Lloyd E. Sc
808 Oaklan

Ann Arbor, Mich.

For final
Thursday June 3, 2-5 Rm 311

STRESS ANALYSIS AND DESIGN OF
ELEMENTARY STRUCTURES

Mortimer E. Cooley Bridge Near Cadillac, Michigan. Deck Cantilever Truss with Curved Lower Chord. Span, 300 feet.

AISC Award, Class C, 1935

Designed by J. H. Cissel

STRESS ANALYSIS AND DESIGN OF
ELEMENTARY STRUCTURES

JAMES H. CISSEL
PROFESSOR OF STRUCTURAL ENGINEERING
UNIVERSITY OF MICHIGAN
MEMBER: AMERICAN SOCIETY OF CIVIL ENGINEERS
AMERICAN CONCRETE INSTITUTE
INTERNATIONAL ASSOCIATION FOR
BRIDGE AND STRUCTURAL ENGINEERS

SECOND EDITION

New York · JOHN WILEY & SONS, Inc.
London · CHAPMAN & HALL, Limited

PREFACE

To the Second Edition

In the second edition of this textbook, I have retained in Part I substantially the same material that was contained in Part I of the first edition. Chapter 2 has been revised to give information on live loads that is consistent with the most recent standards.

Part II, which deals with the design of simple structures, has been completely rewritten to provide subject material that is consistent with the most recent specifications for designing structures. One new chapter, which relates to the design of light-gage steel construction, has been added.

Data for problems have been added at the end of each chapter to aid class instruction.

I acknowledge with gratitude the able assistance of Dr. Leo M. Legatski, who helped with the preparation of problem material.

JAMES H. CISSEL

ANN ARBOR, MICHIGAN
January, 1948

PREFACE

To the First Edition

In this textbook, I have attempted to collect and arrange in a logical order the basic principles and procedures which relate to the stress analysis and design of simple structures. The presentation of material is based on the assumption that the student has completed the study of statics and of strength of materials. Except for the matters of selection of material and arrangement, no claim is made for originality since data have been obtained from many sources.

Many courses of study outlined for fields of engineering other than civil include a course in structures, and it is for such that this book is primarily intended. Usually a limited time is available for such a course, and therefore only a bare introduction or outline of elementary structural analysis and design is possible. In view of this fact, I have attempted to select fundamental, useful, and practical material, such as would generally be of value to an engineer in any field. Courses of study in civil engineering provide sufficient time allowance for the use of more complete and extensive textbooks.

Through the courtesy of the American Institute of Steel Construction, the West Coast Lumberman's Association, the Timber Engineering Company, the American Railway Engineering Association, and others, many tables of data, diagrams, and other material have been reproduced in this textbook. These data have been used with the object of providing a self-contained working book which eliminates the need for auxiliary handbooks. I believe, however, that teachers using this book should advise students as to the utility and value of such handbooks.

I gratefully acknowledge the many helpful suggestions of my colleagues at the University of Michigan and in particular those made by Professors R. H. Sherlock, G. L. Alt, and L. C. Maugh, each of whom read and criticized portions of the manuscript.

JAMES H. CISSEL

ANN ARBOR, MICHIGAN
February, 1940

CONTENTS

PART I   STRESS ANALYSIS

xi

CHAPTER

Part I

STRESS ANALYSIS

FOREWORD

Stress analysis is the determination of the magnitudes and kinds of forces which must be resisted by the material used to form a structure. For an existing structure, it involves a determination of the loads, including the weight of the construction and of the internal forces resulting from the action of these loads. It is assumed that the structure is capable of resisting such internal forces as may be created by the loads and that it will therefore maintain itself in a state of equilibrium. The accuracy of this assumption must of course ultimately be checked and will depend upon the physical properties of the material used in the structure. Such final determinations and the resulting conclusions which must be drawn from them will, for the purposes of this book, be considered as a phase of design and will be discussed in Part II. For a proposed structure, the entire stress analysis is hypothetical, and the loads, weights of construction, and internal forces are those which would exist if the assumed structure is built.

Stress analysis problems are therefore generally reduced to an abstract form which involves only the correct application of mathematics and physics. In solving such problems, however, the ultimate purpose of the solution should be kept in mind, and needless refinement should be avoided. Thus, while a solution producing a value 501,252 pounds for the magnitude of force in a given member of a truss might represent a fine example of mathematical accuracy, the last three numbers might be of no practical significance. The computer should therefore always maintain a reasonable sense of proportion and attempt to secure values sufficiently precise for the purpose for which they are intended.

Chapter 1

INTRODUCTION—DEFINITIONS

1 Structures in General

A structure is an assemblage of elements or parts so arranged and connected as to carry loads and otherwise perform the service for which the structure is intended. Thus a building structure furnishes protection from the elements and supports the loads which develop from its occupancy. A bridge is an assembly which carries loads over a stream or given space at the established roadway level.

The elements or units comprising a structure are called beams, slabs, columns, girders, etc., each performing a special function. For the purpose of analysis or design, a given structure is regarded as divided into the several primary forms or units which comprise the assemblage, and these are then separately studied or designed.

Various materials are used to form the units or elements of a structure, the choice of a given material generally depending on overall economy. The most commonly employed materials are timber, iron, steel, and concrete, and the structures that will hereafter be discussed will be limited to those structures fashioned of such materials.

2 Beams and Girders

Members subjected primarily to transverse forces which produce flexure or bending are called *beams* or *girders*. They may have any convenient shape or cross section and may be made of such material as may be suitable for the purpose. The term *girder* is commonly used to designate a beam which supports other beams; this term is also employed to designate a beam made up of smaller pieces of material suitably fastened together. Thus a plate girder is fashioned out of plates and angles, riveted or welded together to form a cross section similar to the capital letter I.

In ordinary building construction, the beams which directly support the flooring are usually called *joists*. The inclined beams which directly support a roof surface are called *rafters*. The beams placed lengthwise of a bridge to support the floor directly are usually called *stringers* and the beams which are placed crosswise between main girders or trusses and which directly support the stringers are named *floor beams*.

2

3 Slabs

A relatively broad flat piece of material with substantial thickness is called a *slab*. In building construction, floors are frequently made by supporting slabs of reinforced concrete on steel or reinforced concrete beams, and highway bridge floors are usually built in this manner. Such slabs are essentially broad flat beams. Steel slabs are sometimes used to distribute a heavy concentrated load or reaction over supporting areas, and columns are frequently supported on slabs of concrete which distribute the load over the foundation soil.

4 Tension Members

A member which resists the tendency of applied forces to extend or increase its length is called a *tension member*. The term *tie* is sometimes employed to indicate such a member. Structural steel is the material

Eye-Bar Assembly Used in a Suspension Bridge Anchorage.

most commonly employed for tension members. Although timber performs satisfactorily in tension, it is difficult to construct fastenings for wooden tension members, and for this reason such members are not as a rule as economical as steel. Concrete, unless it is properly reinforced with steel bars, is entirely unsuitable because of its brittleness and natural inability to satisfactorily resist tension.

A simple form of metal tension member is a round or square bar with threads cut on the ends so that it may be held in place by means of a nut. If it is of uniform cross section throughout its length, such a mem-

ber will have its critical section at the root of the threads in the threaded portion. For a long member of this type, it is usually economical to upset the ends so that the section at the root of the thread will be the same as the remainder of the bar. Members of this type frequently have clevises or loops forged on the ends and are fastened in the structure by means of pins. Such members are usually provided with turnbuckles so that their length may be adjusted after they are in place.

Eye-bars are made from flat steel, bars or plates, by upsetting the ends to form enlarged heads through which holes are bored to provide for the pins which fasten the eye-bar in the structure.

Built-up or *riveted tension members* must be employed for resisting large forces and in places where simpler types are unsuitable.

5 Compression Members—Columns

Structural members acted upon by forces which tend to diminish their length are called *compression members* or *columns*. *Posts*, *struts*, and *stanchions* are terms also used to indicate members of this type.

Such members may be made of any suitable material, and the common materials such as timber, steel, and reinforced concrete are quite satisfactory for this purpose. Cast iron is a material also frequently employed for compression members.

The shape or form of compression members depends largely upon the materials used in their construction, although their position and function in the assembly are also of real importance. Wooden columns are most frequently rectangular or square in section. Reinforced-concrete columns may be readily made either rectangular, square, or round in section. Cast-iron columns are usually in the form of hollow cylinders or pipes. Structural steel may be fashioned in various forms by fastening together standard shapes, although the most common form is the solid rolled member whose cross section, in the general pattern of a block letter H. is called a *wide-flange* section and is designated by the symbol WF.

6 Trusses

A *truss* is a framework composed of tension and compression members fastened to one another only at their ends. In its elemental form the members are connected by single frictionless pins so that the forces on all the members act in the direction of their lengths. Usually the ends of the truss members are riveted or welded to a common connection plate called a *gusset plate*. Such connections may introduce complications in the action of the truss due to the resistance to any change in the angles between the members, and they must therefore be carefully pro-

portioned and arranged so that errors introduced in this way are as small as possible.

In general the members comprising a truss are arranged in the form of triangles, and the construction supported is usually fastened to the truss at or near the joints of the several triangles thus formed.

7 Frames

In common usage a frame is an assembly of beams and columns such as comprise the structural skeleton of a building.

When the columns, beams, and girders are constructed as a monolith, such as is the common practice in reinforced concrete construction, the frame is termed a *rigid frame*. The word rigid here does not mean that there is no deflection of the component parts but rather that the connections have such rigidity that the action of one part will induce action or stress in the adjoining parts. The degree of rigidity of a frame will depend upon the character of the connections of the members to one another. The analysis or design of a rigid frame is a complicated matter and requires a high degree of specialized technical skill.

A jointed frame is one whose component parts are connected by simple fastenings incapable of transmitting bending in one part to an adjoining part. In such structures the portions are analyzed as simple and separate units.

8 Connections

The manner in which a structural unit is supported or connected to other units in an assembly plays an important part in the analysis and design of structures, particularly for tension members, where the design of the member may be controlled by the arrangement of the connection. In the determination of load capacity of structures, careful consideration must be given to the strength of the connections, for this will frequently limit the loading which may be safely carried by the structure.

For fastening timber members, nails, screws, and bolts are commonly used. Steel members are most frequently fastened by rivets or pins. Electric-arc welding is also frequently used for connections of steel members particularly when welding operations can be performed in the shop.

9 Statically Determinate Structures

A structure is said to be *statically determinate externally* when the external forces can be found by applying the simple laws of statics, $\Sigma H = 0$, $\Sigma V = 0$, and $\Sigma M = 0$. For many structures, assumptions must be made regarding the nature or position of reactive forces in order to reduce the problem to a statically determinate basis. When such

Courtesy Bethlehem Steel Co.

Transmission Line Towers.

assumptions are necessary, they should be made with due regard to the magnitude of the errors introduced so that such errors will not produce unsafe results. For example, a simple beam whose ends rest upon walls which furnish simple bearing resistance is usually regarded as statically determinate by assuming that the resultant of the reactive pressure furnished by the wall is at the center of the bearing area. Obviously, when the beam deflects, as it must under load, the pressures will increase toward the inside edge of the support, and the resultant reactive pressure will actually lie closer to the inside edge of the support than is indicated by this assumption. Since the actual span is shorter than that assumed, the assumption indicated will not produce an unsafe result.

10 Statically Indeterminate Structures

A structure is said to be *statically indeterminate externally* when the external forces cannot be established or determined by the simple laws of statics. For the analysis of such structures, additional equations dealing with the performance of the structure or properties of the external forces must be derived. Usually such equations are determined by considering the elastic behavior of the structure under loading and involve, of course, a thorough understanding of the fundamental principles of elasticity. Beams rigidly attached to the supports and beams continuous over several supports are examples of statically indeterminate structures.

Chapter 2

EXTERNAL FORCES--LOADS

11 Definitions

The external forces which act on a structure are identified as *dead loads*, *live loads*, and *reactions*.

The *dead loads* represent the weight of the materials of which the structure is made; they are fixed in amount and location.

Photograph by Collins Studio, Mt. Pleasant, Michigan.

Variable Floor Load.

(Note that roof trusses are shaped to accommodate loading.)

The *live loads* arise out of the use of the structure and include forces of natural origin such as wind pressure, weight of snow, or dynamic effect of earthquake shock. Live loads vary in amount and character and

8

may be located in any position on the structure which is consistent with the character of the load.

A *distributed load* is one which is spread over a considerable portion of a structure, such as a layer of sand on a floor. A *uniformly distributed load* is such a one as would be caused by a layer of sand uniform in depth.

A *concentrated load* is one which is distributed over a very small area of contact with the structure. In general, such loads are regarded as applied at a point or along a line, but the actual distribution must be considered in connection with determination of local stresses on sections in contact with or in the immediate vicinity of such a load.

Conventional live loadings which simulate the actual loads that will use the structure are generally used for purposes of design. While investigations of the behavior or safety of a structure may be based on an actual load, conventional or standard loads are also frequently used for such studies. The most commonly employed conventional or standard load is the uniformly distributed load, and by general usage many structures, particularly floor systems, are rated in terms of the uniformly distributed load which they will safely support. For railway bridges the conventional load consists of a series of concentrated loads typical of the axle loads of a locomotive, followed by a uniformly distributed load representative of the train load hauled by a locomotive.

The *reactions* are the forces induced by the action of the supports in preventing or retarding motion of the structure under the action of dead and live loads.

12 Weight of Construction

The determination of the dead load acting on a given structure is essentially a matter of computing the volume of material and applying the proper unit weight to the quantities so computed. For a proposed construction, allowance for the probable weight must be made. Such computations require the exercise of good judgment and experience is a useful asset. When a design has been completed, using estimated weights, the dead-load allowances should be checked and corrections made where such allowances are not in accord with the final results. Usually no change is warranted if the assumed dead load is within 10 per cent of the actual weight.

Weights of the common materials of construction are given in Table 1.[1]

---

[1] All tables appear in the Appendix.

13   Weight of Trusses

Empirical formulae are useful for estimating the probable weight of combinations of members forming roof or bridge trusses. Typical of such formulae are the following,

where *W* = total weight of truss in pounds.

   L = span of truss in feet.

   a = distance between trusses in feet.

Wood Roof Trusses (Formula proposed by Ricker) [2]

$$W = \frac{aL^2}{25} + \frac{aL^3}{6000} \tag{1}$$

Steel Roof Trusses (Formula proposed by Fowler)

$$W = 0.06aL^2 + 0.6aL \text{ (for heavy loads)} \tag{2}$$

$$W = 0.04aL^2 + 0.4aL \text{ (for light loads)} \tag{3}$$

For purposes of stress analysis, the total weight of the truss is usually assumed as spread uniformly over the surface which it supports. Thus the weight of a roof truss would be represented by a load such as would be caused by a uniform layer of snow covering the entire roof surface.

14   Floor Loads—Buildings

Loads on floors of buildings are generally caused by crowds of people, furniture, or merchandise and may be closely approximated by a universally distributed load over the floor area. Building ordinances of most cities specify the minimum uniform load which shall be used in the design of floors intended for various purposes. Typical of such requirements are those stipulated by the "1942 Building Laws of the City of New York," which are in part as follows:

(*a*) LIVE LOADS FOR RESIDENCES AND SLEEPING QUARTERS

For private dwellings, multiple dwellings, bedroom floors in hotels and club houses, private and ward room floors in hospitals, dormitories, and for similar occupancies, including corridors, the minimum live load shall be taken as forty pounds per square foot uniformly distributed.

(*b*) LIVE LOADS FOR OFFICE SPACE

For office floors, including corridors, the minimum live load shall be taken as fifty pounds per square foot uniformly distributed.

(*c*) LIVE LOADS FOR PLACES OF ASSEMBLY OTHER THAN THEATRES AND HALLS

For classrooms with fixed seats, including aisles and passageways between seats, for churches with fixed seats, for reading rooms, and for classrooms not exceeding

[2] Bulletin 16, Illinois Experiment Station.

nine hundred square feet of floor area with movable seats, the minimum live load uniformly distributed shall be taken as sixty pounds per square foot, provided that such movable furniture consists, in addition to the instructor's equipment, of individual seatings with or without attached desks.

(d) Live Loads for Theatres and Assembly Halls

For the seating space in theatres and assembly halls with fixed seats, including the passageways between seats, except as provided in subdivision *e* of this section, the minimum live load shall be taken as seventy-five pounds per square foot uniformly distributed.

(e) Live Loads for Public Spaces and Congested Areas

The minimum live load shall be taken as one hundred pounds per square foot, uniformly distributed, for corridors unless otherwise provided for in this section, and for halls, lobbies, public spaces in hotels and public structures, assembly halls without fixed seats, theatre stages, cabarets, barrooms, art galleries and museums, for the ground floors and basements of all hotels, stores, restaurants, shops and office buildings, for skating rinks, grandstands, gymnasiums, dance halls, lodge rooms, stairways, fire escapes and exit passageways, and other spaces where groups of people are likely to assemble. This requirement shall be inapplicable to such spaces in private dwellings, for which the minimum live load shall be taken as in subdivision *a* of this section.

(f) Live Loads for Industrial or Commercial Occupancies and for Garages

In designing floors for industrial or commercial purposes and for garages, the live load shall be assumed to be the maximum caused by the use which the structure or part of the structure is to serve. The following loads in pounds per square foot, uniformly distributed, shall be taken as the minimum live loads permissible for the occupancies listed, and loads at least equal shall be assumed for uses similar in nature to those listed in this section.

Floors to be used for:

1. The display and sale of light merchandise; incidental factory work in not more than twenty-five percent of the floor area   75
2. Factory work, wholesale stores, storage, and stack rooms in libraries   120
3. Stables   75
4. Garages for private passenger cars only   75

When there is floor area sufficient for the accommodation of two or more cars, the design of floors for such garages shall make provision for a concentrated load of two thousand pounds at any one point.

5. Garages for all types of vehicles, other than garages exclusively used for private passenger cars, and for mixed car usage:

For floor construction   175
For beams, columns, and girders   120

The design of floors for such garages shall also make provision for the heaviest concentrated loads to which the floors may be subjected, but in all cases these loads shall be assumed to be at least six thousand pounds concentrated at any point.

Photograph by Collins Studio, Mt. Pleasant, Michigan

Typical Floor Load in Sugar Warehouse.

6. Trucking spaces and driveways within the limits of a structure.

The design of floors for such trucking spaces or driveways shall also make provision for the heaviest concentrated loads to which they may be subjected, but in all cases these loads shall be assumed as at least twelve thousand pounds concentrated at any point.

(g) Live Loads for Sidewalks

The minimum live load for sidewalks shall be assumed to be three hundred pounds per square foot uniformly distributed. Driveways over sidewalks shall be designed for the heaviest concentrated loads to which they may be subjected, but in all cases these loads shall be assumed as at least twelve thousand pounds concentrated at any point.

(h) Roof Loads

Roofs having a rise of three inches or less per foot of horizontal projection shall be proportioned for a vertical live load of forty pounds per square foot of horizontal projection applied to any or all slopes. With a rise of between three inches and twelve inches per foot, inclusive, a vertical live load of thirty pounds on the horizontal projection shall be assumed. If the rise exceeds twelve inches per foot, no vertical live load need be assumed, but provision shall be made for a wind force of twenty pounds per square foot of roof surface acting normal to such surface on one slope at a time.

(i) REDUCTION OF LIVE LOADS

(1) In structures intended for storage purposes all columns, piers, or walls and foundations may be designed for eighty-five percent of the full assumed live load. In structures intended for other uses the assumed live load used in designing all columns, piers, or walls and foundations may be as follows:

> one hundred percent of the live load on the roof
> eighty-five percent of the live load on the top floor
> seventy-five percent of the live load on the floor next below.

On each successive lower floor, there shall be a corresponding decrease in the percentage, provided that in all cases at least fifty percent of the live load shall be assumed.

(2) Girder members, except in roofs and as specified in the following subdivision, carrying a designed floor load the equivalent of two hundred square feet or more of floor area may be designed for eighty-five percent of the specified live load.

(3) In designing trusses and girders which support columns and in determining the area of footings, the full dead loads plus the live loads may be taken with the reductions figured as permitted above.

15 Roof Loads

Roofs serve to shelter the interior of a structure from the action of the elements, and the character of the loading will depend largely upon the degree of exposure and general climatic conditions at the given location. In addition to resisting natural forces, roofs sometimes support interior construction such as suspended balconies, and may carry shafting, hoists, or other equipment.

The weight of snow which may accumulate on the roof surface will depend upon the climatic conditions prevailing at the site of the structure. Data [3] published by the American Standards Association, based upon studies of United States Weather Bureau records, show probable snow loads in various sections of the United States which vary from 2.5 pounds per square foot in the Southern portion to 40 pounds per square foot in northern and mountainous sections. In particular localities, such as the high Sierras in northern California, values as great as 363 pounds per square foot are recorded. Unfortunately for the purpose of establishing probable snow loads, the records show only the total annual cumulative snow fall. For example, in a locality where twelve snow falls, each of 1-inch depth, might occur, the records would show an annual snow fall of 12 inches, and there might actually be no accumulation of more than 1-inch depth of snow on any roof surface at any given time. In most localities, the maximum depth of snow that may accumulate on a flat roof surface will seldom be more than the maximum total snow fall in a month's period of time.

[3] "Minimum Design Loads in Buildings and Other Structures," American Standards Association, 70 East 45th Street, New York, June 19, 1945.

The weight of snow varies from about 5 pounds per cubic foot for freshly fallen dry snow to about 10 for packed snow. The weather bureau estimates that a depth of 6.5 inches corresponds to 1 inch of water, and this assumption produces a snow weight of 9.6 pounds per cubic foot.

Some localities are subject to sleet storms which may cause ice accumulation. This will seldom be as great as $\frac{3}{4}$ inch in thickness, for which thickness the load would be 4 pounds per square foot of roof surface.

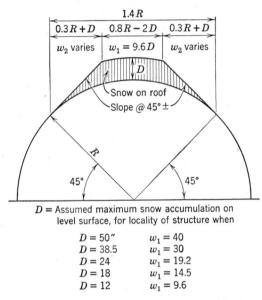

D = Assumed maximum snow accumulation on level surface, for locality of structure when

$D = 50''$	$w_1 = 40$
$D = 38.5$	$w_1 = 30$
$D = 24$	$w_1 = 19.2$
$D = 18$	$w_1 = 14.5$
$D = 12$	$w_1 = 9.6$

Fig. 1.   Snow Loading on Cylindrical Roof Surface.

The shape of the roof or slopes of plane roof surfaces is a factor in establishing roof loading since for steeply pitched surfaces, any substantial snow accumulation may slide off and thus relieve the roof of such load. It is generally agreed that substantially no snow will accumulate on a plane roof surface which slopes more than 45 degrees to the horizontal. Aerodynamic considerations are also of major importance in affecting snow accumulation since air movement across the structure may induce negative roof pressures which actually tend to remove the snow from the surface. For this reason, it is nearly impossible to produce any snow accumulation on a cylindrical roof surface.

Most building codes specify minimum roof loads based upon the horizontal projection of the roof area which are intended to provide for snow load and other forms of possible vertical live load. Typical of

such requirements are those of the National Board of Fire Underwriters [4] which provide as follows:

(*a*) Roofs having a rise of four inches or less per foot of horizontal projection shall be designed for a vertical live load of not less than thirty pounds per square foot of horizontal projection.

(*b*) Roofs having a rise of more than four inches and not more than twelve inches per foot of horizontal projection shall be designed for a vertical live load of not less than twenty pounds per square foot of horizontal projection.

(*c*) Roofs having a rise of more than twelve inches per foot of horizontal projection shall be designed to carry a wind force acting normal to the roof surface, on one slope at a time, of twenty pounds per square foot of such surface, and no vertical live load need be assumed.

The foregoing provisions are obviously intended for roofs made up of plane surfaces. For cylindrical or arch roofs the author recommends the modified loading indicated in Fig. 1. It may be observed that there are few localities in the United States where the maximum accumulation of snow on a level surface will exceed 24 inches.

Wind loads on roof structures are discussed in Article 18.

16   Live Loads for Highway Bridges

Highway bridges must carry loads of a widely divergent nature, such as crowds of people, farm animals, wagons, tractors, automobiles, and trucks. The modern motor truck with its relatively heavy wheel concentration constitutes a comparatively severe load on the floor system of such structures, and such a loading in combination with a uniform load distributed over the surrounding floor area represents the probable maximum condition that is reasonable to impose on principal supporting units such as main girders or trusses.

The 1944 Specifications of the American Association of State Highway Officials specifies that highway live loadings on the roadway of bridges or incidental structures shall consist of standard trucks or of lane loads which are equivalent to truck trains. Two systems of loading are provided, and designated as H loading and H-S loading.

The H loading consists of a two-axle truck or the corresponding lane loading (Fig. 2). In designating this loading, the letter H is followed by a number indicating the gross weight in tons of the standard truck and by a second number which indicates the year of the specification. Thus H20-44 indicates a 20-ton truck under the 1944 A.A.S.H.O. Specification. The lane loading in Fig. 2 is shown for a 20-ton truck. Values for other truck weights may be obtained by proportion.

[4] Building Code Recommended by the National Board of Fire Underwriters, National Board of Fire Underwriters, New York, 1943.

The H-S loadings are illustrated in Fig. 2c and consist of a tractor truck with semi-trailer or of the corresponding lane loading.   H-S lane loading is the same as for H loading indicated above.   These loadings

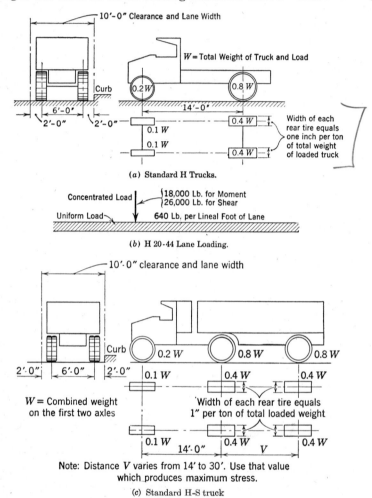

(*a*) Standard H Trucks.

(*b*) H 20-44 Lane Loading.

Note: Distance *V* varies from 14' to 30'. Use that value which produces maximum stress.

(*c*) Standard H-S truck

Fig. 2.   Standard Highway Loading.

are designated by the letter H followed by a number indicating the gross weight in tons of the tractor truck and by the letter S followed by the gross weight in tons of the single axle of the semi-trailer.   The final number indicates the year of the specification.   Thus the designation H20-S16-44 indicates a 20-ton truck and a 16-ton trailer in accordance with the 1944 A.A.S.H.O. Specification.

The 1944 specifications state that highway loadings shall be of five classes: H20, H15, H10, H20-S16, and H15-S12. Loadings H15 and H10 are 75 and 50 per cent, respectively, of loading H20. Loading H15-S12 is 75 per cent of loading H20-S16. For trunk highways, or for other highways which carry or may carry heavy truck traffic, the minimum live load is the H15-S12 loading.

The lane loadings or standard trucks are assumed to occupy traffic lanes, each having a width of 10 feet, corresponding to the standard truck clearance width. Within the curb to curb width of the roadway, the traffic lanes are assumed to occupy any position which will produce the maximum stress but which will not involve overlapping of adjacent lanes nor place the center of the lane less than 5 feet from the roadway face of the curb.

17   Live Loads for Railway Bridges

The live loading carried by railway bridges is naturally quite definitely determined in its character by the purpose of the structure. The usual standard loading for such structures is two heavy locomotives followed by a train of cars, although occasionally it may be necessary to consider loads of special or unusual character. The locomotives furnish heavy concentrations at points corresponding to the axle spacings, and the train load is usually simulated by a moving uniform load.

Because locomotives vary widely in weight and axle spacing, arbitrary standard artificial loadings are generally used instead of actual loadings. These arbitrary loadings are designed to give equivalent or greater effects than would be produced by actual loadings and have the advantage of standardizing the design and analysis of railway structures.

The system of loads which has received the most general acceptance was devised by Theodore Cooper and is known as Cooper's Loading. Cooper's E-60 is shown in Fig. 3 where the loads are given in thousands

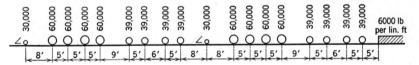

Fig. 3.   Cooper's E-60 Loading.

of pounds on each rail, with axles spaced as shown, and the train load is represented by a uniform load. Where a lighter or heavier loading is to be used, the loads are all changed in the same proportion, but the axle spacing remains constant. Thus for Cooper's E-40 the axle loads and uniform train load are four-sixths of those for the E-60 loading.

The Specifications (1944) of the American Railway Engineering Association for design of steel railway bridges with spans not exceeding 400 feet recommend that the live load on each track be either Cooper's E-72 or two moving concentrated loads of 90,000 pounds each, spaced 7 feet apart and placed in position for maximum effect, whichever loading gives maximum stress to be used.

18 Wind Forces

For determining the pressure on inclined roof surfaces, many building codes use empirical formulae based upon experiments made by Hutton in 1787–88 and Duchemin in 1829. These experiments were conducted on relatively small plates, and the following formulae were deduced for the intensity of pressure normal to the exposed surface.

Hutton's formula:

$$p_n = p(\sin \alpha)^{1.842 \cos \alpha - 1} \tag{4}$$

Duchemin's formula:

$$p_n = p\left(\frac{2 \sin \alpha}{1 + \sin^2 \alpha}\right) \tag{5}$$

where p_n = pressure normal to surface in pounds per square foot.
   p = pressure on a plane surface normal to direction of wind in pounds per square foot.
   α = angle of inclination of surface to direction of wind.

When these formulae are used, the value of p is obtained from the equation

$$p = cv^2 \tag{6}$$

where v = wind velocity in miles per hour.
   c = constant based principally upon the shape and size of the exposed surface. This coefficient is commonly assumed as equal to 0.0033.

The observations by Hutton and Duchemin were made upon small plates isolated from the building structure to which they would necessarily be attached in real practice. Tests in modern wind tunnels show that the formulae are reasonably accurate for such unattached surfaces but that they are grossly in error when applied to roof surfaces [5] attached to a building structure.

The general nature of wind pressure exerted on structures is discussed in some detail in Scientific Paper 523 of the U. S. Bureau of Standards,

[5] *Wind Pressures on Buildings* (Second Series), Danmarks Naturvidenskabelige Samfund, Copenhagen, 1936.

"Wind Pressures on Structures," from which the following has been abstracted:

The nature of the reaction between the wind and an obstacle to its progress is extremely complicated even in the case of a uniform and steady wind. When the air is at rest, there is a distribution of pressure over the surface due to the normal atmospheric pressure. The effect of the motion of the air is a modification of this normal pressure, at some points an increase in pressure, at others a decrease in pressure. The magnitude of these changes is only a small percentage of the normal atmospheric pressure, and the words *suction* or *vacuum* as commonly used in this connection do not imply any large change in density or pressure. The condition indicated by these words is merely a decrease of the normal pressure by amounts which are usually less than 2 per cent of the normal pressure.

The maximum increase in pressure produced by the wind is equal to $\frac{1}{2}\rho V^2$, where ρ is the density [6] of the air and V the wind speed. This pressure is usually termed the velocity pressure.

In aerodynamics it is convenient to express all observed pressure differences as ratios of the pressure difference to the velocity pressure. Although the maximum increase in pressure at any point is equal to the velocity pressure, pressure decreases of greater amount frequently occur and average wind pressures resulting from the surface distribution over an object are frequently greater than the velocity pressure. The advantage of expressing results in this form is that the ratios or *coefficients* are independent of the units used so long as the units are self-consistent.

Expressed in this way, the wind pressure normal to any surface is given by the following formula:

$$p_n = Cq \qquad (7)$$

where p_n = wind pressure normal to surface in pounds per square foot.

C = coefficient determined by experiment.

q = velocity pressure [7] = $\frac{1}{2}\rho V^2$.

The pressures on the surfaces of a typical mill building, with the wind direction making an angle of 90 degrees with the axis of the building, as found by Dryden and Hill,[8] are shown in Fig. 4. The coefficient C to

---

[6] ρ = mass density = $\dfrac{\text{weight density}}{\text{acceleration due to gravity}}$.

[7] For air weighing 0.07651 lb per cu ft corresponding to 15° C at sea level:

$$\rho = \frac{0.07651}{32.2} = 0.002378$$

$$q = \frac{1}{2} \times 0.002378 V^2 \times \left[\tfrac{5280}{3600}\right]^2$$

$$= 0.002558 V^2 \text{ in pounds per square foot}$$

where V = true wind speed in miles per hour.

[8] "Wind Pressure on a Model of a Mill Building," *Research Paper* 301, U. S. Bureau of Standards.

be used in Equation 7 is given for each of the pressure lines shown in this figure.

The pressure lines in Fig. 5 show that the vertical wall on the windward side is the only surface with positive pressure and that all other surfaces are subjected to negative pressure, or suction. This would not be true for a building with a much steeper roof where the windward roof surface would also have a positive pressure. Likewise, if the wind

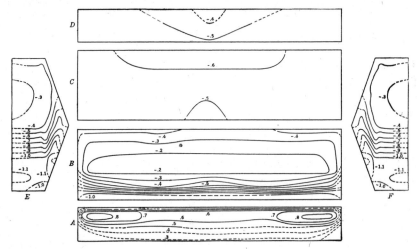

Fig. 4. Distribution of Pressure over the Model without the Monitor; Wind Normal to Face *A*.

The pressures are measured from the static pressure as base and are expressed as ratios to velocity pressure. Minus signs denote that the pressure is lower than the static pressure.

Reproduced from Research Paper 301, U. S. Department of Commerce.

direction were rotated through some angle, the distribution of pressures would be entirely changed. It is very difficult, therefore, to write code specifications which are reasonably simple and yet cover adequately all variations of pressure on sloping or rounded roofs attached to buildings of various proportions. Such an attempt has been made but has not yet been adopted as a code provision.[9] Figure 5 is a diagram by Haven [10] showing uniformly distributed wind pressures on sloping roofs. These pressures are based upon the reports of many investigators and may be assumed to be safe for any reasonable proportions of building and roof slopes. Special consideration should be given to the area

[9] Fifth Progress Report of Subcommittee 31, *Proc. Am. Soc. C. E.*, March, 1936, p. 397.

[10] A. F. Haven, thesis submitted in partial fulfillment of requirements for master's degree, University of Michigan, June, 1934.

ith respect to roofs, these standards provide that they shall be de-
gned to resist $1\frac{1}{4}$ times the foregoing pressures acting outward normal
the surface, and roofs or sections of roofs with slopes greater than
degrees shall be designed to withstand these pressures acting inward
rmal to the surface.

For roofs of semi-cylindrical form, tests made under the direction of
e author show that the maximum pressures should be taken as shown

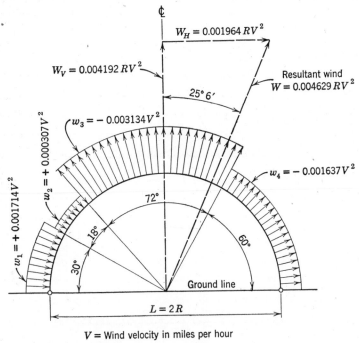

V = Wind velocity in miles per hour
R = Radius of arch rib in feet
W = Pressure on roof surface in lb/sq ft

Fig. 6.

Fig. 6. It will be observed that inward pressure is produced over
nly 48 degrees of the arc on the windward side and that suction is
aduced over the major part of the roof surface.

9 Dynamic Effect of Live Load—Impact

The effect of live loading upon a structure is generally augmented by
he dynamic forces induced by motion of the given loading. Should the
ve load be dropped through a distance and brought to rest by the
esistance of a structure, the energy forces so developed must be added
o the gravity forces induced by the load.

numbered 3 in the diagram, since it is subjected to un
of pressure or suction, depending on the slope of the ro

The American Standards Association [11] in standard
the National Bureau of Standards recommends that bui

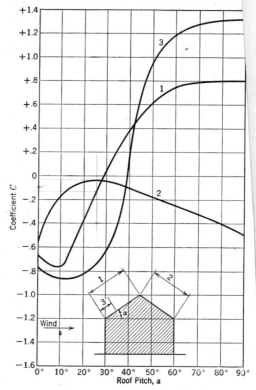

FIG. 5.   Coefficient C for Gable Roofs.

Thesis by A. F. Haven, University of Michigan, 1934.

structures be designed to resist the following horizontal p
wind from any direction:

Height less than 50 ft	20 lb/sq ft
Height 50 to 99 ft	24 lb/sq ft
100 to 199	28 lb/sq ft
200 to 299	30 lb/sq ft

It is also recommended by these standards that all exterio
designed to resist the above pressures acting either inward o

[11] "Minimum Design Loads in Buildings and Other Structures," Amer
ards Association, 70 East 45th Street, New York, June 19, 1945.

Many factors must be considered in determining the dynamic effects which must be taken into account. The nature of the loading, irregularities of floor surface, inertia of the structure, the normal vibration period of the structure, and other complex relationships all enter into a precise solution of this problem. Because of its complexity, a mathematical determination of the dynamic effect is seldom attempted, and empirical formulae or allowances are commonly employed.

The American Railway Engineering Association specifies [12] the following allowances to be made in the design of fixed span steel railway bridges not exceeding 400 feet in length. These allowances for impact are computed as percentages of the static live-load effect and are to be added thereto.

(a) *The rolling effect:* Vertical forces due to the rolling of the train from side to side acting downward on one rail and upward on the other, the forces on each rail being equal to 10 per cent of the axle load.

(b) *The direct vertical effect:* Downward forces, distributed equally to the two rails and acting normal to the top of rail plane.

With steam locomotives (hammer blow, track irregularities, and car impact),

for L less than 100 ft,

$$I = 100 - 0.6L \qquad (8)$$

for L 100 ft or more,

$$I = \frac{1800}{L - 40} + 10 \qquad (9)$$

With electric locomotives (track irregularities and car impact),

$$I = \frac{360}{L} + 12.5 \qquad (10)$$

where L = length in feet, center to center, of supports for stringers, longitudinal girders, and trusses (chords and main members).

Or

L = length of floor beams or transverse girders, in feet, for floor beams, floor beam hangers, subdiagonals of trusses, transverse girders, and supports for transverse girders.

In each case the impact shall not exceed 100 per cent of the static live load.

[12] American Railway Engineering Association Specifications for Steel Railway Bridges, 1944.

For members receiving load from more than one track, the impact percentage shall be applied to the static live load on the number of tracks shown below:

Load received from
  Two tracks:

  For L less than 175 ft: Full impact on two tracks.
  For L from 175 to 225 ft: Full impact on one track and a percentage of full impact on the other as given by the formula $450 - 2L$.
  For L greater than 225 ft: Full impact on one track and none on the other.

  More than two tracks:

  For all values of L: Full impact on any two tracks.

For highway bridges, the Specifications of the American Association of State Highway Officials (1944) give the following allowance:

$$I = S \frac{50}{L + 125} \tag{11}$$

where I = impact stress.
  S = stress due to live load considered as a static load.
  L = length in feet of that portion of the span which is loaded to produce the maximum stress in the member considered.

Impact allowances for live loads which occur in buildings are seldom made except for crane loads, elevators, and similar loads.

Loads which move at comparatively high speed and are forced to follow a curved path will induce centrifugal force which must be resisted by the structure supporting them. A high railroad trestle supporting a curved tack is an example of such a situation.

The 1944 A.R.E.A. Specifications for steel railway bridges state: "On curves, a centrifugal force corresponding to each axle load shall be applied horizontally through a point 6 feet above the top of rail measured along a line perpendicular to the line joining the tops of the rails and equi-distant from them. This force shall equal the percentage $0.00117S^2D$ of the specified axle load without impact,"

where S = speed in miles per hour.
  D = degree of curve.

Tractive forces are those induced by the starting of a live load into motion or the rapid deceleration of a load in motion across the structure.

The starting of a traveling crane in a mill building would develop such a force opposite to the direction of travel and would be the result of friction developed between the wheels and the crane rail; similarly the starting or braking of a locomotive on a railway bridge would produce a tractive force induced by friction at the top of the rail. The railroad specifications previously noted state that the force due to braking shall be 15 per cent of the live load without impact and that the force due to traction shall be 25 per cent of the weight on the driving wheels, without impact. These forces are assumed to act 6 feet above the top of the rail and parallel thereto.

20 Earthquake Shock

Observers have noted that the effect of an earthquake appears to consist of a sudden bump or shove immediately followed by a series of vibrations which seem to produce a swinging motion. In alluvial soils or filled ground there is also a noticeable wave motion.

In the Japanese earthquake of September 1, 1923, the principal vibration had a period of 1.35 seconds and a double amplitude of 3.46 inches. It has been estimated that in the San Francisco earthquake of 1906 the period was about 1 second and the amplitude 2 inches.[13]

The force developed on a structure by virtue of a sudden displacement as caused by an earthquake is a function of the mass of the structure, the amount of the displacement, and the change in the velocity (acceleration) of the movement. It is usually assumed that the motion is simple harmonic,[14] from which

$$a = \frac{4\pi^2 d}{t^2} \tag{12}$$

where a = maximum acceleration.

d = maximum deviation from normal position either way, or amplitude.

t = time of one complete oscillation (from zero to maximum positive to maximum negative to zero).

The values of the amplitude and time may be determined from a consideration of seismic records. It is customary to express the acceleration in terms of that due to gravity; hence a stated acceleration of one-tenth gravity means that a is taken at a value of 3.22 feet per second per second.

[13] Article by Dewell, *Engg. News-Record*, April 26, 1928, p. 650.

[14] Robins Fleming, *Wind Stresses in Buildings*, p. 166. John Wiley and Sons, 1930.

The magnitude of the force exerted on a structure, due to its sudden displacement resulting from earthquake movement, is

$$F = \frac{Wa}{g} \tag{13}$$

where F = maximum force applied to the structure due to the earthquake.

  a = maximum acceleration of earthquake movement.

  g = acceleration due to gravity = 32.2 ft per sec per sec.

  W = weight affected (live and dead load).

It should be noted that the force F is applied at the center of gravity of the weight W. Thus the effect on any horizontal section through a structure would be that of a force F applied at the center of gravity of all loads above the given section.

A value for the acceleration equal to one-tenth gravity (3.22) is used in Tokyo, where probably more severe shocks have been recorded than in any other city on record; hence this may be regarded as a reasonably high allowance. It should be noted, however, that this magnitude applies particularly to rock foundation and that, for structures founded in alluvial soils or on filled ground, the acceleration may reach values three or four times as great.

Observations have shown that, although some vertical movement may be produced, its magnitude is but a fraction of the lateral movement and may be safely disregarded.

21 Lateral Pressure

Structures designed to retain fluids or materials of granular character are subjected to pressures induced by the tendency of the material to flow laterally. For fluids, the pressure exerted on the sides of the containing structure equals that induced on a horizontal plane at the same depth and is computed by multiplying the weight per cubic foot of the material by the depth or *head*.

For materials of a granular nature, such as sand, grain, etc., the action is more complex owing to the presence of such internal resistance to flow as the friction developed by particles sliding or rolling over one another and cohesion, which may exist to a greater or less extent between particles. In such materials as earth, the cohesive action introduces a variable which makes a precise solution impossible.

The first rational theory for the lateral pressure of granular materials was formulated by Coulomb in 1774. According to this theory, a wedge of material, bounded on one side by the wall retaining the material and

on the other by a *plane of rupture*, is assumed as tending to slide and hence to exert pressure against the wall. The *plane of rupture* lies between that corresponding to the *angle of repose* of the given material and the wall surface. When the surface of the material is horizontal and the wall surface vertical, the plane of rupture bisects the angle between the plane of repose and the vertical wall surface. For other conditions graphical methods [15] are generally employed in the determination. Once the *sliding wedge* is determined, various theories are employed for computing the pressures exerted on the wall.

The *Rankine theory*, which was proposed in 1858, is still commonly used for the solution of problems of lateral pressure. While it is essentially an analytical method based upon the principle of conjugate stresses, graphical solutions, using the properties of the ellipse of stress are frequently employed. The principal elements of this theory are

1. In any granular, non-cohesive material the relationship between principal stresses is

$$\frac{q}{p} = \frac{1 - \sin \phi}{1 + \sin \phi} \tag{14}$$

where p = major principal stress.
q = minor principal stress.
ϕ = angle of internal friction.

2. The pressure against a vertical plane will be parallel to the upper surface of the material retained. The inclination of the surface of the material retained must not exceed the angle ϕ with the horizontal.

The pressure of a mass of material whose surface is horizontal, against a vertical plane, Fig. 7a is determined from Equation 14, where $p = wh$, and

$$q = wh \left[\frac{1 - \sin \phi}{1 + \sin \phi}\right] \tag{15}$$

where w = weight per cubic foot of material.
h = depth of material at point of pressure determination.

When the surface of the material is inclined at an angle α to the horizontal (Fig. 7b) the intensity of pressure against a vertical plane is given by the following formula:

$$t = wh \cos \alpha \left[\frac{\cos \alpha - \sqrt{\cos^2 \alpha - \cos^2 \phi}}{\cos \alpha + \sqrt{\cos^2 \alpha - \cos^2 \phi}}\right] \tag{16}$$

[15] Ketchum, *The Design of Walls, Bins and Grain Elevators* (3rd Ed.), McGraw-Hill Book Co.

In the case of a fluid it will be observed that, in the absence of internal friction, $\phi = 0$, and hence $q = wh$. Materials in which internal friction between particles is present may by this theory be regarded as imperfect fluids, the friction serving to reduce the effective weight insofar as lateral

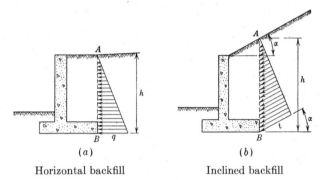

<table>
<tr><td>(a)</td><td>(b)</td></tr>
<tr><td>Horizontal backfill</td><td>Inclined backfill</td></tr>
</table>

Fig. 7.   Earth Pressures According to the Rankine Theory.

pressure is concerned and the pressures determined as if for a fluid weighing w' pounds per cubic foot, where

$$w' = w \left[\frac{1 - \sin \phi}{1 + \sin \phi} \right] \tag{17}$$

The value of ϕ as determined by various investigations [16] varies from 10 to 50 degrees and depends largely upon the coarseness of the material and its moisture content.   In any event, the Rankine theory fails to make any allowance for cohesion between the particles.   For freshly piled earth with normal water content, the value of ϕ is commonly taken as 30 degrees, and with this value it may be determined by Equation 14 that when the surface is level the lateral pressure is one-third the vertical pressure; in other words, the pressures exerted will be the same as those developed by a fluid whose specific gravity is one-third that of the actual earth retained.

Full-size experiments reported by Feld [17] in 1923 indicated that the actual forces may be considerably at variance with those found by applying the Rankine theory.   These experiments were made with sand against a vertical wall, and the following important conclusions were reached:

1. The resultant pressure is inclined to the wall, deviating from the normal by an angle equal to the angle of friction between the fill and the wall.

[16] E. P. Goodrich, "Lateral Earth Pressures and Related Phenomena," *Trans. Am. Soc. C. E.*, Vol. 53, p. 272.

[17] *Trans. Am. Soc. C. E.*, 1923, p. 1448.

2. The resultant acts above the third point and, for a heavy surcharge, as high as the 0.4 point.

3. The horizontal component is given closest by the wedge theory, taking as the angle ϕ the experimentally determined angle of internal resistance of the fill.

The foregoing theories and principles are based on an unlimited extent of material back of the wall and may be regarded as applicable only to cases where the plane of rupture as determined by the Coulomb theory cuts the upper surface of the fill material.

For relatively deep bins the magnitude of vertical and lateral pressures will vary with the characteristics of the material and the character of the wall surface. In such situations the arching action within the material and the frictional resistance of the material to sliding on the wall surface serve to reduce substantially the lateral and vertical pressures. For grain in relatively high bins, the results given by a formula proposed by Janssen [18] have been found by experiment to produce reliable results. Janssen's formula is expressed as follows:

where w = weight of fill material in pounds per cubic foot.

V = vertical pressure per square foot at depth h.

L = lateral pressure per square foot at depth h.

k = ratio of lateral to vertical pressure.

u = coefficient of friction of material on bin wall.

R = hydraulic radius of bin section.

e = base of Napierian logarithm system = 2.71828.

h = depth of material to pressure plane.

Let

$$R = \frac{\text{area of horizontal section of bin in square feet}}{\text{inside perimeter of bin in feet}}$$

Then

$$\frac{kuh}{R} = m$$

$$V = \frac{wR}{ku} (1 - e^{-m}) \tag{18}$$

$$L = kV \tag{19}$$

Experiments by Pleissuer [19] in 1905 indicated that k, the ratio of lateral to vertical pressure, varies with the material and the depth but

[18] "Versuche über Getreidedruck in Silozellen," *Zeitschrift des Vereines deutscher Ingenieure*, 1895, p. 1045.

[19] "Versuche zur Ermittlung der Boden und Seitenwanddrucke in Getreidesilos," *Zeitschrift des Vereines deutscher Ingenieure*, June 23, 1906, p. 976.

increases very little after a depth of two and one-half to three times the diameter of the bin is reached. The value of k as found by experiment varied from about 0.3 to 0.6, depending upon the material and the nature of the bin construction. Experiments made by Jamieson [20] in 1900 on wheat indicated values of about 0.375 to 0.450 for u.

PROBLEMS

2·1 A building floor is supported on Steel I-beams spaced 12 ft apart. The floor consists of a reinforced concrete slab covered with a wood finish and supports a suspended metal lath and plaster ceiling. The concrete slab is 6 in. thick. The wood finish consists of $\frac{7}{8}$-in. maple flooring fastened to screeds or nailing strips which are embedded in a cinder concrete fill 2 in. thick. Determine the amount of dead floor weight which each beam must carry, expressed in pounds per linear foot of beam.

2·2 The steel roof truss shown supports roof construction and loads as follows:

> Trusses with a span of 48 ft are spaced 12 ft center to center and are supported on side walls of building.
> Roofing—wood shingles.
> Sheathing—yellow pine.
> Joists—2 in. x 8 in. at 16 in. center to center, yellow pine.
> Purlins—5-in. x 9-lb channels at panel points.
> Snow load—20 lb per sq ft of roof surface.
> Wind velocity—90 mph.

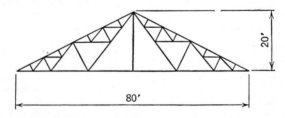

Estimate the weight of the roof truss and calculate the panel loads for dead load, snow load, and wind load.

2·3 *Design Data*

> Trusses with a span of 80 ft are spaced 20 ft center to center and are supported on side walls of building.
> Channel purlins at panel points.

[20] *Engg. News,* 1904, p. 236.

Roofing—24-gage corrugated steel spanning between purlins.

Snow load—10 lb per sq ft of roof surface.

Wind velocity—90 mph.

Required: (a) Estimate the weight of truss by formula, and calculate the panel loads for dead load and snow load. (b) Assume that the wind pressure on a surface normal to the wind $= 0.0033V^2$. Using Duchemin's formula, find the normal pressure on the roof and the panel concentrations for wind load.

2·4 A building with the gable roof shown in Problem 2·3 is to be designed for a maximum wind velocity of 70 mph.

(a) The wind pressures on the wind and leeward slopes to be used for the design of the main structural elements. (b) The wind pressure to be used for the design of exterior roof panels and fastenings.

2·5 A vertical wall is used to retain a level fill of granular material which weighs 90 lb per sq ft and has an angle of internal friction of 45°. According to the Rankine theory, what is the lateral pressure against the wall at a point 22 ft below the surface?

Chapter 3

GRAPHIC STATICS

22 Graphical Representation of Force

A force is represented graphically by a portion of a straight line. The line represents the position and line of action of the force; its length represents its relative magnitude; and an arrow point represents its direction of action.

23 Resolution of a Force

A force may be resolved into any number of components. The relationship between the magnitude and direction of a force and its components may be represented graphically by a *force polygon.*

The components must maintain a continuous line of action so that they and the original force will form a closed polygon. The components may all lie in the line of the force, in which case the force polygon will lie entirely on the line representing the force.

Conversely to the foregoing, the *resultant* of a system of forces is the single force of which the forces in the system are the components. When the forces in the system are concurrent, i.e., intersect in a common point, the resultant must pass through this point.

The *equilibrant* of a system of forces is that force which will neutralize or counteract the resultant. It follows, therefore, that the equilibrant is a force of the same value as the resultant, has the same line of action, but acts in the opposite direction.

24 Couples

Two parallel forces of equal values but acting in opposite directions constitute a *couple.* The magnitude of a couple is measured as a moment equal to the product of either force and the distance separating the forces.

A couple may be transferred to any other point in the plane of the forces without disturbing the equilibrium or value of the system. Thus in Fig. 8a assume that the couple Fz shown at (1) is to be transferred to any position in the plane at (2) so that one of the forces passes through any point a. Continue one of the forces along its line of action to any point b on the proposed line of action through a. The force polygon

bced resolves this force into two components, one having the magnitude
$bc = F$ and the other the magnitude bd. These two components replace
the original force, which is assumed as removed from the force system.
Draw line fg parallel to ab and at a distance z from ab. Continue the
other force F to intersect fg at f and here resolve it into two components
fg and fm by means of the polygon $fgkm$, the component fg having the
magnitude F. Assume this force F replaced by its components fg and

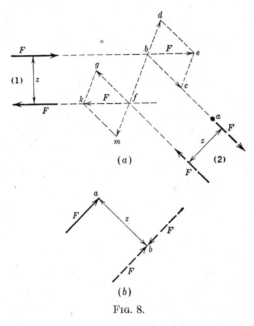

(a)

(b)

Fig. 8.

fm. The original couple has now been replaced by an equivalent set of
forces represented in magnitude and position by bc, bd, fg, and fm. By
construction

$$<kfm = <ebd$$

$$<kfb = <ebf$$

$$fm = bd$$

Hence, components fm and bd cancel each other, leaving the couple Fz
with one force of the couple passing through point a.

Since the forces constituting a couple intersect only at infinity, their
resultant would be a force passing through infinity but with zero magnitude.

A single force or a group of forces can be combined with a couple to
establish a single resultant.

A force may be transferred parallel to itself to any other location in the plane of the forces, provided a couple is added to the force system whose magnitude is the product of the force and the distance through which it is moved. Thus in Fig. 8b the force F at point a is moved through the distance z by adding two equal and opposite forces at b acting parallel to F and combining the original force F with one of the added forces to form a couple of magnitude Fz.

25 Resultant of Force System

A system of co-planar forces is represent in Fig. 9 by F_1, F_2, F_3, and F_4. The resultant of F_1 and F_2 is determined by continuing their lines

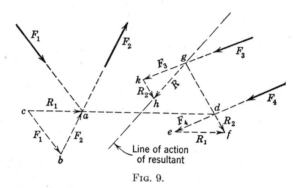

FIG. 9.

of action to intersect at a where a force polygon determines their resultant R_1 in magnitude and direction. The forces F_1 and F_2 may now be replaced by their resultant R_1.

R_1 is now continued along its line of action to intersect any one of the remaining forces, such as F_4, at d, where the same process will determine a second resultant R_2. This force is substituted for R_1 and F_4 and hence replaces forces F_1, F_2, and F_4 of the original force system. By continuing this process, gk is determined as the resultant of the entire system.

26 Force and Equilibrium Polygons

When the forces comprising a given system have such directions that intersections are inconvenient or impossible of determination, as in the case of parallel forces, they may be replaced by components so chosen as to provide convenient intersections. Two separate diagrams are constructed to furnish the necessary data; one diagram, called the *force polygon*, determines graphically the magnitude and direction of the components of the forces; the other diagram, called the *equilibrium*

polygon (or *funicular polygon*), shows the relative position of the several forces and determines the lines of action of their components.

Thus in Fig. 10 the given force system is represented at *a* by the forces F_1, F_2, F_3, and F_4. Force F_1 is resolved at *b* into components aO and Ob, chosen of any convenient magnitudes, and these components are located to intersect at any convenient point *f* on the line of action of F_1. Similarly force F_2 is resolved into components bO and Oc, force F_3 into components cO and Od, and force F_4 into the components dO and Od.

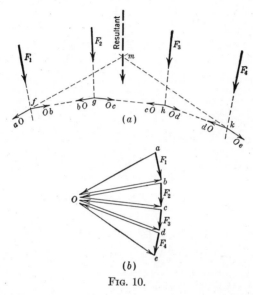

Fig. 10.

Force F_2, as shown at *a*, can be resolved into the selected components bO and Oc at any point on its line of action, and the point *g* which has been selected for this purpose is located at the intersection of component Ob with force F_2. In the same manner point *h* is at the intersection of Oc with F_3, and point *k* is at the intersection of Od with F_4. The entire system of forces F_1, F_2, F_3, and F_4 can now be replaced by an equivalent system which consists of components aO, Ob, bO, Oc, cO, Od, dO, and Oe, and, because of the manner of their selection, the forces of this system will have convenient intersections. The lines of action of these component forces will form the *equilibrium polygon*. Owing to the manner of selecting their magnitude and location, Ob will cancel bO, Oc will cancel cO, and Od will cancel dO, leaving only the two components aO and Oe, which must therefore be components of the resultant. By continuing aO and Oe to intersect at *m*, a point on the resultant of the entire force system is determined.

It is obviously unnecessary to construct the force polygon (10*b*) so that each individual resolution of the several forces into components is indicated as shown in the figure. The *load* line *a*, *b*, *c*, *d*, *e* can be laid off as a continuous sequence of lines and the components, such as *Ob*, *bO*, etc., represented by single lines with *O* as a common point or *pole*.

The forces F_1, F_2, etc., may be laid off in any desired order as in Fig. 11, but it is necessary that the equilibrium polygon be constructed to represent properly the location of component forces thus selected.

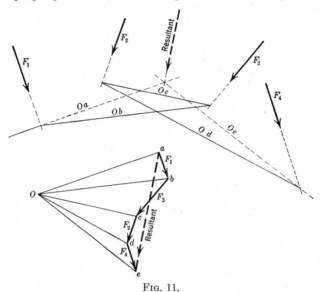

Fɪɢ. 11.

When a force system is in equilibrium both polygons must close. This requirement would be fulfilled in Fig. 11 if the resultant is replaced by the equilibrant.

27 Passing an Equilibrium Polygon through Two Points

The conditions of a problem sometimes require that the equilibrium polygon pass through two points of known location.

Let F_1, F_2, and F_3 (Fig. 12*a*) represent any given system of forces and points *A* and *B* the two known points through which the equilibrium polygon must pass.

At *b*, select any convenient pole as *O'*, and construct the corresponding force and equilibrium polygons to determine the line of action of the resultant of the forces.

At any convenient point on its line of action, resolve the resultant into any two components which will pass through the given points *A*

and B. These components of the resultant force, when drawn in the force polygon, will intersect and determine a pole O which will fulfill the given condition. Note that only the forces which pass *between* the points A and B are involved in this problem.

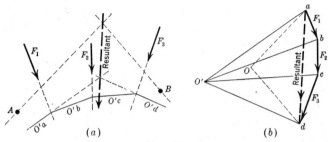

FIG. 12.

An infinite number of polygons can be drawn in the foregoing manner through any two points. An interesting and useful relationship exists between all such polygons in that the poles, infinite in number, will lie on a line parallel to the line through the two given points. This is proved in Fig. 13, where O_1 and O_2 are any two poles chosen in the manner previously outlined.

Draw O_1e through poles O_1 and O_2. By construction Bk is parallel to O_2a, and kg is parallel to de.

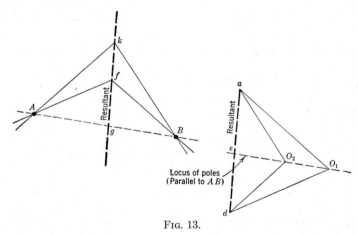

FIG. 13.

Assume the resultant ad to be replaced by its components aO_1 and O_1d acting along the lines fB and fA, respectively. Now if forces dO_2 and O_2a, acting through points A and B, respectively, are added to the force system, the resultant force will be cancelled since these two forces

intersect at k on the line of action of the resultant, and their resultant da is equal and opposite to the resultant ad. Forces dO_2 and O_1d acting at A have O_1O_2 as their resultant acting through A; forces O_2a and aO_1 acting at B have as their resultant the force O_2O_1 acting through B.

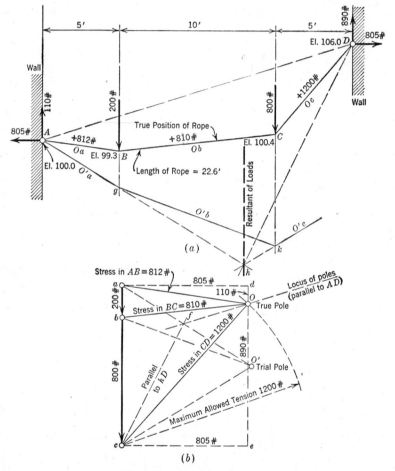

Fig. 14. Cable Suspension.

Since forces O_1O_2 and O_2O_1 are equal they will cancel one another when they lie in the same line of action, hence AB and O_1e must be parallel.

As an example of a problem which can be solved graphically by aid of the foregoing principles, let it be assumed that two weights are suspended from a cable which is attached to walls as shown in Fig. 14a. The cable is to be kept at the highest elevation consistent with a tensile force not to

exceed 1200 pounds. Determine (*a*) the position of the cable, (*b*) the length of cable between supports and (*c*) the stress in all portions of the cable.

The requirements of equilibrium will be met when the rope lies on the line of an equilibrium polygon drawn for the given loads and passing through the points of attachment at *A* and *D*. The force condition will be met when no component force in the force polygon has a greater magnitude than 1200 pounds.

The acting loads and points of support are located at *a* in their relative positions to any convenient scale. The force polygon is constructed at *b* with any convenient pole, such as *O′*, and the corresponding equilibrium polygon *Agk* locates point *h* on the resultant of the loads. Draw any two lines, such as *Ah* and *hd*, so as to intersect on the resultant and pass, respectively, through *A* and *D*. At *b*, lines *af* and *cf* are drawn parallel, respectively, to *Ah* and *hd* and will therefore serve to locate point *f* on the locus of poles. This locus will be parallel to a line through supports *A* and *D*, since the equilibrium polygon must pass through these points. By observation it is apparent that the lower ray in the force polygon will be the longest and, since a condition of the problem requires this to not exceed 1200 pounds, an arc with radius 1200 pounds and center at *c* is found to intersect the locus at *O*, which is the true pole for the stated conditions. The true force and equilibrium polygons are next constructed, and the required information relative to distance and force is determined by scaling the diagrams.

28   Passing an Equilibrium Polygon through Three Points

An equilibrium polygon may be passed through three points, such as *A*, *B*, and *C*, Fig. 15*a*, by finding first the locus of poles for polygons through any two of the three points, and second the locus of poles for polygons through either of the first two points selected, and the remaining point. The intersection of these loci is the pole sought.

In Fig. 15*a*, let *F*$_1$, *F*$_2$, *F*$_3$, and *F*$_4$ represent any set of given forces and *A*, *B*, and *C* the points through which the equilibrium polygon is to pass. If any convenient pole *O*$_1$ (Fig. 15*b*) is selected, the corresponding force and equilibrium polygons will locate a point *k* on the resultant of *F*$_1$ and *F*$_2$. The direction of this resultant is parallel to a line through *a* and *c* in the force polygon. Any convenient point *m* is selected on the line of this resultant and lines *mA* and *mB* determined. In the force polygon, *af* is then drawn parallel to *Am* and *cf* parallel to *mB*, the intersection determining point *f*, which must lie on the locus of all poles which produce equilibrium polygons passing through points *A* and *B*. This locus is then drawn through point *f*, parallel to *AB*.

Similarly the resultant of forces F_3 and F_4 will pass through point p, and any point n selected on the line of this resultant will determine lines nB and nC. At b, line eg drawn parallel to nc and cg drawn parallel to nc will then locate point g on the locus of poles which produce equilibrium polygons passing through points B and C.

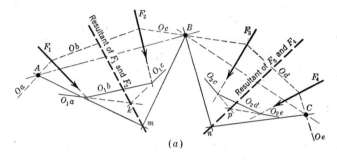

(a)

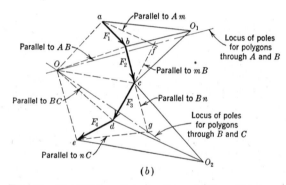

(b)

Fig. 15.　Equilibrium Polygon through Three Points.

Since the polygon is to pass through all three points, the pole must lie on both of these loci, and it therefore coincides with their intersection at O.

A practical application of the problem of passing the equilibrium polygon through three given points is that of determining the reactions of a three-hinged arch. The solution of such a problem is shown in Fig. 30.

29　Distributed Loads

Distributed loads are handled graphically by dividing them into a number of small parts, each such part being then considered as a force. Thus the variable loading shown in Fig. 16 is divided into small parts whose magnitudes can each be conveniently determined, and these are

then assumed to be forces acting at the centers of gravity of the several divisions. The resultant of these assumed forces is then determined in the usual manner. Theoretically the divisions chosen should be infinitesimal in magnitude; practically they must be finite and of such geometric

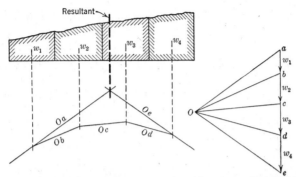

FIG. 16. Graphical Treatment of Distributed Load.

form as will permit easy determination of their magnitudes and centers of gravity. As the number of divisions is increased, there is a corresponding increase in the number of rays in the force polygon and lines of force in the equilibrium polygon. When the divisions are infinitesimal there will be an infinite number of rays and also an infinite number of lines of force, and the corresponding equilibrium polygon, which is the true and correct polygon for such a loading, will be a curve. *The polygon drawn for any number of finite divisions will represent the tangents to*

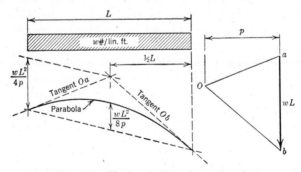

FIG. 17. Uniformly Distributed Load.

the true polygon. In the practical application of graphics to a loading of this character, it is not necessary to employ more divisions than will provide for constructing a smooth inscribed curve such as will closely approximate the true polygon.

The equilibrium polygon for a uniformly distributed loading is a parabolic curve. Some of the convenient properties of this polygon are shown in Fig. 17.

30 Centroids of Areas

The centroid of an area is determined by the same principles that pertain to the finding of the resultant of a force system. The given area is considered as a distributed load acting in any chosen direction. For graphical treatment it is then divided into any number of convenient parts of simple geometric form. The area of each of these parts is then

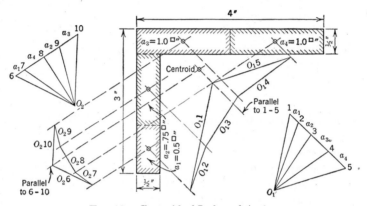

FIG. 18.   Centroid of L-shaped Area.

computed and the location of its centroid established. Each area is then treated as a force having magnitude equivalent to the measure of the area, and all such forces are assumed to constitute a parallel force system. The line of action of the resultant of this assumed force system will then pass through the centroid of the area. The determination of the centroid requires two such solutions with the area loads assumed to act in such directions as will produce a satisfactory intersection of the resultants.

Figure 18 illustrates the graphical determination of the centroid of an L-shaped area.

31 Moment of Inertia

Graphical methods may be used to obtain the moment of inertia of an area. The method developed by Professor Mohr of Aix-la-Chapelle is as follows:

Assume the area shown in Fig. 19 to be subdivided into the elementary areas a_1, a_2, etc. These elementary areas are considered as loads, each

acting at its own centroid and parallel to the axis YY, with reference to which the moment of inertia is to be determined. The force polygon at a is then drawn with a pole distance p of any convenient magnitude. Note that the *pole distance* represents an area to the same scale as is used to lay off a_1, a_2, etc. The corresponding equilibrium polygon is constructed at b and is represented by the polygon *ghkmn*. The tangent lines representing the equilibrium polygon are produced to intersect the axis YY in the points t, p, q, r, s, and v.

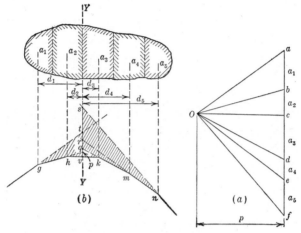

FIG. 19. Moment of Inertia.

By construction triangles gtp and Oab are similar. Therefore

$$\frac{tp}{a_1} = \frac{d_1}{p} \quad \text{and} \quad tp = \frac{a_1 d_1}{p}$$

Hence the product of the intercept tp and the pole distance p gives the statical moment of the area a_1 with respect to the axis YY.

Similarly

$$p \times pv = +a_2 d_2$$

$$p \times qv = -a_3 d_3$$

$$p \times rq = -a_4 d_4$$

$$p \times sr = -a_5 d_5$$

(Counterclockwise moment considered positive.)

The total statical moment is

$$\Sigma ad = p(tp + pv - qv - rq - sr)$$

$$= p \times st$$

Note that when $p =$ unity, the intercepts on the YY axis measure statical moments directly. When p is of any other magnitude these intercepts will measure the statical moment to some scale, depending upon the value of p. Thus, when 1 inch equals n units of distance in the equilibrium polygon, 1 inch of intercept on YY represents a statical moment of np in (units of distance)^3.

Considering again the similar triangles gtp and Oab, we find that

$$a(\text{area } gtp) = tp \times d_1$$

$$= \frac{a_1 d_1}{p} \times d_1 = \frac{a_1 d_1^2}{p}$$

Similar relationships are evident for the other triangles. Hence

$$2(\text{area } gtsnmkhg) = \frac{\Sigma a d^2}{p}$$

And, since $\Sigma a d^2 =$ moment of inertia with respect to YY, it is apparent that the moment of inertia is determined by multiplying twice the pole distance by the area thus obtained from the equilibrium polygon.

Another graphical method, developed by Culmann, produces a value for the moment of inertia by scaling an intercept on the axis of reference. In this method the intercepts tp, pv, vq, gr, etc., are considered as loads applied at the centroid of the corresponding area divisions, a_1, a_2, etc. Thus tp is assumed to replace a_1, pv replaces a_2, etc. Force and equilibrium polygons are then drawn for this second assumed force system, and, by the same process of reasoning used in proving that intercepts tp, pv, etc., represent statical moments of the area, it can be proved that intercepts in this second equilibrium polygon represent moments of inertia of the elemental areas. The total intercept on the YY axis when multiplied by the product of the two pole distances will therefore produce the moment of inertia sought.

The solution of a practical example by each of these methods is shown in Fig. 20. The area is drawn to scale at a and divided into small convenient divisions as shown. These divisions are treated as loads, and the force polygon is constructed at b, and the corresponding equilibrium polygon is drawn at c.

By the Culmann method the intercepts on the axis as determined at c are considered as loads applied at the centroids of the corresponding area divisions. The total intercept ak is used as the load line for the force polygon represented at d, and the loads, which will be positive on one side of the axis and negative on the other, are represented by the

several intercepts. The corresponding equilibrium polygon is represented in Fig. 20e, and the intercept *mn* is scaled. The product of this intercept (measured to the same scale used in laying out the area) with

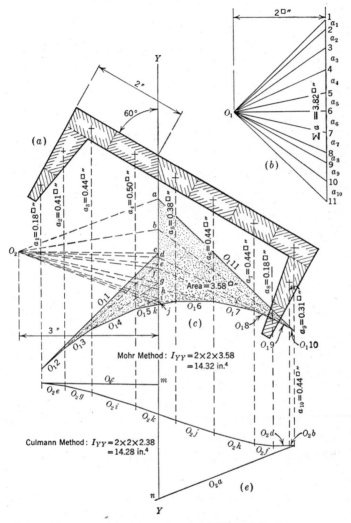

Fig. 20. Moment of Inertia of Channel Section.

the two pole distances gives the moment of inertia of the section with respect to the axis.

It should be noted that theoretically the divisions of the area should be of infinitesimal dimension in a direction normal to the axis. Since

practically they must be finite in size, the resulting equilibrium polygons will actually represent the tangents to the true polygons. The fact that the true polygons are inscribed curves can be utilized in reducing to a minimum the number of area divisions employed.

PROBLEMS

3·1   Find the center of gravity and the moment of inertia about the horizontal axis through the center of gravity.   (*a*) Solve graphically.   (State scales used.) (*b*) Solve analytically.

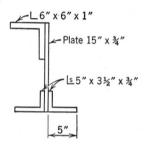

3·2   (*a*) Find position and value of the resultant of the force system *A*, *B*, *C*, and *D*.   Use scale 1 in. = 20 lb, force polygon and 1 in. = 3 ft, equilibrium polygon. (*b*) Check position of the resultant (intersection with line *ad*) analytically.

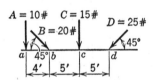

3·3   The loads are applied at the one-third points of lines *AB* and *BC*.   Construct the equilibrium polygon passing through points *A*, *B*, and *D*.   Use scale 1 in. = 10 ft for distances and 1 in. = 15 lb for forces.

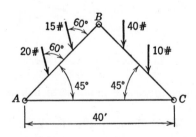

3·4 Find the forces acting in members AB and BC. (*a*) Graphically. (*b*) Analytically.

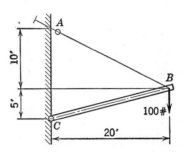

3·5 A system of forces is to be held in equilibrium by a rope passing through points A and B, which are 20 ft apart. (*a*) Determine the length of the suspension ordinates a, b, and c when the tension in the rope at A is 10 lb. (*b*) Determine stress

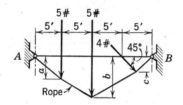

in each part of rope under the conditions of (*a*). (*c*) Assuming that it is permissible for the rope to take any desired form of suspension, what would be the smallest value possible for tension in the rope at B? Use scales $\frac{1}{4}$ in. = 1 ft; 1 in. = 4 lb.

3·6 (*a*) Pass an equilibrium polygon through points G, H, and K. (*b*) Find reactions in direction and amount, graphically. Use scales 1 in. = 10 ft; 1 in. = 10 lb.

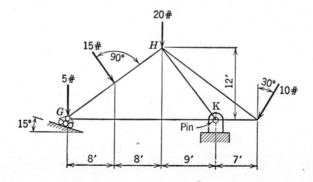

3·7   The forces shown are acting on a chord which is held at A and passes over
a pulley at F.   Neglect weight of chord.   (*a*) Find the form assumed by the chord
when $W = 25$ lb.   Give ordinates from line AF.   (*b*) Find the necessary weight W

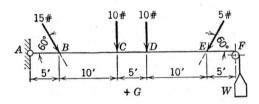

to cause the chord to pass through point G, which is 10 ft below the middle of line
AF.   Use scales 1 in. = 10 ft and 1 in. = 10 lb.

3·8   Pass an equilibrium polygon through points S, M, and K.

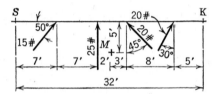

Chapter 4

REACTIONS—SHEAR—BENDING MOMENT

32 Character of Reactions

The supports of a structure may be classed as either (a) *simple*, (b) *hinged*, or (c) *restrained*. These three types are shown diagrammatically in Fig. 21.

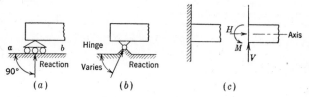

Fig. 21. Reactions.

A *simple support* (Fig. 21a) is one which permits rotation in either direction but prevents translation in one direction. The reaction is therefore a force acting in a line normal to the plane of permitted translation.

A *hinged support* (Fig. 21b) is one which permits rotation in either direction but prevents translation in any direction. The reaction must pass through the center of the hinge, but it may have any line of action through this point.

A *restrained support* (Fig. 21c) is one which provides resistance to rotation and prevents translation in any direction. The resistance of such a support may be regarded as consisting of three component parts: a force to prevent translation in any one given direction, a force to prevent translation in any other direction, and a couple to resist rotation. Usually the two forces preventing translation are regarded in the horizontal and vertical directions, and they are components of the true reaction, which is the resultant of these components and the resisting couple. A support is said to be *fixed* when it develops a resisting couple which prevents rotation of the end of the structure so supported.

If a set of active forces are assumed to act on a body as shown in Fig. 22a, the body can be maintained in a state of equilibrium by a force E, which is equal in magnitude and opposite in direction to the resultant of

the loads.   If equilibrium is to be established by the application of two
or more forces, the force E will be the resultant of such forces.

If the body rests on two simple supports as indicated in Fig. 22b,
equilibrium is possible only when these supports are capable of developing

Typical Support Details.

such resistances as will form the components of the resultant resisting
force E. The reactions shown are the only ones which can maintain
equilibrium of the body for two simple supports with bearing planes at
the given inclinations.   Equilibrium is possible with additional simple
supports in other locations provided that the resultant of the reactive
forces developed at all supports is the force E.   In addition to the foregoing requirement for static equilibrium, the supports must have

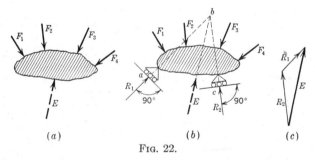

Fig. 22.

sufficient strength to develop resistances of the necessary magnitudes
and directions.

Should the supports be the hinged type as in Fig. 23, the reactions
may have any direction through the hinges but must intersect on the
line of action of the resultant of the loads.   Since the static requirements

for equilibrium can be fulfilled by an infinite number of pairs of reactions, such a problem is termed statically indeterminate. For the solution of such problems it is necessary to take into account the elastic behavior of the structure.

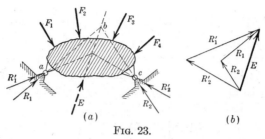

Fig. 23.

When the supports are of the fixed or partially fixed type, the problem is also statically indeterminate, and neither reaction can be established except through a consideration of the elastic behavior of the structure.

33 Graphical Determination of Reactions

Figure 24a represents a beam carrying loads F_1, F_2, and F_3 with a hinged support at the right end and a roller bearing inclined at 45 degrees

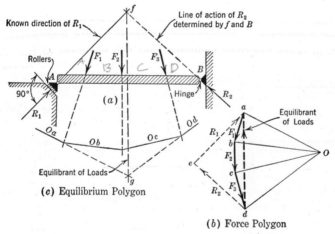

Fig. 24. Graphical Determination of Reactions.

to the horizontal at the other end. In accordance with the principles and methods outlined in Chapter 3, the reactions may be determined graphically as follows:

Lay off the forces F_1, F_2, and F_3 to scale in the force polygon, Fig. 24b, as ab, bc, and cd, and determine the magnitude and directions of

their resultant as *ad*. Select a pole *O* at any convenient point, and construct the force and equilibrium polygons in order to locate the resultant force. Forces may be extended along their lines of action to any convenient location for the equilibrium polygon. Point *g* locates the equilibrant of the forces and is therefore a point on the resultant of the reactions.

Line *gf* through *g* parallel to *da* represents the resultant of the reactions which must intersect a common point on this line. The line of action of R_1 is known so that this point of intersection is located by producing R_1 to intersect line *gf* at *f*, and *fB* gives the direction of R_2.

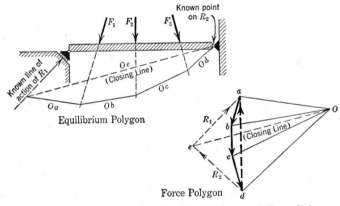

FIG. 25.   Reactions Determined by Equilibrium and Force Polygons.

With the direction of the reactions determined, their magnitudes are determined by drawing *de* and *ea* parallel to *fB* and *Af*.

Figure 25 presents a more direct solution of the same problem and the one which must be used when the reactions intersect at a point inconveniently located on the drawing.

In this solution the equilibrium polygon is drawn so that strings *Oa* and *Od* in the equilibrium polygon will represent components either of R_1 and R_2 or of F_1 and F_3, respectively. Since only one point on R_2 is known, it is obvious that *Od* must be drawn through this point, and the remainder of the equilibrium polygon is thus located with respect to this limited position of string *Od*.

String *Oa* is extended to intersect the known line of action of R_1, and a so-called *closing line* is then drawn from this point to the starting point of the equilibrium polygon at *B*.

A line *Oe* is then drawn in the force polygon parallel to the closing line, and the reactions will intersect on this line and are readily determined from the known direction of R_1.

The proof of this construction is as follows: Assume forces F_1, F_2, and F_3 replaced by their components aO and Ob, bO and Oc, and cO and Od, respectively, the equilibrium polygon locating these components in space. Because of the arrangement all of these components will cancel except component aO of F_1 and Od of F_3. Continue aO to intersect R_1, and at this point assume R_1 resolved into components Oa and eO; component Oa of R_1 will cancel component aO of F_1, leaving only the component eO. Continue Od to intersect R_2, and at this point assume R_2 resolved into components dO and Oe; component dO of R_2 will cancel component Od of F_3, leaving component Oe. Since by construction components eO of R_1 and Oe of R_2 are of the same magnitude and have the same line of action, they will cancel, proving equilibrium of the beam when acted upon by forces thus determined.

34   Analytical Determination of Reactions

Reactions are usually determined by analytical methods. The external forces, loads, couples, and reactions constitute a force system which must be in equilibrium if the structure is to remain at rest. The conditions which must be fulfilled when all the constituent parts of this force system lie in the same plane are expressed by the static equations $\Sigma F_x = 0$, $\Sigma F_y = 0$, and $\Sigma M = 0$, where F_x and F_y represent components of the forces in the directions of any convenient pair of coordinate axes, and M represents either the moment of any force about any point in the plane of the force system or the value of any couple included in the system. When all the parts of the external force system do not lie in the same plane, six equations of condition must be fulfilled, namely $\Sigma F_x = 0$, $\Sigma F_y = 0$, $\Sigma F_z = 0$, $\Sigma M_{xy} = 0$, $\Sigma M_{xz} = 0$, and $\Sigma M_{zy} = 0$. For purposes of analysis and design, most structures can be divided into parts such that the external force system on any part may be considered as lying in a plane.

At each *simple support* the arrangement of the construction will establish the direction and location of the reactive force, hence there is but one unknown left to be determined at each such point. This unknown is the *magnitude* of the reaction. It should be noted that for such a structure as a beam resting on a wall the reaction is distributed over the area of contact or *bearing area*. Such a support is usually regarded as of the simple type, and the reactive force, which is the resultant of the distributed bearing pressures, is considered as acting at the centroid of the bearing area. For an exceptionally long bearing area (measured in the direction of the span) the distance from the inside edge of the support to the reaction is generally arbitrarily assumed to be not greater than one-half the depth of the beam. The *span length* for a simply sup-

ported beam is the distance between the reactions. The *clear span* is the distance between the inside faces of the supports.

At each *hinged support* the reaction must act through the hinge, and there are two unknowns to be determined at each such support. These are the magnitude and the direction of the reaction. Since the horizontal and vertical components of the reactions will completely determine these unknowns, they are the values usually computed. A structure with two hinged supports is statically indeterminate since there are more unknowns than there are equations of static equilibrium. An exception is noted for the three-hinged arch, as will be described later.

For each *restrained* or *fixed support* there are three unknowns: the horizontal component of the reaction, the vertical component, and the couple necessary to restrain or prevent rotation. Hence a structure with more than one fixed or restrained support is statically indeterminate.

As regards reaction determinations, statically determinate structures are therefore limited to those supported by (*a*) *two* simple supports; (*b*) *one* simple support and one hinged support; (*c*) *two* hinged supports, provided that an intermediate hinge is placed in the structure between the supports, as for a three-hinged arch; (*d*) *one* fixed support.

35 Reactions for Fixed Loads

When the position of the loading has been established, the reactions may be determined by solving the equations for static equilibrium. The procedure is illustrated in the following examples:

Example 1 (Fig. 26*a*)

Beam simply supported at A and B; with B as center of moments, write $\Sigma M = 0$.

$$20R_A - (500 \times 16) - (120 \times 10 \times 5) = 0$$

$$R_A = \frac{8000 + 6000}{20} = 700 \text{ lb}$$

From $\Sigma V = 0$

$$R_A - 500 - (120 \times 10) + R_B = 0$$

$$R_B = 500 + 1200 - 700 = 1000 \text{ lb}$$

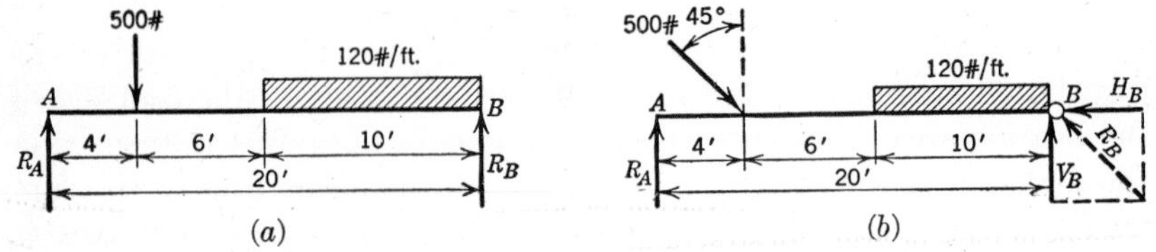

Fig. 26.

Example 2 (Fig. 26b)

Beam simply supported at A and hinged at B.

Resolve 500-lb load into horizontal and vertical components at its intersection with line AB.

$$\text{Horizontal component} = 500 \times 0.7 = 350 \text{ lb}$$

$$\text{Vertical component} \quad = \quad\quad\quad 350 \text{ lb}$$

With B as center of moments, write $\Sigma M = 0$.

$$20R_A - (350 \times 16) - (120 \times 10 \times 5) = 0$$

$$R_A = \frac{5600 + 6000}{20} = 580 \text{ lb}$$

From $\Sigma V = 0$,

$$V_B = 350 + 1200 - 580 = 970 \text{ lb}$$

From $\Sigma H = 0$,

$$H_B = 350 \text{ lb}$$

$$R_B = \sqrt{(350)^2 + (970)^2} = 1030 \text{ lb}$$

Example 3 (Fig. 27)

Truss simply supported at A, hinged at B, and with loads as shown. Note that loads are given in *kips*.[1] The resultant load is 30K and will pass through point D, where it is resolved into horizontal and vertical components.

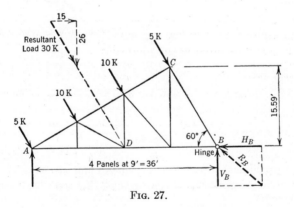

FIG. 27.

$$\Sigma M = 0, \text{ center at } B \quad\quad R_A = \frac{26 \times 18}{36} = 13\text{K}$$

$$\Sigma V = 0 \quad\quad\quad\quad\quad\quad V_B = R_A \quad\quad = 13\text{K}$$

$$\Sigma H = 0 \quad\quad\quad\quad\quad\quad H_B = \quad\quad\quad\quad 15\text{K}$$

[1] The term *kip* is an abbreviation of *kilo-pound* and designates one thousand pounds of force or load. In structural work loads are commonly expressed in *kips* as designated by the symbol K.

Example 4 (Fig. 28)

Beam simply supported at A and B acted upon at section B by a clockwise couple which has a magnitude of 1000 ft-lb.

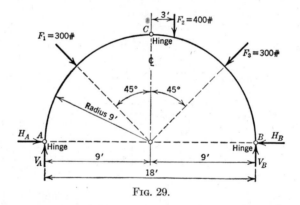

$$\Sigma M_B = 0 - 20R_A + 1000 = 0$$

$$R_A = 50 \text{ lb (acting downward)}$$

$$\Sigma F_v = 0 \qquad R_B = 50 \text{ lb (acting upward)}$$

Fig. 28.

Example 5

If the couple shown in Fig. 28 is applied to the beam in Fig. 26a, the reactions may be found from the solutions of Examples 1 and 4, thus

$$R_A = 700 - 50 = 650 \text{ lb (acting upward)}$$

$$R_B = 1000 + 50 = 1050 \text{ lb (acting upward)}$$

Example 6 (Fig. 29)

Three-hinged arch with loads as shown.   Note that although the hinged reactions at A and B involve four unknowns, the introduction of a hinge at C provides

Fig. 29.

an additional conditional requirement for equilibrium, namely that the forces and reaction acting on segment AC (or segment BC) must have zero moment about C as a center.

F_1 and F_3 may be resolved into horizontal and vertical components at their intersections with AB, thus

Horizontal component $F_1 = 300 \times 0.7 = 210$ lb

Vertical component $\quad F_1 = \qquad\qquad 210$ lb

Horizontal component $F_3 = \qquad\qquad 210$ lb

Vertical component $\quad F_3 = \qquad\qquad 210$ lb

$\Sigma M = 0$ (moment center at hinge B)

$$18V_A - (210 \times 9) - (210 \times 9) - (400 \times 6) = 0$$

$$V_A = 343 \text{ lb}$$

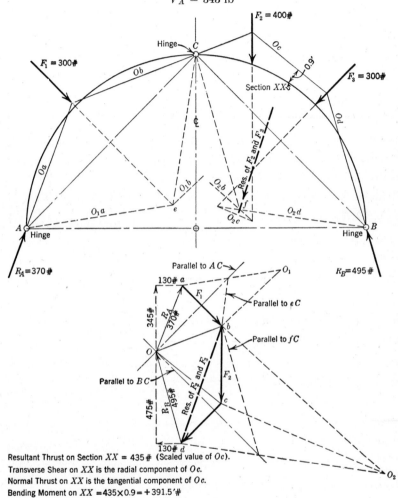

Resultant Thrust on Section XX = 435 # (Scaled value of Oc).

Transverse Shear on XX is the radial component of Oc.

Normal Thrust on XX is the tangential component of Oc.

Bending Moment on XX = $435 \times 0.9 = +391.5'$#

Fig. 30. Graphical Solution for Three-Hinged Arch.

$\Sigma V = 0$

$$V_B + 343 - 210 - 400 - 210 = 0$$

$$V_B = 477 \text{ lb}$$

$\Sigma M_c = 0$ (forces on segment AC, hinge C as center)

$$- 9H_A + (343 \times 9) - (210 \times 9) = 0$$

$$H_A = 133 \text{ lb}$$

$\Sigma H = 0$ (entire structure)

$$133 + 210 - 210 - H_B = 0$$

$$H_A = 133 \text{ lb}$$

$$R_A = \sqrt{(343)^2 + (133)^2} = 368 \text{ lb}$$

$$R_B = \sqrt{(477)^2 + (133)^2} = 495 \text{ lb}$$

The graphical solution of this problem, shown in Fig. 30, involves passing an equilibrium polygon through the three points A, B, and C in accordance with the procedures given in Article 28. Oa will then represent the magnitude and direction of the reaction at A, and dO the magnitude and direction of the reaction at B.

To facilitate computations for a particular type of loading, data may be prepared in the form of a so-called *moment table*, such as is shown in Table 2 for Cooper's E-60 engine loading. The following example illustrates the use of this moment table for computing the reactions of a simply supported span:

Example

Span, 150 ft; axle 7 at a point 100 ft from right support.

Reading under load 7 in set 1, we see that load 1 is 37 ft from load 7 and is therefore on the span. Reading under the end of the uniform load in set 7, we see that the distance from axle 7 to the beginning of the uniform load is 72 ft, and there are, therefore, 28 ft of uniform load on the span. The total moment of all loads about the right support will equal the moment of all axle loads about the last load (or end of the uniform load), plus the product of the sum of such loads and the distance from the last load (or end of the uniform load) to the right support, plus the moment of the uniform load about the right support. Thus

Total wheel loading, loads 1 to 18 inclusive	= 426,000 lb	
Distance from end of uniform load to right support	= 28 ft	
Moment of wheel loads 1 to 18 inclusive about the end of the uniform load (read under end of uniform load set 1)	=	24,546,000 ft-lb
426,000 $\times$ 28	=	11,928,000
Moment of uniform load = 3000 $\times$ 28 $\times$ 14	=	1,176,000
Total moment about right support	=	37,650,000 ft-lb

$$R_L = \frac{37,650,000}{150} = 251,000 \text{ lb}$$

36 Reactions Caused by Live Loads

The live loading applied to a structure is commonly of such character that it may shift its position, or move from point to point in the span; hence it is necessary to place this loading in the position which produces maximum effect on the structure. Since the live load may be changed in position or even entirely removed, whereas the dead load is fixed, it is desirable to determine separately the effect of each loading, assuming that each acts independently of the others. The results may then be combined in accordance with the nature and probability of coincidence of the several loadings considered.

The effect of the position of a load on the reaction can be studied by considering a single load of unity moving across the span. Thus in Fig. 31 the load $F = 1$ pound is assumed to move across the span from

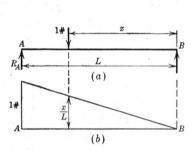

Fig. 31. Influence Line for Reaction.

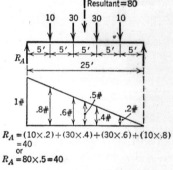

$$R_A = (10 \times .2) + (30 \times .4) + (30 \times .6) + (10 \times .8)$$
$$= 40$$
or
$$R_A = 80 \times .5 = 40$$

Fig. 32. Reaction Determined from Influence Line.

B to A. The distance x will thus vary from $x = 0$, when the load is directly over B, to $x = L$, when the load is directly over A. For the load at any given point between B and A as shown at a, the value of $R_A = x/L$. All the possible values of R_A are given by the graph at b, where AB represents the span to scale, and the ordinate represents the scale value of R_A when the unit load is at a corresponding point in the span. This graph is called an *influence line*.

For a load of magnitude F, $R_A = Fx/L$; hence the reaction equals the product of such a load and its corresponding influence line ordinate. If several loads occupy the span, $R_A = \Sigma(Fx/L)$; hence the reaction is the sum of the products of loads and their corresponding influence line ordinates (Fig. 32). Since the ordinates in this influence line are each proportional to x, the value of R_A for a system of concentrated loads will equal the product of the resultant of the loads and the influence line ordinate corresponding to such resultant. The maximum value of R_A

will therefore be obtained when the resultant of the loads is located as near A as possible; thus with the loads in Fig. 32 moved 5 feet to the left, $R_A = 80 \times 0.7 = 56$. With any further movement to the left, F_1 will be removed from the span thus creating a new load system whose resultant again must be placed as near A as possible. This condition will place load F_2 at A and $R_A = (30 \times 1) + (30 \times 0.8) + (10 \times 0.6) = 60$. To determine the maximum possible value of R_A, all load positions must thus be studied.

The reaction for a partial uniform loading may be obtained from the influence line as in Fig. 33. Thus the reaction at A produced by an element of loading $w\,dx$ is $(w\,dx)y$, and for the entire load

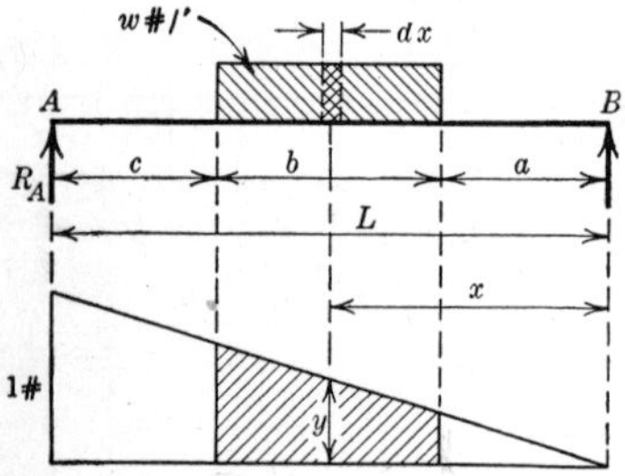

$$R_A = \int_a^{a+b} w\,dx \cdot y = w \int_a^{a+b} y\,dx \quad (20)$$

Hence the reaction is equal to the product of the load per unit of span length and the area of the portion of the influence line diagram that is in projection under the uniform load. The maximum reaction for such a load would be produced by placing the load immediately adjacent to the support and, for a uniform load of unlimited extent, by loading the entire span.

Fig. 33. Uniformly Distributed Load Applies to Influence Line.

37   Internal Forces

The internal forces which exist at any point in a structure may be determined by dividing the structure into two parts by a cutting section at the point to be investigated and establishing the complete force system necessary to produce equilibrium of either portion. Thus the internal forces on a section located 6 feet from A in the beam shown in Fig. 26b are determined by cutting the beam at this point and applying the equations of static equilibrium to the force system acting on either portion as in Fig. 34. Thus for the part on left of section

$$\Sigma H = 0 \qquad N = 500 \times 0.7 = 350 \text{ lb (horizontal)}$$

$$\Sigma V = 0 \qquad V = 580 - (500 \times 0.7) = 230 \text{ lb (vertical)}$$

$$\Sigma M = 0 \text{ (moment center at intersection of } N \text{ and } V)$$

$$M = (580 \times 6) - (500 \times 0.7 \times 2) = 2780 \text{ ft-lb}$$
$$\text{(counterclockwise)}$$

Thus the forces N and V, together with the couple M, will combine with the loads and reaction on this part of the beam to provide a force system in equilibrium. The resultant of the loads and reaction on this part of the beam is the resultant force on the section. The resultant of

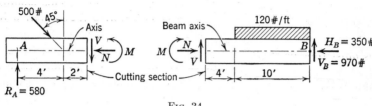

FIG. 34.

N, V, and the couple M must be equal and opposite to that for the loads and reactions on this part. Similarly, considering portion on right,

$$\Sigma H = 0 \qquad N = H_B = 350 \text{ lb}$$

$$\Sigma V = 0 \qquad V = (120 \times 10) - 970 = 230 \text{ lb}$$

$\Sigma M = 0$ (moment center at intersection of N and V)

$$M = (970 \times 14) - (1200 \times 9) = 2780 \text{ ft-lb (clockwise)}$$

For beams, it is the conventional practice to pass the cutting section in a direction normal to the axis of the beam and to determine the components N and V, of the resultant force on the section, normal and parallel respectively to this section. N is located at the intersection of the axis of the beam with the cutting section (through the centroid of the effective cross section) and is called the *normal thrust*. V acts in the plane of the section and is called the *transverse shear* or *shear*. When N and V are determined in accordance with the above convention, M is known as the *bending-moment*.

For frames, such as the one represented in Fig. 27, the members are assumed to be joined by pins in such a manner that the force in any member will coincide with the axis of the member. The forces in such members as are cut by the section which divides the structure into parts will, together with the loads and reaction on any such part, constitute a force system in equilibrium.

38 Shear and Bending-Moment Due to Fixed Loads

When all the forces on one side of the section are resolved into components parallel and normal to the section, the shear will equal the algebraic sum of the components parallel to the section. In a hori-

zontal beam it will equal the algebraic sum of the vertical components of those loads and the reaction, which are on one side of the section.

For convenience in identifying the direction of shearing action in a horizontal structure, the shear is called positive when the resultant force

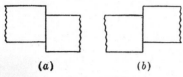

(a)   **(b)**

Positive Shear.   Negative Shear.

FIG. 35.

on the left of the section acts upward, thus producing the tendency shown at Fig. 35a; action in the opposite direction is called negative shear (Fig. 35b).

A *shear diagram* is the graphical record of the shears which occur simultaneously on all sections of a structure (Fig. 36a). Such diagrams are usually plotted on a base normal to the direction of the cutting sections (for a beam, the base would be drawn parallel to the axis) with positive shear plotted above the base line and negative shear below.

Bending-moment was defined as the algebraic sum of the moments of the forces (including N and V) on one side of a section with reference to a selected moment center. For beams, the moment center is conveniently chosen at the intersection of the axis of the beam with the cutting section; hence the bending-moment will equal the algebraic sum of the moments of such loads and the reaction, which are on one side of the section with respect to this center. For trusses, moment centers are located at the truss joints.

For convenience in identifying the direction of bending-moment action, a resultant clockwise rotation of the forces and reaction on the left of the section, with respect to the moment center, is called positive. Negative bending-moment thus indicates a resultant tendency of the loads and reaction to rotate that part of the structure on the left of the section in a counterclockwise direction. In a horizontal beam, it will be noted that positive bending-moment causes the beam to sag downward or to assume a curvature which has its center above the axis of the beam. Positive bending-moment will therefore tend to produce tension in the bottom fibers of a beam, and negative bending-moment will tend to produce compression in the bottom fibers.

Simultaneous values of the bending-moments on all sections of a structure may be recorded graphically in the form of a *bending-moment diagram* (Fig. 36b).

Values of the maximum bending-moment and form of the bending-moment diagram for cases of simple loading on horizontal beams should be memorized. Thus for a single concentrated load, the bending-moment diagram is a triangle with maximum ordinate under the load; the

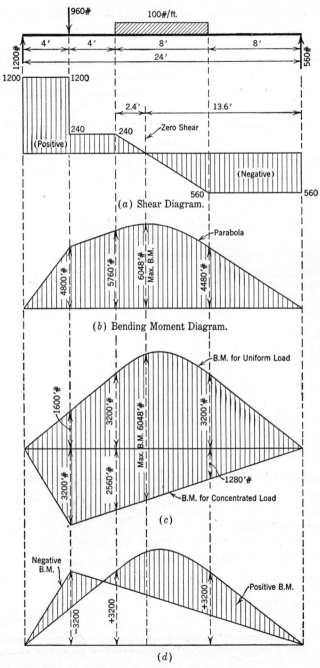

(a) Shear Diagram.

(b) Bending Moment Diagram.

(c)

(d)

FIG. 36.   Shear and Bending-Moment Diagrams.

maximum bending-moment equals the product of the load with the lengths of the two segments into which its position divides the span, divided by the span length. For a uniformly distributed load of w lb per sq linear ft the bending-moment diagram is a parabola with maximum ordinate at the center of the span equal to $wL^2/8$.

39   Relationship between Shear and Bending Moment

When a beam is acted upon by a system of loads perpendicular to its axis, it can be shown [2] that the shear is the first derivative of the bending-moment $(V = dM/dx)$. Since dM/dx measures the slope of the bending-moment curve, it follows that a maximum (or minimum) bending-moment will occur at the points where $dM/dx = V = 0$. Thus sections of zero shear identify locations of potential maximum bending-moment.

Another useful relationship is obtained by integrating the expression $dM = V\,dx$. Thus if M_1 and M_2 represent the values of the bending-moments on two sections located at distances a_1 and a_2, respectively, from the left support,

$$\int_{M_1}^{M_2} dM = \int_{a_1}^{a_2} V\,dx$$

and $M_2 - M_1 =$ area of shear diagram between the two given sections. Referring to Fig. 36a, we note that the bending-moment at a point 8 feet from the left support is 5760 foot-pounds; at 4 feet from the support the bending-moment is 4800-foot-pounds. The difference is 960 foot-pounds and equals the area of the shear diagram between these two points, or $240 \times 4 = 960$ foot-pounds.

This relationship may be used to compute the bending-moment at any section, since

$$M_2 = M_1 + \text{(area of shear diagram between sections)}$$

Thus the bending-motion at the left end of the uniform load is

$M_1 = $ bending-moment at the concentrated load $= 4800$ ft-lb

Area of shear diagram between concentrated load and uniform load $= 240 \times 4$ $=\ \ \ 960$ ft-lb

$M_2 = 4800 + 960$ $= 5760$ ft-lb

If section 1 is located adjacent to the support, where $M_1 = 0$, it will be seen that the bending-moment on any other section equals the net area

[2] S. Timoshenko, *Strength of Materials*, Part I, p. 108, D. Van Nostrand Co., 1930.

of that portion of the shear diagram which is on either side of such a section. Thus for the section 8 feet from the *right* support

$$M = (1200 \times 4) + (240 \times 4) + (\tfrac{1}{2} \times 240 \times 2.4) - (\tfrac{1}{2} \times 560 \times 5.6)$$

$$= 4800 + 960 + 288 - 1568 = 4480 \text{ ft-lb}$$

It should be noted that, for restrained or fixed beams, M_1 must be included in the computation of bending-moment.

40 Superposing Shear or Bending-Moment Values

It is sometimes convenient to separate the loads on a structure into individual units or groups, calculating the value of the shear, bending-moment, or other effect separately for each unit or group and finally combining these separately determined results to obtain the effect of the combined loading. Thus, for the beam shown in Fig. 36, if the concentrated load is considered as acting alone, the bending-moment under the load is 3200 foot-pounds. For the uniform load acting alone, the bending-moment on this same section is 1600 foot-pounds. When these loads are applied simultaneously, the bending-moment is the algebraic sum of these separately determined values, or 4800 foot-pounds.

The bending-moment diagram for one portion of the loading may be superposed on that for another in such a manner that the ordinates combine graphically to show the resultant effect of the combined loading. The bending-moment diagram for the foregoing beam is thus constructed as shown at *c*. The effect produced by reversing the direction of the concentrated load which would introduce negative bending-moments, to be combined with the positive bending-moment, is as shown at *d*.

41 Influence Line for Shear

The shear on a given section produced by live loading may be studied by means of influence lines constructed in a similar manner to those for reactions as discussed in Article 36. It is necessary to recognize two types of structural conditions: (1) where the loads are applied directly to the structure, and (2) where loads are applied to a floor system or intermediate construction which is supported by the main structure.

The influence line for shear (Fig. 37*b*) on any section of a structure representing the first type is a combination of the influence lines for the reactions at either end of the structure as shown at *a*. With a unit load in the position shown, $R_A = \tfrac{1}{3}$ pound, and, since there are no other forces acting on the portion of the structure on the left of xx, this is also the value of the shear on this section and is represented by the ordinate

in the influence line under the load. The influence line for shear may be employed in finding the shear caused by a number of loads or by a uniformly distributed load in the same manner as discussed in Article 36. Thus in Fig. 37 assume two concentrated loads of 1000 pounds each located at 8 feet and 12 feet, respectively, from B. The influence-line ordinate under the load nearer the support is $+\frac{1}{3}$ pound and under the

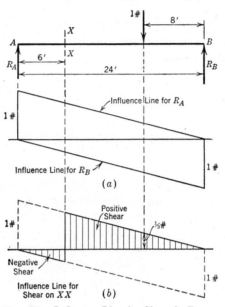

Fig. 37.   Influence Line for Shear in Beam.

other load $+\frac{1}{2}$ pound. The shear is then equal to $(1000 \times \frac{1}{3}) + (1000 \times \frac{1}{2}) = +833$ pounds. It will readily be seen from the influence line that these loads will produce greater shear if moved toward the section, since the influence-line ordinates will correspondingly increase. The influence line is thus useful in visualizing load positions which produce maximum shear. For a uniformly distributed load, since the shear equals the intensity of loading (load per unit of span length) multiplied by the projected area of the influence line under the load, it will be noted that maximum positive shear will occur on section xx when such a load extends from B to the section. For a uniform load of 100 pounds per foot, the maximum positive shear may then be computed as follows:

Influence-line ordinate at section $= \frac{18}{24} \times 1 = \frac{3}{4}$ lb

Area of influence-line diagram under load $= \frac{1}{2} \times \frac{3}{4} \times 18 = \frac{27}{4}$

Shear $= 100 \times \frac{27}{4} = +675$ lb

The second type of structural arrangement is illustrated in Fig. 38. In this type, the live loading is applied to an intermediate construction or superstructure whose reactions produce loads on the main structure at a, b, c, d, and e. Usually this intermediate construction is an arrangement of simple beams, and in such a case the reactive forces at these panel points are determined in accordance with the principles previously outlined for reactions. Thus, any loading applied on the superstructure between c and d would produce loads on the main structure only at these two points. The reasoning applied to the construction of the influence line in Fig. 38 is as follows: For a unit load acting on the superstructure at any point between c and e, the only force acting on that portion of the main structure on the left of section xx is R_A; therefore, the influence line corresponding with such load positions will coincide with that for R_A. Now if the unit load is moved into panel bc, starting from c, R_A will increase as indicated by its influence-line ordinates, but a reactive load will also be created at b which must be subtracted

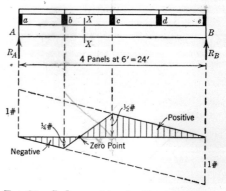

Fig. 38. Influence Line for Shear in Girder.

from R_A to determine the shear on the section at xx. The joint load at b varies directly with the position of the unit load in panel bc, from a value of zero when the unit load is at c to unity when it is placed at b. This produces the sloping portion of the influence line between c and b. When the unit load arrives at b, the deduction is unity and the influence line hence coincides with that for R_B. The zero point is a significant feature of this influence line, any load to the right of this point causing positive shear and to the left producing negative shear. It may readily be located from point c by the following proportion:

Let x = distance from c to zero point.

Then by similar triangles

$$\frac{x}{6} = \frac{\frac{1}{2}}{\frac{1}{2} + \frac{1}{4}}$$

$$x = \frac{6 \times \frac{1}{2}}{\frac{3}{4}} = 4 \text{ ft}$$

A uniform load will produce maximum positive shear on section xx when

it extends from support B to the zero point; it will produce maximum negative shear when it extends from support A to the zero point.

42 Influence Line for Bending-Moment

The influence line for bending-moment is developed by applying principles previously discussed. Thus in Fig. 39 let a unit load act at any point on the right of section xx. Since $R_A = x/L$ is the only force on the left of xx, the bending-moment will equal xa/L and is plotted as an ordinate under the given position of the unit load.

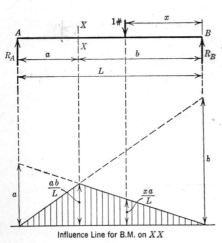

Other positions of the load produce ordinates which define that portion of the influence line corresponding to segment b of the structure. When the unit load acts on the left of section xx, $R_B = (L - x)/L$ and the bending-moment equals $(L - x)b/L$.

Influence Line for B.M. on XX

Fig. 39. Influence Line for Bending Moment.

From this influence line it is readily seen that a load at any point causes positive bending-moment on any given section; that a single concentrated load will produce maximum bending-moment when placed at the section; and that a uniform load will produce maximum positive bending-moment when it extends over the entire span.

43 Concentrated Load Systems—Maximum Shear

When a series of concentrated live loads is applied to a beam, it is apparent from a consideration of the shear influence line that to produce maximum shear the loads should be spaced as closely as permissible. Let a, b, c, etc., represent those minimum distances, and consider the condition where loads are applied directly to the structure as in Fig. 40. If it is assumed that the loading moves across the structure from right to left as at a, the positive shear will increase as the loads move toward the left until load 1 arrives at a point immediately to the right of the section as at b. If W_1 represents the total load on the structure and $W_1 x_1$ the total moment of all loads about the right support, the shear on the section is

$$V_1 = \frac{W_1 x_1}{L} \qquad (21)$$

Now if the loads are moved further to the left as at *c*, load 1 will produce negative shear, and as the loads move further to the left the negative shear caused by load 1 will diminish while the positive shear caused by the remaining loads will increase. If the shear is increased by this shift in position of the loading, the movement to the left should be continued

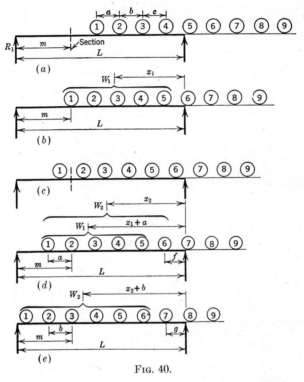

FIG. 40.

until load 2 reaches the section, as at *d*, when a second determination of the shear must be made. With the loading in this position, the shear on the section will be

$$V_2 = \frac{W_2 x_2}{L} - P_1 = \frac{W_1(x_1 + a)}{L} + \frac{P_6 f}{L} - P_1$$

$$= \frac{W_1 x_1}{L} + \frac{W_1 a}{L} + \frac{P_6 f}{L} - P_1 \tag{22}$$

Similarly the next position to consider will be that shown at *e* and

$$V_3 = \frac{W_2 x_2}{L} + \frac{W_2 b}{L} + \frac{P_7 g}{L} - P_1 - P_2 \tag{23}$$

Comparing these values, we see that

$$V_2 > V_1 \text{ when } \left[\frac{W_1 a}{L} + \frac{P_6 f}{L}\right] > P_1 \tag{24a}$$

$$V_3 > V_2 \text{ when } \left[\frac{W_2 b}{L} + \frac{P_7 g}{L}\right] > P_2 \tag{24b}$$

In accordance with the foregoing procedure the criterion for comparing values of shear produced, by any two positions of the loading, is as follows. With the loading assumed to move across the structure from right to left, let A refer to any position with a given load P_n at the section. Let B refer to a position with any succeeding load at the section,

where V_A = value of shear on section with loading in position A.

     V_B = value of shear on section with loading in position B.

     W = sum of all loads on span when loading is in position A (include loads over supports).

    ΣP = sum of all loads, including P_n, which cross the section in shifting loading from position A to position B.

      c = distance loading moves from right to left in shifting from position A to position B.

    M_L = moment about the left support of all loads which run off the span in shifting from position A to position B.

    M_R = moment about the right support of all loads which come on the span in shifting from position A to position B.

Then

$$V_B > V_A, \text{ when } \left[\frac{Wc - M_L + M_R}{L}\right] > \Sigma P \tag{25}$$

When the loads are transmitted to the structure through an intermediate construction (Fig. 41) a more direct procedure may be used. From a consideration of the influence line at b it is apparent that for positive shear in panel ab, panel point b is the critical load point, and the loads must be located with one of the loads at this point. With loads arranged to meet this requirement as at a,

where W = total load on the span.

     W_1 = total load in the panel where the section is located.

     W_2 = total load on that part of the structure on the left of the given panel.

The actual loads delivered by the floor system to the structure will be those shown at c and the shear on section xx is

$$V = R_L - W_2 - r \qquad (26)$$

$$= \frac{Wx}{L} - W_2 - \frac{W_1 x_1}{p} \qquad (27)$$

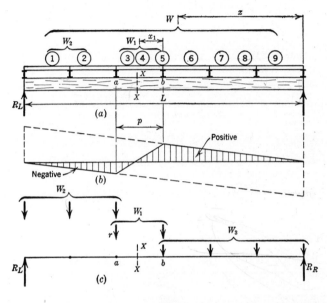

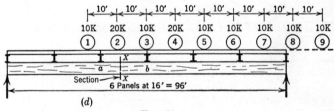

FIG. 41.

If this position of load produces maximum shear, the value dV/dx will pass through zero as the load at b crosses panel point b; hence,

$$\frac{dV}{dx} = \frac{W}{L} - \frac{W_1}{p} = 0 \qquad (28)$$

and

$$\frac{Wp}{L} = W_1 \qquad (29)$$

Note that dx_1 equals dx since the loads remain at fixed distances apart, and that it is assumed that no loads come on or run off the span when the loading is moved an infinitesimal distance right or left.

As the particular load at b moves across this point, the value of W_1 will change from

W_1 (min) = total load in panel ab excluding the individual load at point b

to

W_1 (max) = total load in panel ab including the individual load at point b.

For maximum shear, therefore, the loads must be so arranged on the span that

$$\frac{Wp}{L} \genfrac{}{}{0pt}{}{< W_1 \text{ (max)}}{> W_1 \text{ (min)}} \tag{30}$$

At d the live loading shown is spaced at 10-foot intervals and may occupy any position on the span. When the loading is arranged on the span in the manner shown, with load 3 at point b,

$$\frac{Wp}{L} = \frac{90 \times 16}{96} = 15 \genfrac{}{}{0pt}{}{< W_1 \text{ (max)} = 30}{< W_1 \text{ (min)} = 20}$$

This position does not satisfy the criterion and hence will not cause maximum shear in panel ab. Try placing the loading with load 2 at point b.

$$\frac{Wp}{L} = \frac{80 \times 16}{96} = 13\tfrac{1}{3} \genfrac{}{}{0pt}{}{< W_1 \text{ (max)} = 30}{> W_1 \text{ (min)} = 10}$$

This position satisfies the criterion, thus indicating a potential maximum, and the corresponding shear must therefore be computed. Try placing the loading with load 4 at point b.

$$\frac{Wp}{L} = \frac{100 \times 16}{96} = 16\tfrac{2}{3} \genfrac{}{}{0pt}{}{< W_1 \text{ (max)} = 30}{> W_1 \text{ (min)} = 10}$$

This position also satisfies the criterion and the corresponding shear must also be computed. Since other positions will obviously produce

less positive shear, the maximum positive shear is computed as follows:

Load 2 at b

Left reaction R_L = 28.5 kips

Total load between R_L and a = 0

Joint load at $a = \dfrac{10 \times 10}{16} = \underline{6.25}$

6.25

___

Shear on xx = +22.25 kips

Load 4 at b

Left reaction R_L = 47.8 kips

Total load between R_L and a = 30

Joint load at a due to loads in panel $= \dfrac{10 \times 10}{16} = \underline{6.25}$

36.25

___

Shear on xx = +11.55 kips

Maximum shear is therefore obtained by placing load 2 at *b*.

The same principles apply for determining negative shear with *a* as the critical point at which one of the loads must be placed.

44 Concentrated Load Systems—Maximum Bending-Moment

From a consideration of the influence line for bending-moment (Fig. 39), it is apparent that every load placed on the structure produces positive bending-moment and that the loads should be spaced at minimum distances apart. As the given system of concentrated loads moves from right to left across the span, the bending-moment will steadily

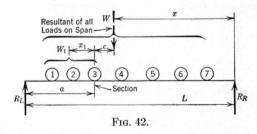

Fig. 42.

increase until the first load reaches the section. If the loading is moved further to the left, the effect of load 1 will diminish and that of the remaining loads will increase. If the total bending-moment has been increased by such additional movement of the loads, it is therefore

obvious that this increase will continue until the next load arrives at the section.   It can therefore be concluded that the maximum bending-moment will always occur when one of the loads is at the given section. In Fig. 42, the loads are placed to fulfill this condition and

$$R_L = \frac{Wx}{L} \qquad (31)$$

$$M = R_L a - W_1 x_1 = \frac{Wxa}{L} - W_1 x_1 \qquad (32)$$

where W = total load on the span.
  Wx = moment of all loads about right support.
  W_1 = total load on left of section.
  $W_1 x_1$ = moment of all loads on left of section about a point on the section.

In order for this position of loading to cause maximum bending-moment, the value dM/dx must pass through zero as the individual concentrated load at the section crosses this point; hence

$$\frac{dM}{dx} = \frac{Wa}{L} - W_1 = 0 \qquad (33)$$

and

$$\frac{Wa}{L} = W_1 \qquad (34)$$

As the individual concentrated load at the section moves across this point in the span, the value of W_1 will successively equal all values between W_1 (min), excluding the individual load at the section, to W_1 (max), including the individual load at the section; therefore for maximum bending-moment

$$\frac{Wa}{L} \begin{array}{c} < W_1 \text{ (max)} \\ = \\ > W_1 \text{ (min)} \end{array} \qquad (35)$$

Example

  For a practical application of this criterion, refer to Fig. 42 and assume that $L = 40$ feet and $a = 15$ feet, with the loads spaced at 4-foot intervals and of magnitudes, in kips, corresponding to the load numbers.   For the loading in the position shown

$$\frac{Wa}{L} = \frac{28 \times 15}{40} = 10.5 \text{ kips} \begin{array}{l} > W_1 \text{ (max)} = 6 \text{ kips} \\ > W_1 \text{ (min)} = 3 \text{ kips} \end{array}$$

The criterion is not fulfilled, and therefore this position does not produce maximum bending-moment.   It is also obvious that there is insufficient load on the

left of the section. Try position with load 5 at section; load 1 will now be off the span.

$$\frac{Wa}{L} = \frac{27 \times 15}{40} = 10.1 \text{ kips} \quad \begin{array}{l} < W_1 \text{ (max)} = 14 \text{ kips} \\ > W_1 \text{ (min)} = 9 \text{ kips} \end{array}$$

Observation indicates this to be the only position which will satisfy the criterion, and therefore it will cause maximum bending-moment on the section.

When the loads are applied to the structure through an intermediate construction, the greatest bending-moments will occur at the panel points or joints, and usually they are computed only at such points. In applying the criterion and computing the bending-moments at panel points of structures of this type, the concentrated loads may be assumed to be applied directly to the structure at the points where such loads act on the superstructure. Referring to Fig. 41, it is easily computed that the bending-moment on a section at b, determined from the actual loads on the structure indicated at c, is the same as is obtained at this point by using the original loads shown at a. If, however, the bending-moment on an intermediate section, such as xx, is desired, the actual loads, as at c, must be taken into account. The criterion previously developed for placing loadings to produce maximum bending-moment will therefore not be applicable for such intermediate sections.

45   Absolute Maximum Bending-Moment

Let Fig. 42 represent a simply supported beam loaded with a system of concentrated loads. Since maximum bending-moments will always be obtained when the loads are as closely spaced as is permissible, it will be assumed that the distances between loads are of minimum values and that they remain constant when the loading is moved. From a consideration of the bending-moment diagram which may be drawn for the loading in any given position, it is seen that the greatest bending-moment in the span will occur on a section taken at one of these concentrated loads. With respect to a section at any one of the loads, the value of the bending-moment can be expressed in the general form

$$M = \frac{Wxa}{L} - W_1 x_1$$

With reference to any given load, as for example load 3, the only variables in the above equation are x and a, hence the value of the bending-moment on any section under this concentrated load will be maximum only when $x = a$. Stated in other words, the loads must be so placed on the span that the center of the span is midway between the given concentrated load and the resultant of all the loads then on the span. In

addition to fulfilling this requirement, the arrangement must be such as will satisfy the criterion (Equation 35) developed in Article 44; hence W_1 must be equal to reaction R_L. The greatest bending-moment in the span will, therefore, occur on a section taken at one of the concentrated loads adjacent to the resultant, when the loads are placed in accordance with the foregoing rule.

Example

Consider the loading shown at *a* in Fig. 43, and determine the greatest possible bending-moment that this loading can produce in a 40-ft simply supported span.

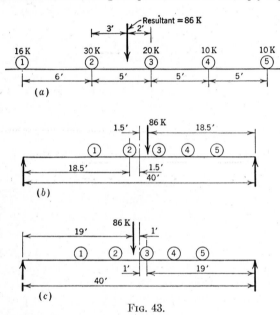

Fɪɢ. 43.

The position of the resultant of the loads is first determined as shown. The loading is now placed in accordance with the requirement $x = a$, and it will be noted that two positions are possible as shown at *b* and *c*. Applying the criterion for maximum bending-moment at a given section to each of these positions, for position as in *b*, we have

$$\frac{Wa}{L} = \frac{85 \times 18.5}{40} = 39.4 \quad \begin{matrix} < W_1 \text{ (max)} = 46 \\ > W_1 \text{ (min)} = 16 \end{matrix}$$

The criterion is therefore satisfied when the loading is in this position. For position as in *c*,

$$\frac{Wa}{L} = \frac{85 \times 21}{40} = 44.6 \quad \begin{matrix} < W_1 \text{ (max)} = 66 \\ < W_1 \text{ (min)} = 46 \end{matrix}$$

This position will therefore be rejected. The position shown in *b* must therefore produce the greatest bending-moment in the span, and it is then computed as follows:

$$\text{Bending-moment (under load 2)} = \left[\frac{85 \times 18.5}{40}\right] \times 18.5 - (16 \times 6)$$

$$= 631 \text{ ft-kips}$$

PROBLEMS

4·1 Find the reactions at *A* and *B* graphically.

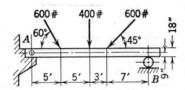

4·2 (*a*) Find reactions graphically. (*b*) Find reactions analytically.

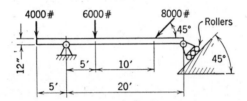

4·3 (*a*) Find R_1 and R_2 graphically. (*b*) Find R_1 and R_2 analytically. (*c*) Draw shear and bending-moment diagrams.

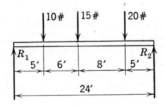

4·4 Determine the reactions at *A* and *B* due to the fixed loads shown.

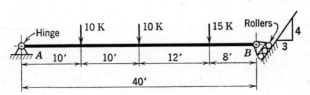

4·5 Determine the horizontal and vertical components of the reactions at *A* and *B*. (*a*) Analytical solution.   (*b*) Graphical solution.

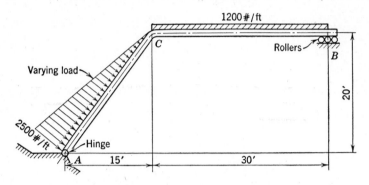

4·6 The member *ABC* is hinged at *A* and *D* and is loaded with a uniform of load 1 kip per ft.   Draw the shear and bending-moment diagrams for *ABC* and give the value of the controlling ordinates.

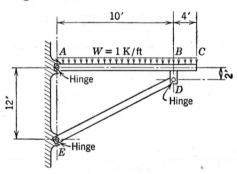

4·7 Compute the resultant forces or components acting at hinges *A*, *B*, and *C* of the three-hinged arch shown.   Solve both algebraically and graphically.

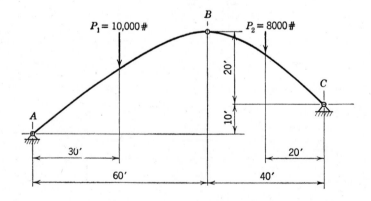

4·8 Determine graphically the reactions at hinges *A* and *B* of the three-hinged arch due to the 6 loads shown. Use a scale of 1 in. = 60 ft and 1 in. = 60 kips.

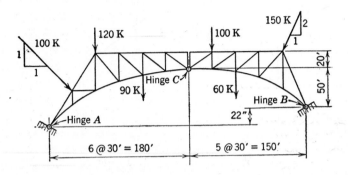

4·9 Determine reactions at *A* and *B* graphically, and check results analytically.

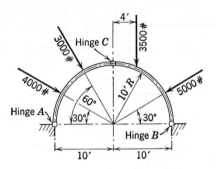

4·10 A three-hinged arch has forces acting on it as shown in the sketch. (*a*) Find algebraically the forces acting at the hinges. (*b*) Calculate the maximum bending-moment.

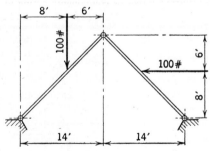

4·11 In the three-hinged structure shown, determine the reactions at A and B.

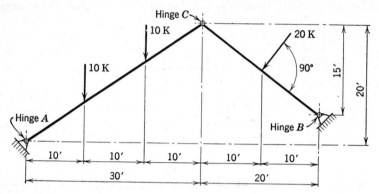

4·12 (a) Calculate the reactions R_1 and R_2. (b) Draw the shear and bending-moment diagrams.

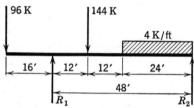

4·13 (a) Draw the shear and bending-moment diagrams for the structure ACB in Problem 4·5. (b) Calculate the shear, bending-moment, and normal (axial) force at a section 10 ft from A in member AC, Problem 4·5.

4·14 Draw the shear and bending-moment diagrams and give the numerical values of the controlling ordinates.

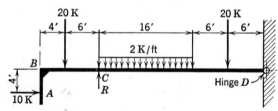

4·15 (a) Calculate the reactions and draw the shear and bending-moment diagrams for the structure shown. (b) Make a graphical solution for the reactions.

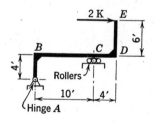

4·16 (*a*) Determine the reactions at *A* and *B* both algebraically and graphically. (*b*) Compute the value of the normal force, the shearing force, and bending-moment at point *C*.

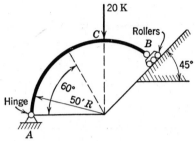

4·17 Calculate the reactions and draw the shear and bending-moment diagrams.

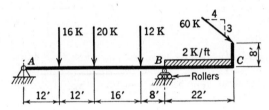

4·18 (*a*) Draw an influence diagram for the horizontal component at the hinge *A* for a unit vertical load moving across *AB*. (*b*) Draw an influence diagram for the

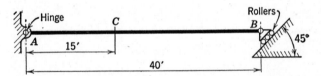

vertical component at *A*. (*c*) Draw an influence diagram for the bending-moment at *C*.

4·19 Draw the influence line for shear at point *A*, indicating the value of the controlling ordinates. From this influence line, calculate the maximum positive

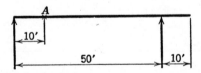

shear at *A* due to a moving uniform live load of 2 kips per ft. Also calculate the maximum negative shear at *A* due to a moving uniform live load of 2 kips per ft.

4·20 For the beam in Problem 4·19 draw the influence line for moment at point *A*, indicating the value of controlling ordinates. From this influence line determine the maximum positive and negative bending moments at *A* due to a moving uniform live load of 2 kips per ft.

4·21 If the reactions at b and c act either up or down, draw influence diagrams for the shear and moment at section 1–1.

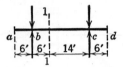

4·22 (a) Draw influence line for shear on section aa located 8 ft from left support. (b) Draw influence line for moment on section aa. (c) Using the diagram for

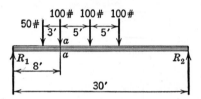

(a), determine shear on section aa due to loading shown. (d) Using the diagram for (b), determine the bending-moment on section aa due to loading shown.

4·23 The reactions at R_1 and R_2 can act either downward or upward. (a) Draw the influence lines for shear and bending-moment at sections m and n, and give values of the controlling ordinates. (b) Determine the maximum positive and negative

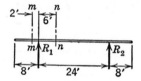

shear at sections m and n for a uniform live load of 1000 lb per linear ft. (c) Determine the maximum positive and negative moment at sections m and n for a uniform live load of 1000 lb per linear ft.

4·24 A simply supported beam of 60-ft span carries the moving concentrated load system shown. (Loading is not reversible.) For a section 15 ft from the left

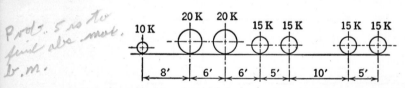

*Probs. 5 is to
find abs. mo.
b·m·*

end of the beam find: (a) The maximum bending-moment, and (b) The maximum shear.

4·25 A Cooper's E-60 loading is moved from right to left across a simply supported beam of 75-ft span. For a section 20 ft from the left end find the maximum positive shear and also the maximum bending-moment.

4·26 Determine the maximum bending-moment, due to the moving concentrated loads shown, at a point 15 ft from the left end of a simply supported beam of 50-ft span.

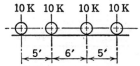

4·27 (*a*) Compute the maximum shear at section 1 for the moving live load shown. (*b*) Compute the maximum bending-moment at section 1 for the same live load.

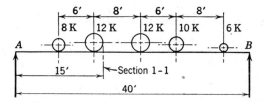

4·28 (*a*) Compute the maximum shear that can occur for the same beam and loads in Problem 4·27. (*b*) Compute the absolute maximum bending-moment for the beams and loads in Problem 4·27.

4·29 For girder *A*: (*a*) Plot influence lines for shear in panels 0–1 and 1–2. (*b*) From an inspection of the influence line, determine where a single concentrated load

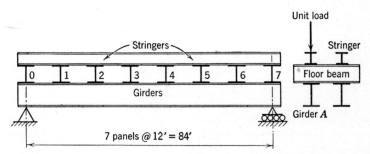

should lie to cause maximum positive shear in panel 1–2. (*c*) Compute by the "influence-line method," the exact maximum positive shear produced in panel 1–2 by a uniform live load of 2000 lb per ft, and check this result by computing the shear analytically.

4·30 Draw the influence line for shear in panel 2–3, and from this determine the maximum positive and maximum negative shear due to a uniform moving live load of 2 kips per ft.

4·31. Draw the influence line for reaction at A. Draw the influence line for shear in panel 3–4. Draw the influence line for moment at 5. From these influence lines and using a movable uniform load of 4 K per ft, determine: The maximum

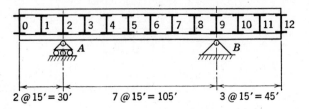

2 @ 15′ = 30′   7 @ 15′ = 105′   3 @ 15′ = 45′

negative reaction at A. The maximum positive shear in panel 3–4. The maximum negative moment at 5.

4·32 For the moving load system shown (a) Calculate the maximum positive shear in panel 1–2 of girder AB. (b) Calculate the maximum moment in the girder at panel point 3.

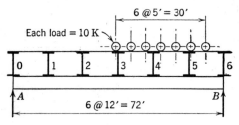

Chapter 5

RESTRAINED AND CONTINUOUS BEAMS

46 Definitions

A beam is said to be *restrained* when its supports, or some other external agency, prevent or restrict free rotation of the ends of the beam. The terms *fixed* or *partially fixed* are frequently employed to indicate a condition of restraint. A *fully restrained* or *fixed* beam is generally one whose ends are rigidly attached to an immovable support; a *partially restrained* or *partially fixed* beam is one whose ends may rotate to a lesser extent than the ends of a similar simply supported beam.

A *continuous* beam is one which is supported at more than two points. Such a beam may be fixed, partially fixed, or simply supported at its extreme ends. Any single span of a continuous beam may be partially or fully restrained by the elastic resistance of the adjoining spans.

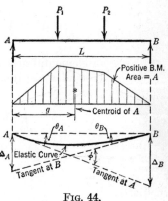

FIG. 44.

47 Elastic Behavior of Simply Supported Beams

Consider the simply supported beam shown in Fig. 44 with any system of loads,

I = moment of inertia of the beam section; assumed constant over the span AB.

A = area of the bending-moment diagram produced by the transverse loads, with the beam considered as simply supported.

g = distance from support A to the centroid of the bending-moment diagram.

Under the action of the loading, the beam will bend and conform to the elastic curve shown. In the study of strength of materials it is shown

85

that the elemental angle between two successive tangents to the elastic curve is given by the equation [1]

$$d\phi = \frac{M\,dx}{EI} \tag{36}$$

The magnitude of the total angle between the end tangents at A and B, respectively, is obtained by integrating Equation 36 over the length L, and, since E and I are constant,

$$\phi = \frac{A}{EI} = \theta_A + \theta_B \tag{37}$$

Since $d\phi$ is infinitesimal, $\tan d\phi = d\phi$, and successive tangents will subtend distances $x\,d\phi$ on a vertical through A. We see that the total of these will equal

$$\Delta_A = \int_0^L x\,d\phi = \frac{1}{EI} \int_0^L Mx\,dx \tag{38}$$

$M\,dx$ is an elemental area of the bending-moment curve and $Mx\,dx$ represents the moment of this elemental area bout the origin at A, hence

$$\int_0^L Mx\,dx = Ag$$

and

$$\Delta_A = \frac{Ag}{EI} \tag{39}$$

Similarly,

$$\Delta_B = \frac{A(L-g)}{EI} \tag{40}$$

Since θ_A and θ_B are relatively small angles,

$$\theta_A = \frac{\Delta_B}{L} = \frac{A(L-g)}{EIL} \tag{41}$$

$$\theta_B = -\frac{\Delta_A}{L} = -\frac{Ag}{EIL} \tag{42}$$

$$\frac{\theta_A}{\theta_B} = \frac{L-g}{g} \tag{43}$$

[1] S. Timoshenko, *Strength of Materials*, Part I, p. 150, D. Van Nostrand Co., 1930.

For symmetrical loading,

$$\Delta_A = \Delta_B = \frac{AL}{2EI} \tag{44}$$

$$\theta_A = -\theta_B = \frac{1}{2}\phi = \frac{A}{2EI} \tag{45}$$

Note that positive values of θ_A or θ_B indicate a clockwise direction of rotation of the respective end tangents. This convention for the signs of these angles will be followed in the remaining derivations.

For a uniformly distributed load of w pounds per unit of span length,

$$A = \frac{wL^2}{8} \times \frac{2}{3}L = \frac{wL^3}{12}$$

$$g = \tfrac{1}{2}L$$

$$\phi = \frac{wL^3}{12EI} \tag{46}$$

$$\Delta_A = \Delta_B = \frac{wL^4}{24EI} \tag{47}$$

$$\theta_A = -\theta_B = \frac{wL^3}{24EI} \tag{48}$$

When couples are combined with loads as is usually the condition in problems involving restrained or continuous beams, it is necessary to adopt a conventional system of signs to indicate the directions of rotation of such couples. A positive couple will hereafter be considered as one which acts *on the beam* in a clockwise direction and a negative couple as one which acts *on the beam* in a counterclockwise direction. Such couples are induced by resistance of the support to rotation for fixed or partially restrained beams. It should be observed that the sign of a couple may be opposite to the sign of the bending-moment which it induces in the beam.

When the only external loading on a simply supported beam is a positive couple, acting at one of the supports, as at A in Fig. 45a, equilibrium of the beam as a whole requires the development of a downward reaction at A and an upward reaction at B as shown. These reactions constitute

a couple whose magnitude equals that of the applied couple M_{AB} and,

$$\phi = \frac{M_{AB}L}{2EI} \tag{49}$$

$$\Delta_A = \frac{M_{AB}L^2}{6EI} \tag{50}$$

$$\Delta_B = \frac{M_{AB}L^2}{3EI} = 2\Delta_A \tag{51}$$

$$\theta_A = \frac{M_{AB}L}{3EI} \tag{52}$$

$$\theta_B = -\frac{M_{AB}L}{6EI} = -\frac{1}{2}\theta_A \tag{53}$$

When M_{AB} acts on the beam in a counterclockwise (negative) direction, or opposite in direction to that represented in Fig. 45a, the beam will be

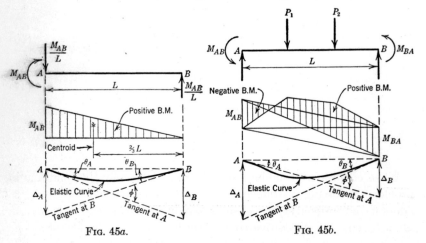

Fig. 45a.   Fig. 45b.

bowed upward, and the deflections and rotations of the end tangents will therefore be opposite in direction to those produced by the loading shown in Fig. 44.

A positive (clockwise) couple M_{BA} acting at B will produce the following values:

$$\theta_A = -\frac{M_{BA}L}{6EI} \tag{54}$$

$$\theta_B = +\frac{M_{BA}L}{3EI} \tag{55}$$

When the beam is acted upon simultaneously by a transverse loading and a positive couple at each support, the separate effects expressed by the foregoing equations will combine as follows:

$$\theta_A = \frac{A(L-g)}{EIL} + \frac{M_{AB}L}{3EI} - \frac{M_{BA}L}{6EI} \tag{56}$$

$$\theta_B = -\frac{Ag}{EIL} - \frac{M_{AB}L}{6EI} + \frac{M_{BA}L}{3EI} \tag{57}$$

48 Partially and Fully Restrained Beams

When a couple applied at either end acts in such a direction as to produce a direction of rotation of end tangents opposite to that induced by the transverse loading, it will within certain limits of value constitute a *restraining* couple. Thus, referring to Fig. 45b, M_{AB} will serve to restrict the rotation of the tangent at A when

$$M_{AB} < -\frac{3A(L-g)}{L^2} + \frac{M_{BA}}{2}$$

The beam will be fully restrained or fixed at A when $\theta_A = 0$ and there is no rotation of the end tangent at A. For this condition,

$$M_{AB}^F = -\frac{3A(L-g)}{L^2} + \frac{M_{BA}}{2} \tag{58}$$

A restraining couple may be caused by some external force condition, or it may be induced by resistance of the support to rotation when the beam is rigidly attached to the support.

The following additional equations may be derived from Equations 56 and 57:

For a beam fixed at B and simply supported at A.

$$\theta_B = 0$$

$$M_{BA}^F = +\frac{3Ag}{L^2} + \frac{M_{AB}}{2} \tag{59}$$

For a beam fixed at both ends,

and

$$\theta_A = \theta_B = 0,$$

$$M_{AB}^F = -\frac{2A(2L-3g)}{L^2} \tag{60}$$

$$M_{BA}^F = -\frac{2A(L-3g)}{L^2} \tag{61}$$

It should be noted that, for a symmetrical loading, $g = \frac{1}{2}L$, and

$$M_{AB}^F = -M_{BA}^F = -\frac{A}{L} \tag{62}$$

When the loading consists of concentrated loads, for each concentrated load,

$$A = \frac{Pab}{2}, \quad \text{and} \quad g = \frac{1}{3}(2a + b)$$

where a and b are the distances from any load to the left and right supports, respectively. For such a loading,

$$M_{AB}^F = -\sum \frac{Pab^2}{L^2} \tag{63}$$

$$M_{BA}^F = +\sum \frac{Pa^2b}{L^2} \tag{64}$$

Values of fixed-end moments for various span and load conditions are given in Fig. 46.

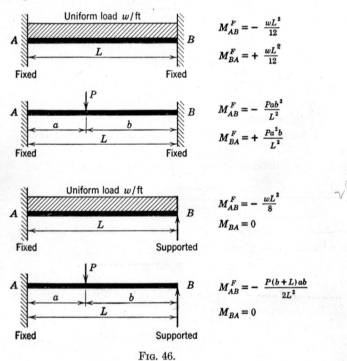

$$M_{AB}^F = -\frac{wL^2}{12}$$

$$M_{BA}^F = +\frac{wL^2}{12}$$

$$M_{AB}^F = -\frac{Pab^2}{L^2}$$

$$M_{BA}^F = +\frac{Pa^2b}{L^2}$$

$$M_{AB}^F = -\frac{wL^2}{8}$$

$$M_{BA} = 0$$

$$M_{AB}^F = -\frac{P(b+L)ab}{2L^2}$$

$$M_{BA} = 0$$

Fig. 46.

49 Relative Stiffness and Carry-Over Moment

When a beam fixed at one end is acted upon by a couple applied at the free end, the value of restraining couple at the fixed end is determined by Equation 58 or 59. The effect of the couple applied at the free end is represented by the second term, $\frac{1}{2}M_{BA}$ or $\frac{1}{2}M_{AB}$, and is seen to be independent of the loading. This term is known as the *carry-over moment*, and its use will be explained later.

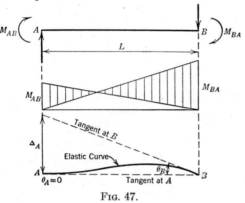

F_{IG}. 47.

With reference to the beam shown in Fig. 47, which is fixed at A,

$$\theta_B = -\frac{M_{AB}L}{6EI} + \frac{M_{BA}L}{3EI} \; ; \quad M_{AB} = \tfrac{1}{2}M_{BA}$$

Therefore

$$\theta_B = -\frac{M_{BA}L}{12EI} + \frac{M_{BA}L}{3EI} = +\frac{M_{BA}L}{4EI} \tag{65}$$

$$M_{BA} = +\left(\frac{4EI}{L}\right)\theta_B = +4E\theta_B k \tag{66}$$

The quantity $4EI/L$ measures the stiffness of the beam when one end is fixed, and is the value of M_{BA} when $\theta_B =$ unity. When E is constant, the relative stiffness may be measured by the ratio

$$k = \frac{I}{L} = \text{stiffness factor} \tag{67}$$

Should the fixity at A be removed, thus making the beam free to rotate at this end, $M_{AB}^F = 0$ and

$$M_{BA} = +\left(\frac{3EI}{L}\right)\theta_B = +3E\theta_B k \tag{68}$$

Such a beam would therefore have three-fourths the actual or relative stiffness of a similar fixed end beam.

50   Moment Distribution at a Joint

Consider the frame shown at Fig. 48a, where the members AB, BC, and BD are rigidly connected at B. Assume that the members are

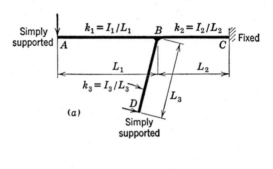

(a)

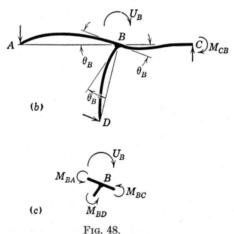

(b)

(c)

Fig. 48.

freely supported at A and D and that member BC is fixed at C. The stiffness factors for each of these members, determined as outlined in Article 49, will be as represented on the diagram of the frame.

Let a couple, of magnitude U_B, act on the frame at point B as shown in Fig. 48b. Neglecting any translation of point B, the members at this point will be rotated in the direction of U_B until sufficient resistance is developed internally to produce equilibrium of the joint and when equilibrium of the joint has been established, it will have rotated through the angle θ_B. Passing a cutting section around joint B to produce the

free body shown at (c), the moments on the cut sections must fulfill the requirement that $\Sigma M = 0$; hence

$$M_{BA} + M_{BD} + M_{BC} = U_B \tag{69}$$

Now consider each of the beams separately, each as a free body produced by a cutting section adjacent to point B. Beam AB will be acted upon by the clockwise couple M_{BA}, and from Equation 68

$$M_{BA} = 3E\theta_B k_1$$

Similarly, beam BC will be acted upon by the clockwise couple M_{BC}, and from Equation 66

$$M_{BC} = 4E\theta_B k_2$$

Beam BD will be acted upon by the clockwise couple M_{BD}, and from Equation 68

$$M_{BD} = 3E\theta_B k_3$$

therefore,

$$3E\theta_B k_1 + 4E\theta_B k_2 + 3E\theta_B k_3 = U_B \tag{70}$$

and

$$\frac{M_{BA}}{U_B} = \frac{3E\theta_B k_1}{3E\theta_B k_1 + 4E\theta_B k_2 + 3E\theta_B k_3} \tag{71}$$

$$M_{BA} = \left[\frac{\frac{3}{4}k_1}{\frac{3}{4}k_1 + k_2 + \frac{3}{4}k_3}\right] U_B \tag{72}$$

$$M_{BC} = \left[\frac{k_2}{\frac{3}{4}k_1 + k_2 + \frac{3}{4}k_3}\right] U_B \tag{73}$$

$$M_{CD} = \left[\frac{\frac{3}{4}k_3}{\frac{3}{4}k_1 + k_2 + \frac{3}{4}k_3}\right] U_B \tag{74}$$

Thus, when a couple, or unbalanced moment, acts at a joint in an elastic frame, the sum of the relative stiffness factors of the several members joined measures the total stiffness of the joint; members which are simply supported at the end away from the joint are considered as having a relative stiffness of $\frac{3}{4}k$ when this is used in conjunction with members which are fixed at their extremity. The total unbalanced moment, or couple, applied to the joint distributes itself to the members in proportion to their relative stiffness. It should be noted that the couples distributed to the several members will all have the same direction of rotation and that this direction will be the same as that of the unbalanced moment or couple.

51   Continuous Beam Moments by Moment Distribution

The method of successive approximation known as the *moment distribution* method is convenient for the analysis of continuous beams. This method, which was developed by Professor Hardy Cross,[2] makes use of the foregoing principles and by successive corrections produces results within any desired percentage of error. It can best be explained in connection with the solution of a simple problem.

Example

Consider the beam with loading shown at *a* in Fig. 49 resting without restraint on supports *A* and *B* and fixed at *C*. Let *I* of all sections of span *AB* = 2. Let *I* of all sections of span *BC* = 3.

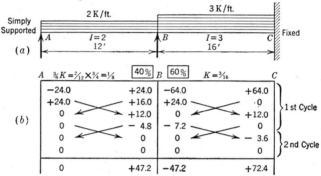

FIG. 49.   Continuous Beam.

Step 1.   Assume external couples applied to the beam at each point of support sufficient to *fix* it at these points. The beam will then consist of two fixed spans, and the end couples acting on these spans may be computed from Equation 62 or as shown in Fig. 46.

$$M_{AB} = -24 \text{ ft-kips}$$

$$M_{BA} = +24 \text{ ft-kips}$$

$$M_{BC} = -64 \text{ ft-kips}$$

$$M_{CB} = +64 \text{ ft-kips}$$

Step 2.   The couples computed in Step 1 are now corrected to accord with the true conditions relative to the fixity of supports. Since actually no fixing couples are developed by the supports, the values of the assumed external fixing couples in Step 1 are not balanced by internal bending-moment at these points. To correct the error of this assumption, an external couple equal in magnitude to the unbalanced internal moment must be applied at each of the supports. Each support is considered separately and corrections determined with the as-

[2] *Proc. Am. Concrete Institute*, 1929; also *Trans. Am. Soc. C. E.*, Vol. 196, 1932.

sumption that the other supports will remain fixed. The values of the end couples developed in the separate spans by these corrective couples are determined in accordance with the principles of distribution outlined in Article 50. Since support C is in fact a fixed support, no error was made at this point.

Support A

> Unbalanced moment $= -24$ ft-kips
> Correction couple applied at A $= +24$ ft-kips
> Correction applied to M_{AB} $= +24$ ft-kips

Support B

> Unbalanced moment $= (+24 - 64) = -40$ ft-kips
> Total correction couple applied at B and to
>   be distributed between M_{BA} and M_{BC} $= +40$ ft-kips

$$k_1 = \tfrac{2}{12} = \tfrac{1}{6} \qquad\qquad\qquad k_2 = \tfrac{3}{16}$$

$$\frac{\tfrac{3}{4}k_1}{\tfrac{3}{4}k_1 + k_2} = 0.4 \qquad\qquad\qquad \frac{k_2}{\tfrac{3}{4}k_1 + k_2} = 0.6$$

> Correction applied to $M_{BA} = 0.4 \times 40 = +16.0$ ft-kips
> Correction applied to $M_{BC} = 0.6 \times 40 = +24.0$ ft-kips

Support C

> Unbalanced moment $= 0$ ft-kips
> No correction couple is needed at this support

Step 3. Since the other supports were assumed to remain fixed when a correction couple is applied at a given support, the distributed correction couples determined in Step 2 will develop carry-over moments at the opposite ends of the span. These are determined as follows:

> Carry-over moment at $M_{AB} = 0.0$ ft-kips
> Carry-over moment at $M_{BA} = \tfrac{1}{2} \times 24.0 = +12.0$ ft-kips
> Carry-over moment at $M_{BC} = 0$ ft-kips
> Carry-over moment at $M_{CB} = \tfrac{1}{2} \times 24.0 = +12.0$ ft-kips

Step 4. This step is a repetition of Step 2 for the unbalanced values again produced by Step 3. Hence at

Support A

> Unbalanced moment $= 0$ ft-kips
> Correction applied to $M_{AB} = 0$ ft-kips

Support B

> Unbalanced moment $= -0 + 12.0$ ft-kips $= +12$ ft-kips
> Correction applied to $M_{BA} = 0.4 \times -12.0 = -4.8$ ft-kips
> Correction applied to $M_{BC} = 0.6 \times -12.0 = -7.2$ ft-kips

Support C

> Unbalanced moment $= 0$ ft-kips
> Correction applied to $M_{CB} = 0$ ft-kips

Summation of the original fixed end couples and corrections determined in steps 2, 3, and 4 will complete the *first cycle* and give approximate values of the true couples at the supports as follows: $M_{AB} = 0$, $M_{BA} = +47.2$, $M_{BC} = -47.2$, $M_{CB} = +76.0$. The work may be concluded here if these approximate values are sufficiently precise. If more accurate results are desired, however, the work may be continued through as many additional cycles as necessary. Each subsequent cycle will consist of two steps: (1) determination of carry-over moments as in Step 3, and (2) applying correction couples and distributing them as in Step 4. It is seldom necessary to carry results beyond four cycles.

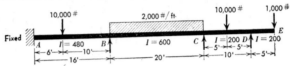

Beam is fixed at A and simply supported at B, C, and D,

Fixed End Moments:

Span AB, $M_{AB}^{f} = -\dfrac{10,000 \times 6 \times 100}{256} = -23.44$ ft-kips

$M_{BA}^{f} = +\dfrac{10,000 \times 36 \times 10}{256} = +14.06$ ft-kips

Span BC $M_{BC}^{f} = -\dfrac{2,000 \times 400}{12} = -66.67$ ft-kips

$M_{CB}^{f} = \qquad\qquad +66.67$ ft-kips

Span CD $M_{CD}^{f} = -\dfrac{10,000 \times 15 \times 25}{200} = -18.75$ ft-kips

M_{DC}^{f} = zero for simply supported end support

Overhang DE $M_{DE}^{f} = -1,000 \times 5 = -5.00$ ft-kips

A	$k=30$	B 0.50	0.50	$k=30$	C 0.67	0.33	$\tfrac{3}{4}k=15$	D 1.00	0	$k=0$
0									0	
−23.44		+14.06	−66.67		+66.67	−18.75		0	−5.00	
0		+26.30	+26.31		−31.95	−15.97		+5.00	0	
+13.15		0	−15.98		+13.15	+2.50		0	0	
0		+7.99	+7.99		−7.83	−7.82		0	0	
+4.00		0	−3.91		+4.00	0		0	0	
0		+1.96	+1.95		−2.67	−1.33		0	0	
+0.98		0	−1.34		+0.98	0		0	0	
0		+0.67	+0.67		−0.65	−0.33		0	0	
+0.34		0	−0.32		+0.34	0		0	0	
0		+0.16	+0.16		−0.23	−0.11		0	0	
−4.97		+51.14	+51.14		+41.81	−41.81		+5.00	−5.00	

The bending-moments on beam sections taken at the supports are:
At support A, Bending-moment = 4,970 ft-lb, negative
B, Bending-moment = 51,140 ft-lb, negative
C, Bending-moment = 41,810 ft-lb, negative
D, Bending-moment = 5,000 ft-lb, negative

FIG. 50.   Continuous Beam Solution by Method of Moment Distribution.

The solution of a continuous beam by moment distribution is most conveniently done by arranging the computations in tabular form. A tabular arrangement of the preceding computations is thus shown at *b* in Fig. 49, and here it will be noted that a complete solution is obtained at the end of two cycles. Another typical solution involving different load and span conditions is given in Fig. 50.

52 Theorem of Three Moments

This theorem for the solution of continuous beams was first published by Clapeyron in 1857. Its derivation may be found in any standard treatise on strength of materials [3] and will not be repeated here.

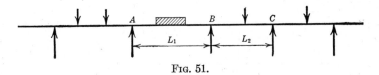

FIG. 51.

The theorem is expressed by the following general equation, applicable to any pair of adjacent spans of a continuous beam (see Fig. 51).

$$M_A \frac{L_1}{I_1} + 2M_B \left(\frac{L_1}{I_1} + \frac{L_2}{I_2}\right) + M_C \frac{L_2}{I_2} = -\frac{6A_1 g_1}{L_1 I_1} - \frac{6A_2(L_2 - g_2)}{L_2 I_2} \quad (75)$$

where M_A = bending-moment on section at support A.

M_B = bending-moment on section at support B.

M_C = bending-moment on section at support C.

L_1 = length of span AB.

L_2 = length of span BC.

I_1 = moment of inertia of all sections of span AB.

I_2 = moment of inertia of all sections of span BC.

A_1, A_2 = area-of-bending-moment diagram for spans AB and BC, respectively, considering each as a simply supported beam.

g_1, g_2 = distance from centroid of A_1 or A_2, respectively, to support A or B.

It is assumed in the derivation of this equation that the reactions at A, B, C, etc., act either upward or downward to prevent vertical movement of the beam at the supports.

This equation is most frequently written in the form

$$M_A \frac{L_1}{I_1} + 2M_B \left(\frac{L_1}{I_1} + \frac{L_2}{I_2}\right) + M_C \frac{L_2}{I_2}$$

$$= -\frac{1}{I_1} \Sigma[P_1 L_1^2 (k_1 - k_1^3)] - \frac{1}{I_2} \Sigma[P_2 L_2^2 (2k_2 - 3k_2^2 + k_2^3)] \quad (76)$$

[3] Timoshenko and McCullough, *Elements of Strength of Materials*, D. Van Nostrand Co.

where (see Fig. 52) P_1 = any concentrated load in span AB.

k_1 = ratio of distance between A and load, to span length L_1.

P_2 = any concentrated load in span BC.

k_2 = ratio of distance from B to load, to span length L_2.

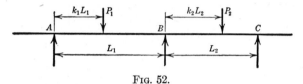

Fig. 52.

For uniform loading

$$P_1 = w\, dx$$

$$k_1 = \frac{x}{L_1}$$

$$\frac{1}{I_1} \Sigma P_1 L_1^2 (k_1 - k_1^3) = \frac{1}{I_1} \int w\, dx\, L_1^2 \left(\frac{x}{L_1} - \frac{x^3}{L_1^3}\right) \tag{77}$$

$$\frac{1}{I_2} \Sigma P_2 L_2^2 (2k_2 - 3k_2^2 + k_2^3) = \frac{1}{I_2} \int w\, dx\, L_2^2 \left(\frac{2x}{L_2} - \frac{3x^2}{L_2} + \frac{x^3}{L_2^3}\right) \tag{78}$$

where the limits are determined by the extent of the uniform load. When the uniform load extends over the entire span, either integration produces the result

$$\frac{1}{4} \frac{wL^3}{I} \tag{79}$$

When a beam is fixed at the end support, an imaginary span $L_0 = 0$ is added, and the equation is then applied to this imaginary span and the adjacent span; thus for the beam in Fig. 53a, noting that I is constant,

Example

(a)
$$M_0 = 0$$

(b)
$$0 + 2M_A(0 + 20) + 20M_B = -0 - \frac{2 \times (20)^3}{4}$$

$$40M_A + 20M_B = -4000$$

(c) $20M_A + 2M_B(20 + 16) + 16M_C = -4000 - [12 \times (16)^2 \times \tfrac{195}{512}]$

$$20M_A + 72M_B + 16M_C = -5170$$

(d)
$$M_C = -(4 \times 4) = -16 \text{ ft-kips}$$

Combining (c) and (d),

$$20M_A + 72M_B = -4914$$
$$20M_A + 10M_B = -2000$$

$$62M_B = -2914$$
$$M_B = -47.0 \text{ ft-kips}$$

$$M_A = \frac{-4000 - 20M_B}{40} = -76.5 \text{ ft-kips}$$

53 Continuous Beam Reactions

With the bending moments on sections at the supports established in value and kind, the reactions are determined from principles of statics. Thus, for the beam shown in Fig. 53a,

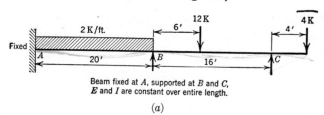

Beam fixed at *A*, supported at *B* and *C*,
E and *I* are constant over entire length.

(a)

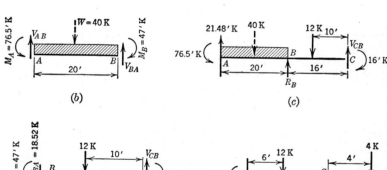

(b)

(c)

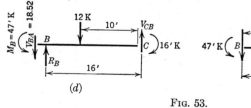

(d)

(e)

Fig. 53.

Example

$$M_A = -76.5 \text{ ft-kips}$$

$$M_B = -47.0 \text{ ft-kips}$$

$$M_C = -16.0 \text{ ft-kips}$$

Passing a cutting section immediately left of support B and considering portion AB as a free body (Fig. 53b),

$\Sigma M = 0$ (moment center at B)

$$20V_{AB} - 76.5 - (40 \times 10) + 47 = 0$$

$$R_A = V_{AB} = 21.48 \text{ kips (acting upward)}$$

$\Sigma V = 0$

$$V_{AB} - 40 + V_{BA} = 0$$

$$V_{BA} = 40 - 21.48 = 18.52 \text{ kips (negative shear)}$$

Passing a cutting section left of support C and considering portion A–C as a free body (Fig. 53c) and writing $\Sigma M = 0$ with moment center at C gives

$$16R_B - 76.5 + (21.48 \times 36) - (40 \times 26) - (12 \times 10) + 16 = 0$$

$$R_B = 27.96 \text{ kips (acting upward)}$$

Note that the above computation for R_B could have been based on the free-body diagram indicated in Fig. 53d in which case

$$16R_B - 47 - (18.52 \times 16) - (12 \times 10) + 16 = 0$$

$$R_B = 27.96 \text{ kips}$$

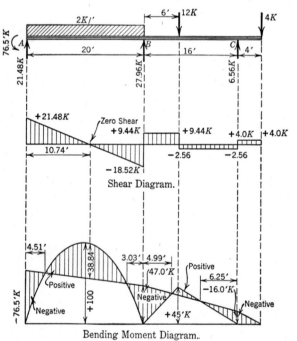

Bending Moment Diagram.

FIG. 54.   Continuous Beam.   Shear and Bending-Moment Diagrams.

Considering as a free body the portion on right of a section at B (Fig. 53e), writing $\Sigma M = 0$ with moment center at B, gives

$$16R_C - (4 \times 20) - (12 \times 6) + 47 = 0$$

$$R_C = 6.56 \text{ kips (acting upward)}$$

Computing $\Sigma V = 0$ for entire beam,

Forces (acting upward) $= 21.48 + 27.96 + 6.56 = 56$ kips
Loads (acting downward) $= 40 + 12 + 4 \qquad\quad = 56$ kips

$\qquad\qquad\qquad\qquad\qquad\qquad\qquad\qquad$ Check   0

The shear and bending-moment diagrams may now be determined as outlined in Chapter 4. (See Fig. 54.)

54   Vertical Displacement of Supports

The procedures outlined in Articles 51, 52, and 53 were based upon the condition that the supports remained at their initial elevation and that the reactive forces at each support were sufficient to produce this relationship. If any support moves vertically, when the loads are applied, values based on this condition must be adjusted accordingly. If it is assumed that any support movement will be relatively small and that coincidental lateral effects may be neglected, the computations based on the loading will not be changed, and the effect of support movement may be studied by considering the behavior of the beam with the loading removed.

Referring to Fig. 55a, we see that no moments will be induced in the simply supported beam AB by a settlement of support B through a very small distance d. If, however, the beam is fixed at A, a couple M_{AB} will be induced at A sufficient in magnitude and direction to rotate the tangent at A through the angle θ_A, as illustrated at b. Since $\theta_A = -d/L$, from Equation 52,

$$M_{AB} = -\frac{3EId}{L^2} \qquad (80)$$

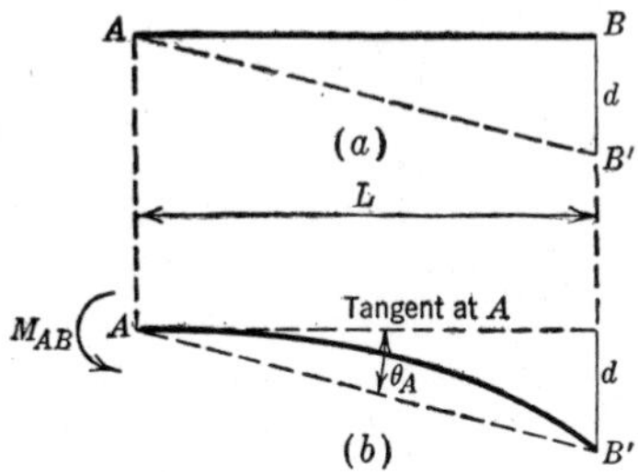

FIG. 55.

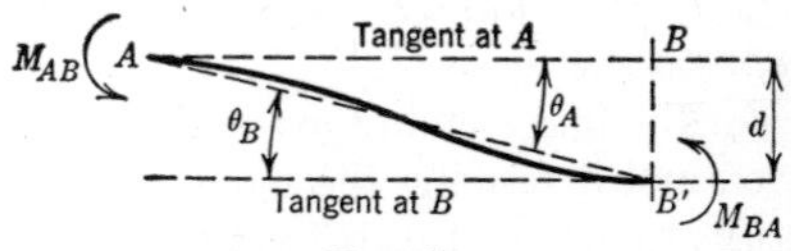

FIG. 56.

Note that M_{AB} is negative when the movement of support B is downward and that the direction of M_{AB} will be reversed should support B move upward from its original position.

For a beam fixed at both ends as shown in Fig. 56, the values of end couples induced by a change in the relative elevation of the support may be determined from Equations 56 and 57.

$$\theta_A = -\theta_B = -\frac{d}{L} \tag{81}$$

$$M^F_{AB} = M^F_{BA} = -\frac{6EId}{L^2} \tag{82}$$

It should be noted that both end couples are negative (counterclockwise) when support B moves downward relative to support A and that these couples will be positive when support B moves upward relative to support A.

Example

The structural steel beam shown in Fig. 57 is to be computed for a $\frac{1}{2}$-inch settlement of support B, the other supports remaining at their original level.

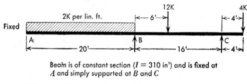

Beam is of constant section ($I = 310$ in') and is fixed at
A and simply supported at B and C

When supports remain at same level:

0.00	$k = 1.29$	0.52	0.48	$\frac{3}{4}k = 1.21$	1.00	0.00
−66.7		+66.7	−28.1		+16.9	−16.0
0		−20.0	−18.6		− 0.9	0
−10.0		0	− 0.5		0	0
0		+ 0.3	+ 0.2		.0	0
+ 0.2		0	0		0	0
0		0	0		0	0
−76.5		+47.0	−47.0		+16.0	−16.0

Correction for $\frac{1}{2}$ in. settlement of support B:

−39.7		−39.7	+31.0		0	0
0		+ 4.5	+ 4.2		0	0
+ 2.3		0	0		0	0
0		0	0		0	0
Final Moment −113.9		+11.8	−11.8		+16.0	−16.0

Fig. 57. Moments Caused by Settlement of Support.

For the first step in the solution, assume that all supports remain at the same level, and determine the moments at the supports in the usual manner. The results by moment distribution are shown in Fig. 57.

Now consider span AB, and assume that the beam is fixed at supports A and B. From Equation 82,

$$M^F_{AB} = M^F_{BA} = -\frac{6 \times 29{,}500 \times 310 \times 0.5}{240 \times 240 \times 12} = -39.7 \text{ ft-kips}$$

Next, consider span BC with the beam fixed at B and simply supported at C. From Equation 80,

$$M_{BC}^F = +\frac{3 \times 29,500 \times 310 \times 0.5}{192 \times 192 \times 12} = +31.0$$

For the second step in the solution, these correction moments, which are due to the settlement of support B, are added to the previous values, and the moments are adjusted by moment distribution to produce the final corrected values. The solution of this part of the problem is shown in the lower tabulation of Fig. 57.

PROBLEMS

5·1 Bending-moments (B.M.) at the supports of the continuous beam shown have been computed and are of the values and sign indicated. Plot the shear and bending-moment diagrams to the following scales:

Horizontal—1 in. = 6 ft

Vertical—(shear)   1 in. = 10,000 lb

(moment) 1 in. = 10,000 ft-lb

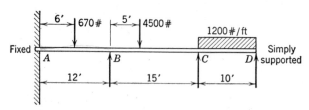

Bending-moments

At A, B.M. = $-1,460$ ft-lb

B, B.M. = $-4,370$ ft-lb

C, B.M. = $-11,360$ ft-lb

D, B.M. =   0 ft-lb

Indicate magnitude and location of all controlling ordinates and points of zero shear and bending-moment.

5·2 Compute the value of the fixed end moments for each of the spans shown.

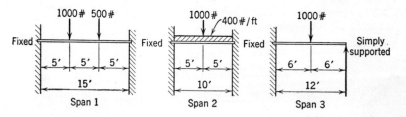

Span 1   Span 2   Span 3

5·3 E and I are constant. The moments at the supports of the above continuous beam have been determined as follows:

$$M_{AB} = -76.4 \text{ ft-kips}$$
$$M_{BA} = +47.0 \text{ ft-kips}$$
$$M_{BC} = -47.0 \text{ ft-kips}$$
$$M_{CB} = +16.0 \text{ ft-kips}$$
$$M_{CD} = -16.0 \text{ ft-kips}$$

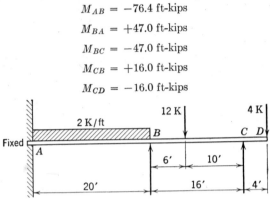

Determine the reactions and plot shear and bending-moment diagrams. Indicate values of controlling and critical ordinates.

5·4   Span AB $I = 30$
                 BC $I = 10$ E is constant
                 CD $I = 36$

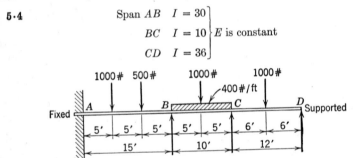

Determine moment at each support of the above continuous beam by method of "moment distribution." Express results in foot-kips.

5·5   (*a*) Determine the value of the bending moments at the supports. The beam is simply supported at A, continuous over B and C, and fixed at D. EI is constant for all spans. (*b*) Draw the shear and bending-moment diagrams.

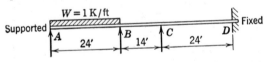

5·6   Determine the reactions at A and B, also the maximum positive and negative moments. EI is constant.

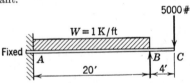

5·7 $I = 4800$ in.⁴ for all spans. (*a*) Compute the moments at the supports A, B, C, and D for the continuous beam shown. (*b*) Calculate the reactions at A and B. (*c*) Draw the shear and bending-moment diagram for the span *ab*.

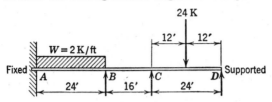

5·8 (*a*) Determine the bending moments at supports A, B, and C by the moment distribution method. Carry results through not more than two cycles, and express values to the nearest tenth. (*b*) Determine the value of reaction R_c.

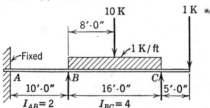

5·9 (*a*) Compute the moments at the supports of the continuous beam shown. I is constant for all spans. (*b*) Calculate the reactions and draw the shear and bending-moment diagrams. Record the values of the controlling ordinates on the diagram.

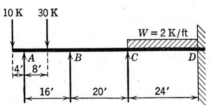

5·10 Compute the moments at the supports B, C, and D for the beam shown. $I = 2000$ in.⁴ for both spans. There are no supports at A and E.

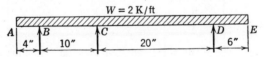

5·11 Determine the moments at supports A, B, C, and D using the moment-distribution method carried through four cycles (EI is constant.)

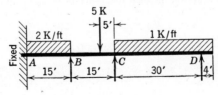

5·12   In Problem 5·11, if the moments at the supports A, B, C, and D are as listed below, determine the reactions at the supports, and draw the shear and bending-moment diagrams for the beam.

$$M_A = -55,996 \text{ ft-lb} \qquad M_C = -76,693 \text{ ft-lb}$$

$$M_B = -508 \quad \text{ft-lb} \qquad M_D = -8,000 \text{ ft-lb}$$

5·13   Determine the moments and reactions at supports A, B, and C. Assume E and I as constant.

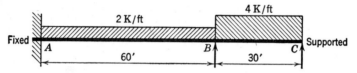

5·14   Find the positive bending moment at the centerline of span BC. The beam is of constant section.

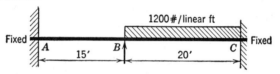

5·15 EI is constant. Determine the moments at the supports A, B, and C.

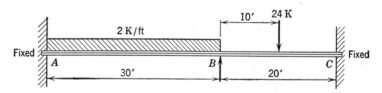

5·16   If EI is a constant, determine the moments at each of the four supports using the moment-distribution method carried through four cycles.

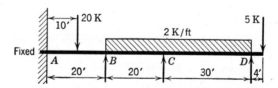

5·17   Draw the shear and moment diagrams for beam of Problem 5·16. Use

$$M_A = -58.94 \text{ ft-kips}$$

$$M_B = -32.12 \text{ ft-kips}$$

$$M_C = -162.58 \text{ ft-kips}$$

$$M_D = -20.00 \text{ ft-kips}$$

5·18 Determine the moments and reactions at the supports. Assume *E* and *I* as constant.

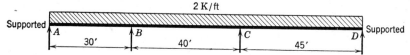

2 K/ft

Supported | A | 30' | B | 40' | C | 45' | D | Supported

5·19 (*a*) Compute the moments at supports *A* and *B* by moment distribution. *I* = 10 for all spans. (*b*) Compute the value of reaction R_A.

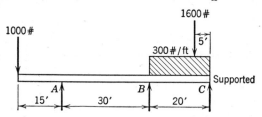

1000#

1600#

300#/ft | 5'

Supported

A | 15' | 30' | B | 20' | C

5·20 Assuming *EI* to be constant, determine the moments and reactions at supports *A*, *B*, and *C* using the moment-distribution method.

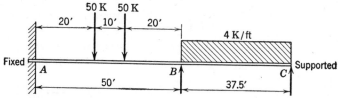

15' | 60 K

2 K/ft

4 K/ft

Fixed | A | 30' | B | 45' | C | Supported

5·21 Assume *EI* constant. Draw the bending-moment diagram. Use moment-distribution method for moments at supports.

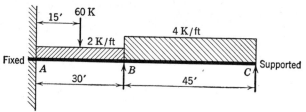

50 K   50 K

20' | 10' | 20'

4 K/ft

Fixed | A | 50' | B | 37.5' | C | Supported

5·22 For spans *AB* and *CD*, *I* = 122 in.⁴, for span *BC*, *I* = 442 in.⁴ (*a*) Determine the bending moments on sections at *A*, *B*, *C*, and *D* using the moment-distribution method. Continue computations through *two cycles only*, and express values in

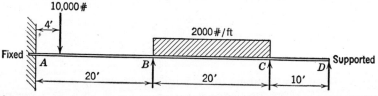

10,000#

4'

2000#/ft

Fixed | A | 20' | B | 20' | C | 10' | D | Supported

ft-kips to one decimal only. (*b*) Sketch form of bending-moment diagram for the entire beam, showing values of controlling ordinates. (*c*) Compute value of reaction at *D*.

Chapter 6

TRUSSES

55 Definitions

A *truss* is an arrangement of tension and compression members fastened together at their ends by pins or other suitable devices. The simplest arrangement is three members in the form of a triangle as at *a* in Fig. 58; if supported at *A* and *B*, such a frame will resist change in form

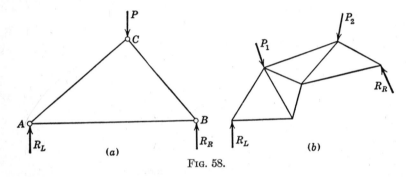

Fig. 58.

and will thus, within the limitation imposed by the strengths of its members, be capable of carrying the load *P*. A truss may be regarded as an assemblage of such triangles as at *b* in Fig. 58. The arrangement is determined by the position and direction of the applied loads and reactions; also by practical design limitation of the individual members themselves.

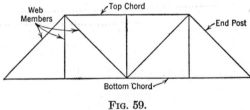

Fig. 59.

The series of top members (horizontal or inclined) of a truss (Fig. 59) is called the *top chord*; the series of bottom members, usually horizontal, is called the *bottom chord*; the members connecting the top and bottom

chords are referred to collectively as *web members* and individually as *diagonals* or *verticals*.

Some of the common truss forms are illustrated in Fig. 60.

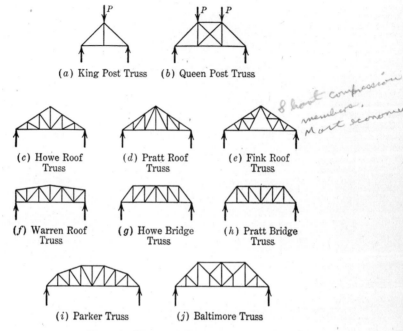

(*a*) King Post Truss   (*b*) Queen Post Truss

Short compression members. Most economical

(*c*) Howe Roof Truss   (*d*) Pratt Roof Truss   (*e*) Fink Roof Truss

(*f*) Warren Roof Truss   (*g*) Howe Bridge Truss   (*h*) Pratt Bridge Truss

(*i*) Parker Truss   (*j*) Baltimore Truss

FIG. 60.   Types of Trusses.

56   Primary and Secondary Stress

The total axial force induced in any member of a truss is called *stress*. Primary stresses are those which are computed in accordance with the assumption that members of the truss are connected by frictionless pins located at the intersections of the axes of the members; that the loads are all applied initially to these pins; and that the truss will not deform or deflect under the action of the loading. Secondary stress results from errors in the foregoing assumptions. Thus, where the members are rigidly connected by rivets to a common gusset plate, the change in geometrical form of the truss due to its deflection will develop bending in the members and induce secondary stress. Transverse loads applied directly to members will produce secondary stress in such members due to bending.

In general, secondary stresses are computed only for large and important structures or for special obvious situations as, for example,

Typical Riveted Truss Joint.

where transverse loads are applied to members at intermediate points in their length.

57 Joint Loads

As stated in Article 56, primary stresses are premised on the assumption that the external forces acting on the truss are applied to the pins, real or imaginary, which connect the members meeting at a common point; therefore, the first step in any stress analysis is the determination of these external forces or *joint loads.* A truss generally supports secondary construction on which the loads are directly applied. The actual loads acting on the truss, therefore, are the reactions developed by such auxiliary construction.

Roof trusses are spaced at intervals over the length of the space that is roofed over, and they support the weight of the roofing, beams, and other construction which bridges the space between roof trusses. The usual arrangement (Fig. 61), from the exterior surface inward, consists of the roof covering, which is supported on sheathing, in turn supported by rafters which run in a direction corresponding to the slope of the roof; the rafters, in turn, are supported on purlins, which are beams spanning

the space between trusses. <u>The purlin reactions therefore constitute the actual loads on the roof truss.</u> To avoid excessive secondary bending stresses in the top chord, purlins are generally supported by the roof truss at or near top-chord joints. Usually, for simplicity in construction, the truss joints are arranged to divide the top chord of the truss into

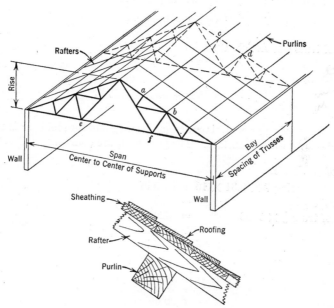

Fig. 61. Details of Roof Construction.

equal spaces, and the trusses are spaced at equal intervals. Determination of joint loads for typical roof construction is illustrated in the following problem:

Example 1

Construction Data

Roofing	Common shingles
Sheathing	1-in. yellow pine
Rafters	2 × 6 yellow pine at 16 in. on centers
Purlins	6 × 10 yellow pine at top-chord joints
Truss	Wooden truss with steel ties, Howe type (Fig. 60c), span 50 ft; pitch $\frac{1}{4}$; spacing of trusses 16 ft

Dimensions

Rise of roof $= \frac{1}{4} \times 50 = 12.5$ ft

Length of rafter $= \sqrt{(12.5)^2 + (25)^2} = 27.95$ ft

Spacing top-chord joints $= \frac{1}{3} \times 27.95 = 9.31$ ft

Weight per Square Foot of Roof (see Table 1 in the Appendix)

Shingles   = 2.5 lb
Sheathing   = 2.5 lb
Rafters $2.5 \times \dfrac{2 \times 6}{12} \times \dfrac{12}{16}$ = 2.0 lb

Distributed load $\overline{7.0}$ lb per sq ft

Purlins $2.5 \times \dfrac{6 \times 10}{12} \times 16 = 200$ lb each

Roof truss (see Article 13)

$$W = \frac{16 \times \overline{50}^2}{25} + \frac{16 \times \overline{50}^3}{6000}$$
$$= 1600 + 333 = 1933 \text{ lb}$$

Joint Loads

For purposes of stress analysis or design, the weight of the roof truss is assumed distributed over the roof surface.   The joint loads are then computed as follows:

Intermediate Joints

Roof covering $7 \times 9.31 \times 16$ = 1045 lb
Purlin   = 200
Roof truss $\frac{1}{6} \times 1933$ = 320
                                         $\overline{}$
                          Total = 1565 lb

End Joints

Roof covering $7 \times \dfrac{9.31}{2} \times 16$ = 520 lb
Purlin   = 200
Roof truss $\frac{1}{2} \times 320$ = 160
                                         $\overline{}$
                          Total = 880 lb

(These loads are shown as acting on the truss at *a* in Fig. 62.)

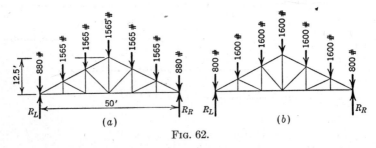

FIG. 62.

For practical purposes and for preliminary analysis made before the actual sizes of members are established, it is sufficiently accurate to estimate the total dead weight of the construction and assume this as a

distributed load over the roof surface. On this basis, the joint loads would be as follows:

Example 2

Total weight roof covering = $7 \times 27.95 \times 2 \times 16$ = 6250 lb
Total weight purlins   = 7×200 = 1400
Total weight roof truss   = 1930
               ———
       Total weight of construction = 9580 lb

Joint Loads

Intermediate = $\frac{1}{6} \times 9580$ = 1600 lb
End $\frac{1}{2} \times 1600$ = 800 lb

(These loads are shown as acting on the truss at *b* in Fig. 62.)

The loads computed in the foregoing are for the intermediate trusses supporting the roof. The trusses at the ends would carry only one-half as much roof surface, and their loads would therefore be correspondingly less.

Any live load superimposed on the roof surface is carried to the top-chord joints of the truss by the roof construction. Even though the sheathing, rafters, and purlins are continuous over their supports, the reactions developed on the truss by purlins are computed as though such elements of the construction were non-continuous and simply supported. Thus, in Fig. 61, if a load were placed in the roof area bounded by purlins *ac* and *bd*, it would create reactions or joint loads at *a*, *b*, *c*, and *d* in proportion to its relative position in that area. A load at the center would be equally divided among the four points; if closer to *ac*, joint loads at *a* and *c* would be proportionately larger than joint loads of *b* and *d*; if closer to truss joints *a* and *b*, these joint loads would be proportionately larger than joint loads of *c* and *d*.

Loads are sometimes applied to or suspended from truss members. In such cases, the member is regarded as acting first as a simply supported beam delivering reactions to the joints at its ends. Thus (Fig. 61) a load suspended from member *ef* would cause that member to act as a beam, and the joint loads at *e* and *f* would be equal to the reactions of this beam.

It is generally necessary to determine the joint loads for any loading applied to a truss before analyzing the internal stresses in the truss.

Bridge trusses are generally arranged in pairs with the floor of the bridge passing between the trusses, in *through bridges*, and over the top of the trusses in *deck bridges*. For either type bridge, the usual arrange-

ment is to attach transverse *floor beams* to the trusses (Figs. 63 and 64) with longitudinal *stringers* resting on or attached to these floor beams.

Typical Roof Framing.

The flooring, which usually is a reinforced concrete slab for highway bridges and cross ties for open-deck railroad bridges, rests on the longitudinal stringers. Although variations in this general arrangement

Fig. 63.

Fig. 64.

may at times be employed, they produce the same net result, namely that the weight of the floor system and of the live load superimposed on the floor is delivered to the trusses by the transverse floor beams, and the reactions of these beams, therefore, constitute the loads applied to the truss. To avoid secondary bending stress in truss members, floor beams are preferably attached to the trusses at or near joints of the truss. The effect of the weight of the trusses themselves plus the weight of bracing and other auxiliary construction, which is not part of the floor system, is usually allowed for by assuming a uniformly distributed load of the same gross magnitude spread over the floor of the bridge. For large trusses, where the distribution of truss weight may appreciably affect member stresses, the weight of the truss may be assumed equally divided between top- and bottom-chord joints and the weight of the bracing and of the floor system applied to the truss at the joints to which or near which such construction is attached. The vertical members are the only ones which are affected by changing the load distribution between the top and bottom chord joints.

The following examples illustrate the determination of dead-load joint (panel) loads for a typical truss bridge:

Example 3

Construction Data

> Through highway truss bridge
> Span, 110 ft center to center of truss bearings
> Roadway, 24 ft curb to curb
> Trusses, 5-panel Pratt (Fig. 59h), spaced 29 ft apart.   Total estimated weight trusses and bracing is 90,000 lb
> Curb, 9 in. wide and 15 in. high (concrete)
> Floor beams, 30 in. × 110 lb
> Stringers, 7 lines of 16-in. × 45-lb I-beams
> Floor slab, reinforced concrete average $t = 7\frac{1}{2}$
> Wearing surface, allow 20 lb per sq ft for future

Intermediate-Joint Loads (see Fig. 65a)

> Wearing surface and floor slab $(20 + 94) \times \frac{110}{5} \times 24 \times \frac{1}{2}$ = 30,100 lb
> Curb, $9 \times 15 \times \frac{150}{144} \times 22$ = 3,090
> Stringers, $7 \times 45 \times \frac{110}{5} \times \frac{1}{2}$ = 3,470
> Floor beam, $110 \times 29 \times \frac{1}{2}$ = 1,600
> Truss and bracing, $\frac{1}{2} \times 90,000 \times \frac{1}{5}$ = 9,000

> Total = 47,260 lb

End-Joint Load

> $\frac{1}{2} \times 47,260 = 23,630$ lb

If the weight of truss and bracing is to be more accurately distributed, the results would be as follows:

Example 4 (same data as for Example 3).

Intermediate-Joint Loads (see Fig. 65b)

    Top-Chord Joints

      Truss and bracing, $\frac{1}{2} \times 90,000 \times \frac{1}{5} \times \frac{1}{2} = 4,500$ lb

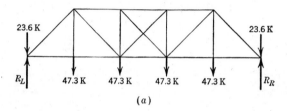

(a)

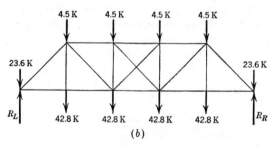

(b)

Fig. 65.

Bottom-Chord Joints

Wearing surface and floor slab	=	30,100 lb
Curb	=	3,090
Stringers	=	3,470
Floor beam	=	1,600
Truss and bracing	=	4,500
		42,760 lb

End-Joint Load

$\frac{1}{2} \times 4,500 = 2,250$ lb
$\frac{1}{2} \times 42,760 = 21,380$

23,630 lb

Live loads are transmitted to the trusses by the floor system, which is generally assumed to act as a system of simply supported beams. In accordance with this assumption, it is not necessary to compute indi-

vidual slab and stringer reactions as any load will be distributed to the joints of the two trusses proportionate to its position in the panel. To produce maximum effect, a concentrated load should be placed near one truss.

Example 5

Consider a standard H20 truck (see Fig. 2) placed on the foregoing highway bridge floor (Example 3) with its rear axle over the floor beam at L_2 (Fig. 66a).

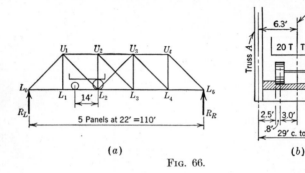

(*a*)   (*b*)

Fig. 66.

The truck is placed with the wheel against the curb (Fig. 66b), and the joint loads on truss A are computed as follows:

$$\text{Weight of truck, 20 tons} \quad = 40 \text{ kips}$$

$$\text{Rear axle, } 0.8 \times 40 \quad = 32 \text{ kips}$$

$$\text{Front axle, } 0.2 \times 40 \quad = \ 8 \text{ kips}$$

$$\text{Proportion of load to truss } A = \frac{22.7}{29}$$

Joint Load L_1

$$\text{Front axle, } \ 8 \times \frac{22.7}{29} \times \frac{14}{22} = \ 4.0 \text{ kips}$$

Joint Load L_2

$$\text{Front axle, } \ 8 \times \frac{22.7}{29} \times \frac{8}{22} = \ 2.3 \text{ kips}$$

$$\text{Rear axle, } \ 32 \times \frac{22.7}{29} \quad = \underline{25.0 \text{ kips}}$$
$$27.3 \text{ kips}$$

These joint loads are used to determine the stresses in the truss for the truck in the given position.

For a uniformly distributed load over the floor surface the determination would be as follows for the structure of Example 3.

Example 6
Location of Load

Assume a uniformly distributed load of 100 lb per sq ft covering the entire width of roadway and extending from L_5 to a point midway between L_1 and L_2.

$$\text{Load per lineal foot of bridge} = 100 \times 24 = 2.4 \text{ kips}$$

$$\text{Load per lineal foot of truss} = \tfrac{1}{2} \times 2.4 = 1.2 \text{ kips}$$

Joint Loads

At L_1 $\dfrac{1.2 \times 11 \times 5.5}{22} =$ 3.3 kips

At L_2 $\dfrac{1.2 \times 11 \times 16.5}{22} = 9.9$

$1.2 \times 22 \times \tfrac{1}{2} = \underline{13.2}$

23.1 kips

At L_3 and L_4 1.2×22 $=$ 26.4 kips

At L_5 $1.2 \times 22 \times \tfrac{1}{2} =$ 13.2 kips

58 Truss Reactions

The truss reactions are determined in accordance with the principles outlined in Chapter 4. Although they are produced by action of the joint loads on the truss, they may be determined directly from the initial loading and its relative position in the span.

Thus, for the roof truss shown in Fig. 62a, assuming it simply supported, $R_L = R_R = (\tfrac{1}{2} \times 1565 \times 5) + 880 = 4790$ lb. For the bridge truss shown in Fig. 65 $R_L = R_R = (2 \times 47.3) + 23.6 = 118.2$ kips.

For live loading it is sometimes convenient to compute separately the amount contributed to the reaction by each joint load. Thus, for the bridge truss given in Example 3 of Article 57,

Example 1

Using joint loads determined in Example 5, Article 57,

Truss reaction produced by joint load $L_1 = 4.0 \times \tfrac{4}{5} = 3.2$ kips
Truss reaction produced by joint load $L_2 = 27.3 \times \tfrac{3}{5} = 16.4$ kips

Total truss reaction, $R_L = 19.6$ kips

Here, however, it would have been more convenient to compute the amounts contributed to the reaction from the initial loading as shown in Fig. 66, without

consideration of the individual joint loads. Thus, noting that the load on the floor is transmitted to truss A in the proportion $22.7/29$, the reaction R_L is as follows:

$$\text{Truss reaction produced by front axle } = \ 8 \times \frac{22.7}{29} \times \frac{80}{110} = \ 4.6 \text{ kips}$$

$$\text{Truss reaction produced by rear axle } = 32 \times \frac{22.7}{29} \times \frac{3}{5} = 15.0 \text{ kips}$$

$$\text{Total truss reaction, } R_L = 19.6 \text{ kips}$$

Example 2

The individual joint loads which result from the uniform loading used for Example 6, Article 57, will each contribute the following amounts to the value of R_L:

Load at L_1	$3.3 \times \frac{4}{5} =$	2.64 kips
Load at L_2	$23.1 \times \frac{3}{5} =$	13.86
Load at L_3	$26.4 \times \frac{2}{5} =$	10.56
Load at L_4	$26.4 \times \frac{1}{5} =$	5.28
Load at L_5	$13.2 \times 0 =$	0

$$\text{Total truss reaction, } R_L = 32.34 \text{ kips}$$

It is much simpler here to compute the reactions directly from the initial loading:

Total load on span	$= 2.4 \times 77$	$= 184.8$ kips
Load delivered to truss A	$= \frac{1}{2} \times 184.8$	$= 92.4$ kips
Distance from resultant of load to right reaction	$= \frac{1}{2} \times 77$	$= 38.5$ ft

$$R_L = 92.4 \times \frac{38.5}{110} = 32.34 \text{ kips}$$

Reactions may also be determined by graphical methods as outlined in Chapter 4.

59 Stresses in Truss Members

The primary stress in an individual member of the truss is determined by dividing the structure into parts as stated in Article 37 and computing the force system necessary to maintain the equilibrium of any such part. Since the members are assumed to be connected by frictionless pins, the force in a member must coincide with its axis and pass through the pins at each end. Thus, if a section is passed through panel L_1L_2 of the truss shown in Fig. 66, the force system acting on the portion on the left of this section will be as represented at a in Fig. 67; the force system acting on the portion on the right of this section is shown at b. In each system it will be observed that the members cut by the section are represented by the stresses in such members. The reaction, joint loads, and stresses

in either of these groupings thus constitute a force system in equilibrium and must fulfill the static conditions $\Sigma H = 0$, $\Sigma V = 0$, and $\Sigma M = 0$.

Sections are generally chosen in such a manner as to cut not more than three members. When the arrangement of members is such that this cannot be done, the structure is termed *statically indeterminate internally*, and other methods of analysis must be employed. Such a condition may be noted by sectioning the center panel of the above truss and considering the portion on the left of this section (Fig. 67c). For such an

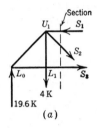

(a)

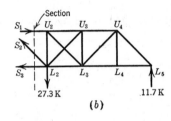

(b)

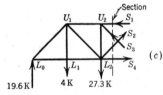

(c)

FIG. 67.

arrangement, however, a solution by statics is made possible by so constructing the diagonals that they are incapable of resisting compressive stress; thus $S_3 = 0$, and the three remaining unknowns may be determined by statics.

Tension stress in a member is generally indicated by the symbol $+$, compression by the symbol $-$.

The force or stress in members may also be found from a consideration of the individual joints. Since the pin (real or imaginary) connecting the members at a given joint is in equilibrium, the forces in the members acting on such a pin must form a concentric force system in equilibrium and fulfill the equations $\Sigma H = 0$ and $\Sigma V = 0$. Obviously, not more than two unknowns may be included in such a determination. Typical joints of the foregoing truss are represented in Fig. 68. Analysis of joint L_0 (Fig. 68a) shows that the vertical component of stress in L_0L_1 equals the truss reaction, and, since $\Sigma H = 0$, the stress in L_0L_1 must equal the horizontal component of the stress in L_0U_1; analysis of

joint L_1 (Fig. 68b) shows that the stress in L_1L_2 must equal the stress in L_0L_1 and that the stress in U_1L_1 must equal the load at L_1; proceeding to joint U_1 (Fig. 68c), we find the stresses in U_1U_2 and U_1L_2 by writing $\Sigma H = 0$ and $\Sigma V = 0$. This method of analysis is particularly useful in determining stresses in hangers such as U_1L_1 and vertical posts such as U_2L_2. It also forms the basis of graphical solutions, since the forces acting on a pin, laid out to scale and direction, must form a closed polygon.

Stresses are usually computed for each separate loading or load arrangement. The dead-load stresses are first computed and recorded;

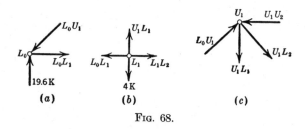

$$(a) \qquad\qquad (b) \qquad\qquad (c)$$

Fig. 68.

then each live loading is separately considered and stresses recorded for such arrangements of this live loading as will produce maximum effects on given members. Finally, the combined stress resulting from rational load combinations is determined by adding the stresses obtained from the separate analyses.

60   Roof Trusses—Dead-Load Stresses

Stresses in roof trusses are frequently obtained by graphical methods. The truss diagram is laid out to convenient scale as at a in Fig. 69, and all spaces are lettered or numbered. The forces acting on a given joint are identified by reading the letters or numbers around the joint in a clockwise [1] direction. Thus the forces on the end joint are identified as reaction AB, joint load BC, and stresses $C1$ and $1A$. Figure 69b is a collection of force polygons drawn for each joint and superimposed upon one another. Thus, the left end joint being considered, AB is laid off to scale and direction and lettered ab to read in its direction of action; bc in similar manner indicates the joint load; forces $c1$ and $1a$ must then complete a closed force polygon and act on the pin in the direction indicated by reading their identifying letters or numbers. Thus force

[1] Forces may be read in a counterclockwise direction if preferred; however, the same direction must be maintained throughout the solution.

$c1$ is a compression stress and $1a$ is tensile. Similar procedures are followed for the other joints, and the values of all stresses are obtained by scaling the diagram.

In the construction of the force polygons which make up the force or stress diagram, it will be noted that only two unknowns can be solved

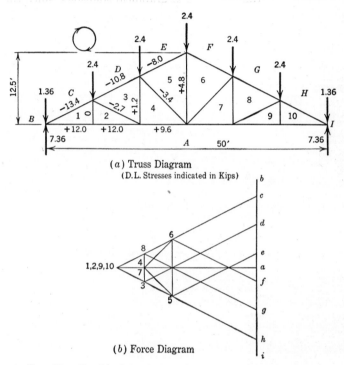

(*a*) Truss Diagram
(D.L. Stresses indicated in Kips)

(*b*) Force Diagram

FIG. 69.   Graphical Analysis of Stress.   Howe Roof Truss.

at each joint, and the selection of the order in which joints are solved must be in accordance with this limitation. For the Fink roof truss shown in Fig. 70, joints L_0, U_1 and L_1 are solved in order without difficulty. Because of the presence of three unknowns at each of the next top- or bottom-chord joints, the order of progress is temporarily halted. It will be noted, however, that although joint U_3 has three unknowns, two of these have the same line of action, which makes it possible to solve for the third unknown and the resultant of the other two forces. Thus the force polygon (Fig. 70*b*) $ef6'5'e$ is drawn with stress 6–5 in assumed or temporary location, but, since $f6$ and $e5$ are parallel, it will be noted that $6'5'$ represents the correct stress in truss member 6–5.

Joint M_3 now represents a similar situation, and the force polygon $5'6'7'4'5'$ can be constructed with the length $4'5'$ representing the correct stress in member 4–5. Joint U_2 can now be solved and forces $5'4'$ and $5'6'$ shifted to their correct positions.

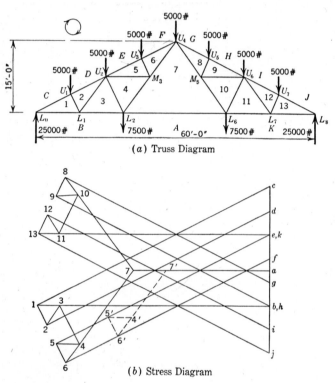

(*a*) Truss Diagram

(*b*) Stress Diagram

Fig. 70. Graphical Analysis of Stress. Fink Roof Truss.

Figure 71 represents another solution of this problem. In this solution, a temporary member *mn* is substituted for members 5–4 and 6–5, and the solution proceeds to the finding of the stress in member *F*6. The temporary member is then removed and stresses determined in the actual members.

In these graphical constructions, the layout of the truss diagram should be of such size as will permit accurate determination of the slopes of all members. For the stress diagram, since stresses are commonly recorded to the nearest 500 pounds of value, a scale of 1 inch = 4000 pounds is usually satisfactory. When the truss and loading are symmetrical, the stress diagram will also be symmetrical, and only one-

half of this diagram need be constructed; however, the stress in such a member as $A4$ in Fig. 69 or $A7$ in Fig. 70 should then be computed analytically as a check on the accuracy of the graphical work.

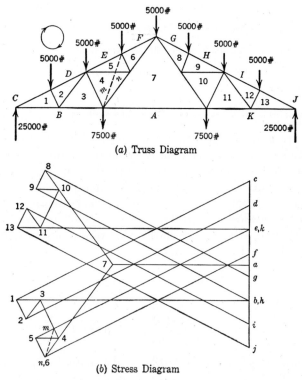

(a) Truss Diagram

(b) Stress Diagram

Fig. 71. Graphical Analysis of Stress. Fink Roof Truss. Substitute Member Method.

61 Roof Trusses—Live-Load Stresses

Live loads on roofs consist primarily of snow, ice, and wind pressure. In addition, loads such as shafting, balconies, and hoists are frequently suspended from the roof truss. The stresses must be determined for each such load, and, if it is one which may vary in position on the structure, the effect of such changes in location must be taken into account.

Snow and ice loads are usually regarded as applied uniformly over the entire roof surface and therefore produce effects similar to dead load. The stresses due to these loads may, therefore, be found by proportion. Thus, for the truss illustrated in Fig. 69 (see the typical roof problem in Article 57 for construction data), stresses due to ice or snow loads may be determined as in the following example.

Example 1

Ice load	$= 10$ lb per sq ft of roof surface
Snow load	$= 8$ lb per sq ft of roof surface
Total ice load	$= 10 \times 27.95 \times 2 \times 16 = 8900$ lb
Total snow load	$= 8 \times 27.95 \times 2 \times 16 = 7200$ lb
Total dead load	$= 14{,}700$ (see Article 58)
Ice-load stress	$= \frac{8.9}{14.7} \times$ (dead-load stress)
Snow-load stress	$= \frac{7.2}{14.7} \times$ (dead-load stress).

For the given truss, the stresses in individual members are recorded in Fig. 74.

The force of the wind is generally expressed in terms of pressure exerted against a vertical plane surface, and this in turn is reduced to an equivalent pressure normal to the windward roof surface. Although recognized as an erroneous practice, the suction present on the leeward side is commonly neglected.[2] Based upon a wind intensity of 20 pounds per square foot against a vertical plane (corresponding to a wind velocity of about 80 mph), the pressure on the windward roof surface of the roof of Example 1 would be as follows:

Example 2

$$\text{Rise of roof truss} = 12.5 \text{ ft}$$

$$\text{Length of rafter} = 27.95 \text{ ft}$$

$$\text{Sin } \alpha = \frac{12.5}{27.95} = 0.45$$

Using Duchemin's formula (see Article 18), the pressure on the windward roof surface is

$$p_n = 20 \left(\frac{2 \times 0.45}{1 + (0.45)^2} \right) = 15 \text{ lb per sq ft}$$

$$\text{Total wind force} = 15 \times 27.95 \times 16 = 6.71 \text{ kips}$$

$$\text{Joint load} = 15 \times 9.31 \times 16 = 2.23 \text{ kips}$$

If one end of the truss is free to move horizontally, the entire horizontal component of the wind force must be resisted at the opposite support. The vertical and horizontal components of the total wind force are

$$W_V = \frac{25 \times 6.7}{27.95} = 6.0 \text{ kips}$$

$$W_H = \frac{12.5 \times 6.7}{27.95} = 3.0 \text{ kips}$$

[2] See Fifth Progress Report of Subcommittee 31, *Proceedings Am. Soc. C. E.*, March, 1936, p. 398.

Wind acting left to right (Fig. 72a)

Right reaction

Vertical component $= \left[\dfrac{6.7 \times 27.95}{2} \right] \div 50 = 1.9$ kips

Horizontal component $= 3$ kips
Left reaction $= 6.0 - 1.9 = 4.1$ kips

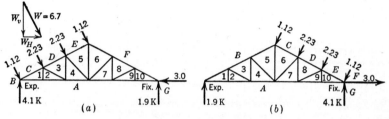

FIG. 72. Wind Loads and Reactions.

Wind acting right to left (Fig. 72b)

Left reaction $= 1.9$ kips
Right reaction

Vertical component $= 6.0 - 1.9 = 4.1$ kips
Horizontal component $= 3.0$ kips

The graphical analysis of stresses is performed in the manner outlined in Article 60 (Fig. 73), and the summary of stresses due to assumed combinations of loading is shown in Fig. 74.

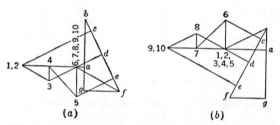

Wind acting left to right.   Wind acting right to left.

FIG. 73. Stress Diagrams.

62 Roof Trusses—Combined Stresses

The stress in each member having been determined for each loading which may act on the structure, consideration must then be given to the manner in which these loadings and corresponding stresses may be combined. This is a matter which entails the application of common sense and judgment in order to arrive at logical results. Thus it would not

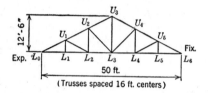

(Trusses spaced 16 ft centers)

Loads:

Dead Load (D. L.) per joint = 2.4 kips
Ice   = 10/□' of roof surface
Snow = 8/□' "   "   "
Wind = 20/□' on vertical plane

Combinations:

Case I. D. L. + Ice + Snow
  II. D. L. + Ice + Snow + ½ Wind
  III. D. L. + Ice + Wind
  IV. D. L. + Wind

STRESS IN MEMBERS   + Denotes Tension
  (Kips)   −   "   Compression

Member	D. L.	Ice	Snow	Wind		Combined Stresses			
				L to R	R to L	Case I	Case II	Case III	Case IV
L_0L_1	+12.0	+7.3	+5.9	+5.7	+3.8	+25.2	+28.1	+25.0	+17.7
L_1L_2	+12.0	+7.3	+5.9	+5.7	+3.8	+25.2	+28.1	+25.0	+17.7
L_2L_3	+ 9.6	+5.8	+4.7	+3.2	+3.8	+20.1	+22.0	+19.2	+13.4
L_3L_4	+ 9.6	+5.8	+4.7	+0.8	+6.2	+20.1	+23.2	+21.6	+15.8
L_4L_5	+12.0	+7.3	+5.9	+0.8	+8.7	+25.2	+29.6	+28.0	+20.7
L_5L_6	+12.0	+7.3	+5.9	+0.8	+8.7	+25.2	+29.6	+28.0	+20.7
L_0U_1	−13.4	−8.1	−6.6	−6.9	−4.2	−28.1	−31.6	−28.4	−20.3
U_1U_2	−10.8	−6.5	−5.3	−5.3	−4.2	−22.6	−25.3	−22.6	−16.1
U_2U_3	− 8.0	−4.8	−3.9	−3.6	−4.2	−16.7	−18.8	−17.0	−12.2
U_3U_4	− 8.0	−4.8	−3.9	−4.2	−3.6	−16.7	−18.8	−17.0	−12.2
U_4U_5	−10.8	−6.5	−5.3	−4.2	−5.3	−22.6	−25.3	−22.6	−16.1
U_5U_6	−13.4	−8.1	−6.6	−4.2	−6.9	−28.1	−31.6	−28.4	−20.3
U_1L_1	0	0	0	0	0	0	0	0	0
U_1L_2	− 2.7	−1.6	−1.3	−2.8	0	− 5.6	− 7.0	− 7.1	− 5.5
U_2L_2	+ 1.2	+0.7	+0.6	+1.3	0	+ 2.5	+ 3.2	+ 3.2	+ 2.5
U_2L_3	− 3.4	−2.1	−1.7	−3.5	0	− 7.2	− 9.0	− 9.0	− 6.9
U_3L_3	+ 4.8	+2.9	+2.4	+2.5	+2.5	+10.1	+11.4	+10.2	+ 7.3
L_3U_4	− 3.4	−2.1	−1.7	0	−3.5	− 7.2	− 9.0	− 9.0	− 6.9
U_4L_4	+ 1.2	+0.7	+0.6	0	+1.3	+ 2.5	+ 3.2	+ 3.2	+ 2.5
L_4U_5	− 2.7	−1.6	−1.3	0	−2.8	− 5.6	− 7.0	− 7.1	− 5.5
U_5L_5	0	0	0	0	0	0	0	0	0

FIG. 74.   Summary of Stresses in Roof Truss.

be logical to combine wind forces of maximum intensity with full snow load as such a wind would probably blow the snow off the roof.

Typical combinations of roof loads for the roof used in previous examples and the resulting combined stresses due to these load combinations are shown in Fig. 74. The maximum combined stresses are used in the design or final analysis of the structure, due consideration being given to the symmetry of the structure. Careful consideration must also be given to possible reversals of stress in members. Thus a given member may for one condition of loading carry tension while for a different combination the stress may be compression. Such reversals of stress must be noted and the members designed for the maximum of each kind of stress.

In the given example, the maximum stress in each member occurs under Case II loading except for U_1L_2 which is determined by Case III, and there are no reversals. The stresses given by Case I will probably control the design of this structure, however, since accepted practice permits a $33\frac{1}{3}$ per cent increase in allowed unit stress when wind force is included.

63 Mill Bent—Hinged Column Bases

In the construction illustrated in Fig. 61, the lateral or horizontal component of the wind force must be resisted by one of the walls supporting the roof. This means that a force of considerable magnitude will be applied horizontally to the top of the wall, and the stability of the entire construction will depend upon the ability of the wall to resist such a force. Walls of substantial construction, such as brick or concrete, will ordinarily be required, except for very short span roofs, and, to increase their stability further, pilasters are frequently included in the wall construction.

It is frequently desirable, particularly for shops and simple mill construction, to use relatively inexpensive wall construction and support the trusses on columns designed to resist the horizontal wind forces. The most common arrangement is to attach the end of the truss to the top of the column and connect the nearest lower-chord joint to the column at a point near the top by a *knee brace*, as at *a* in Fig. 75. For a flat roof as shown at *b*, the knee braces may be omitted. In this type of construction, the columns are attached to footings which must be capable of resisting the horizontal wind force in addition to supporting the vertical loadings. Depending upon the rigidity of the connections of columns to footings and the resistance of footings to overturning, the columns may be considered as either hinged or fixed at their bases. The criterion is the rigidity of the base, and, since the fulfillment of the assumption of

fixity requires that there be no movement whatsoever of the bases or footings, the columns should be assumed to be hinged unless it is certain that definite fixity exists.

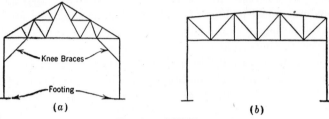

(a)   (b)

FIG. 75.   Mill Bent.

The action of a bent with hinged column bases under lateral force is illustrated in Fig. 76.   If we assume no lateral loading applied to the columns and neglect any distortion of the truss and knee braces, the upper end of each column will remain vertical, and each hinge will deflect the same amount relative to the top of the column.   If the windward column is considered as a free body as at b, it will be acted upon by the resistance offered by the truss, represented by components P_1 and P_2; by the force S in the knee brace; and by the reaction at the hinged base, represented by components V_L and H_L.   The forces on the column may be divided into two groups: force P_1 applied at a, S_v applied at b, and V_L applied at c are axial forces producing compression but not contributing to the initial deflection; force P_2 acting at a, S_H acting at b,

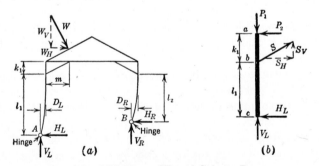

FIG. 76.   Mill Bent.   Hinged Column Bases.

and H_L acting at c are transverse forces which induce bending.   Usually the distance k will be less than one-fourth the length of the column, and the elastic curve of the column may be assumed to remain vertical at b without introducing excessive error for the comparative purpose here employed.   Based on this assumption, deflection D_L will equal that of a

cantilever fixed at b and loaded with a force H_L at its extremity; hence, for the left-hand column, where I_L = moment of inertia of column section,

$$D_L = \frac{H_L l_1^3}{3EI_L} \text{ (approx.)} \tag{83}$$

In a similar manner, for the right-hand column,

$$D_R = \frac{H_R l_2^3}{3EI_R} \tag{84}$$

and since

$$D_L = D_R$$

$$\frac{H_L}{H_R} = \frac{l_2^3 I_L}{l_1^3 I_R} \tag{85}$$

$$H_L + H_R = W_H \tag{86}$$

$$H_L = W_H \left[\frac{l_2^3 I_L}{l_2^3 I_L + l_1^3 I_R} \right] \tag{87}$$

$$H_R = W_H \left[\frac{l_1^3 I_R}{l_2^3 I_L + l_1^3 I_R} \right] \tag{88}$$

When the columns are of the same section and length,

$$H_L = H_R = \tfrac{1}{2} W_H \tag{89}$$

With the values of H_L and H_R determined as above, the values of V_L and V_R are computed from the equation for $\Sigma M = 0$, applied to the entire structure choosing moment centers successively at the supports. For the column as a free body (Fig. 76b)

With moment center at b

$$P_2 = \frac{H_L l_1}{k} \tag{90}$$

With moment center at a

$$S_H = \frac{H_L (l_1 + k)}{k} \tag{91}$$

From the known slope of the knee brace

$$S_V = S_H \left(\frac{k}{m} \right) \tag{92}$$

From $\Sigma V = 0$

$$P_1 = V_L + Sp \tag{93}$$

A similar procedure is followed for the leeward column.

Stresses in the roof truss may now be determined as described in Article 60, noting that forces P_1 and P_2 constitute the components of the reaction at the end joint of the truss, and the force S in the knee brace acts as a load applied at the joint to which it connects. Unit stresses in the column are determined from the bending-moments,

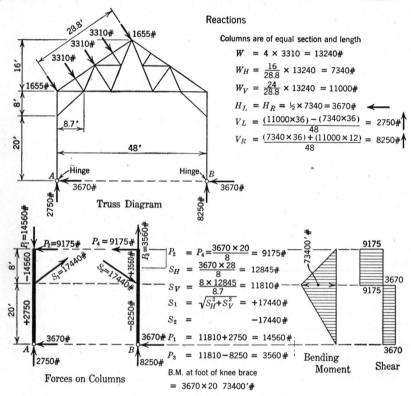

Reactions

Columns are of equal section and length

$$W = 4 \times 3310 = 13240\#$$

$$W_H = \frac{16}{28.8} \times 13240 = 7340\#$$

$$W_V = \frac{24}{28.8} \times 13240 = 11000\#$$

$$H_L = H_R = \frac{1}{2} \times 7340 = 3670\# \quad \longleftarrow$$

$$V_L = \frac{(11000 \times 36) - (7340 \times 36)}{48} = 2750\#\uparrow$$

$$V_R = \frac{(7340 \times 36) + (11000 \times 12)}{48} = 8250\#\uparrow$$

Truss Diagram

$$P_2 = P_4 = \frac{3670 \times 20}{8} = 9175\#$$

$$S_H = \frac{3670 \times 28}{8} = 12845\#$$

$$S_V = \frac{8 \times 12845}{8.7} = 11810\#$$

$$S_1 = \sqrt{S_H^2 + S_V^2} = +17440\#$$

$$S_2 = \qquad\qquad = -17440\#$$

$$P_1 = 11810 + 2750 = 14560\#$$

$$P_3 = 11810 - 8250 = 3560\#$$

B.M. at foot of knee brace
$$= 3670 \times 20 \; 73400'\#$$

Forces on Columns

Bending Moment

Shear

Fig. 77.   Mill Bent with Hinged Column Bases.   Typical Solution.

shears, and axial stress in portions ab and of Fig. 76b. The complete solution of a typical mill bent with hinged column bases is shown in Figs. 77 and 78.

When the exterior walls are supported by girts attached to the columns, the wind pressure on the windward wall is transmitted directly to the column. It is usually considered as a horizontal uniformly distributed load over the length of the windward column, and account must be taken of this load condition on the windward column in writing the deflection equations.

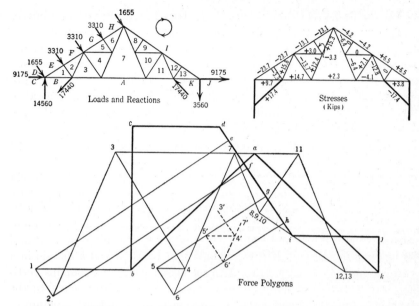

FIG. 78. Mill Bent with Hinged Column Bases. Stresses in Roof Truss.

64   Mill Bent—Fixed Column Bases

The action of a bent whose columns are fixed at their bases is illustrated at a in Fig. 79, where it is assumed that the column base and the attachment of the column thereto are sufficiently rigid to hold the column axis, at the bottom of the column, in its original position. Neglecting the distortion of the truss and knee braces, points a and b will remain

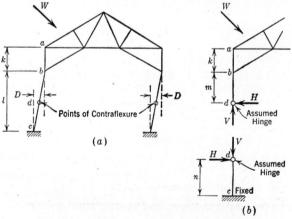

FIG. 79.   Mill Bent.   Fixed Column Bases.

in a vertical line and the column will be bent in the form of an S curve, the bending-moment reversing at some point d, between the foot of the knee brace at b, and the column base at c. At point d, therefore, the bending-moment in the column must be zero, and this point is known as the *point of contraflexure*. For purposes of analysis, the columns are assumed cut at the points of contraflexure and hinges inserted as at b. The portion of the structure above these imaginary hinges may then be solved as a bent with hinged column bases and the portion of the columns below the hinges solved as a vertical cantilever beam with forces H and V applied at its free end.

If the column is considered as a free body (Fig. 80), the external forces will consist of the components of the truss reaction P_1 and P_2 acting at a; the stress S in the knee brace acting at b; and the shear H, direct force V, and couple M_c acting on the base section of the column. These external forces and couple will produce the bending-moment and shear diagram shown. If it is assumed that points a and b remain in a vertical line and that the tangent to the elastic curve at c remains vertical, the deflection of points a and b, respectively, with respect to the tangent at c may be computed by area-moments as follows (column of constant section):

$$D_1 = \text{deflection of } a \text{ with respect to tangent at } c$$

$$= \frac{Hml}{2}(\tfrac{1}{3}l + k) + \frac{Hmk}{2}(\tfrac{2}{3}k) - \frac{Hnl}{2}(\tfrac{2}{3}l + k) \qquad (94)$$

$$D_2 = \text{deflection of } b \text{ with respect to tangent at } c$$

$$= \frac{Hml}{2}(\tfrac{1}{3}l) - \frac{Hnl}{2}(\tfrac{2}{3}l) \qquad (95)$$

Since $D_1 = D_2$

$$\frac{ml}{2} + \frac{mk}{3} - \frac{nl}{2} = 0 \qquad (96)$$

Substituting $n = l - m$ and solving for m gives

$$m = \frac{l}{2}\left(\frac{1}{1 + \dfrac{k}{3l}}\right) \qquad (97)$$

From Equation 97 it is seen that for a column of constant section, the position of the point of contraflexure depends upon the ratio of k to l. Since this ratio is usually small (generally less than one-fourth), it is customary to neglect it entirely and assume that

$$m = n = \tfrac{1}{2}l \qquad (98)$$

$D_A = D_B$

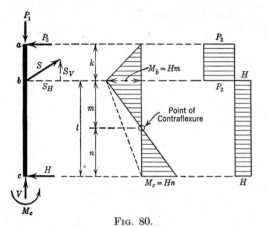

FIG. 80.

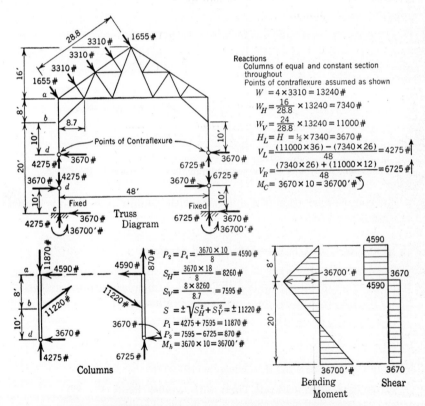

FIG. 81.   Mill Bent with Fixed Column Bases.   Typical Solution.

The foregoing equations take no account of any lateral load on the columns. When the construction is such that the side walls are supported directly by the columns, a uniformly distributed load must be included in the forces acting on the column and the bending-moments, shears, and deflection equations altered accordingly.

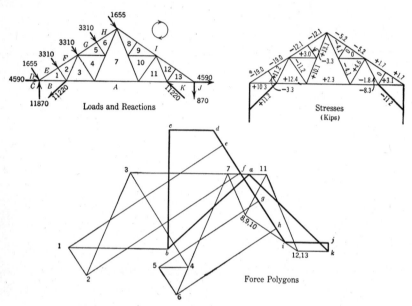

FIG. 82.   Mill Bent with Fixed Column Bases.   Stresses in Roof Truss.

The complete solution of a mill bent with column bases fixed is shown in Figs. 81 and 82.

65   Parallel-Chord Truss—Dead-Load Stresses

Stresses in the members of a truss with parallel chords are best determined by analytical methods utilizing the principles outlined in Article 59. The application of these principles is illustrated in the solution of the following typical bridge truss problem:

Example 1

Highway Bridge—Span 150 ft, roadway width 20 ft

    Truss data—Riveted Pratt Truss, with parallel chords (Fig. 83)
            Spacing of trusses, 25 ft center to center
            Height of truss, 27 ft center to center of chords
            Span 150 ft; 6 panels at 25 ft

Estimated weights

Floor slab, stringers, and floor beams	258.0 kips
Bottom lateral bracing	1.3
Top lateral bracing	6.6
Trusses	94.1

Total weight of bridge = 360.0 kips = dead load

Assume all dead load applied at lower-chord joints.

Dead load (per truss) = $\frac{1}{2} \times 360$ = 180 kips
Joint load   = $180 \times \frac{1}{6}$ = 30 kips
Reaction   = $2\frac{1}{2} \times 30$ = 75 kips

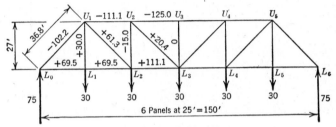

FIG. 83.   Pratt Bridge Truss.

It will be noted that the half-panel loads at joints L_0 and L_6 have been omitted since they do not cause stress in truss members. They must be included, however, in the total load on the support.

Because of the symmetry of both the truss and the loads it is necessary to compute stress only in the members on one side of the center of the span, since corresponding members on the other side will receive the same stress in both kind and amount.

Chord stresses are determined by sectioning the structure successively in each panel and writing $\Sigma M = 0$ for the forces acting on that part of the structure on *one side only* of the section. For a section through panel L_2L_3, and considering the part of the truss on the left of the section (Fig. 84a), the force S is obtained by writing $\Sigma M = 0$ with moment center at L_3. A similar result would be obtained by using the portion of the truss on the right of the section as at b. It will also be observed that the algebraic sum of the moments of the reaction and loads on either portion about L_3 is the bending-moment on a section through L_3, and the force S must equal this bending-moment divided by the height of the truss h. Similarly, the stress in L_2L_3 equals the bending-moment on a section through U_2 divided by the height of truss. It can be stated in general that, whenever three members are cut by a section as in

Fig. 84, *the stress in any member equals the algebraic sum of the moments of truss loads and reaction about the point of intersection of the other two members, divided by the normal distance from centerline of the member to this point of intersection.* It may also be observed that, should the diagonal in this panel extend from L_2 to U_3 instead of as shown, the moment centers for top- and bottom-chord stress will reverse, i.e., stress in U_2U_3 equals bending-moment at L_2 divided by h, and stress in L_2L_3 equals bending-moment at U_3 divided by h.

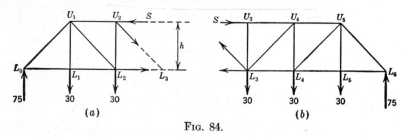

(a) (b)

FIG. 84.

Bending-moments are most readily computed by expressing values algebraically. Thus, for the truss of Example 1 (Fig. 83),

Example 2

Where W = joint load   = 30 kips
       p = panel length = 25 ft
       h = truss height = 27 ft

Reaction at $L_0 = 2\frac{1}{2}W$
Bending-moments

    at L_1, B.M. $= 2\frac{1}{2}Wp$
    at L_2, B.M. $= (2\frac{1}{2}W \times 2p) - Wp = 4Wp$
    at L_3, B.M. $= (2\frac{1}{2}W \times 3p) - 2Wp - Wp = 4\frac{1}{2}Wp$

Since

$$\frac{Wp}{h} = \frac{30 \times 25}{27} = 27.78$$

The stresses are

Member	Moment Center	Stress		
L_0L_1 and L_1L_2	U_1	$2\frac{1}{2}$	$\times\ 27.78 =$	$+69.5$ kips
L_2L_3	U_2	4	$\times\ 27.78 =$	$+111.1$ kips
U_1U_2	L_2	4	$\times\ 27.78 =$	-111.1 kips
U_2U_3	L_3	$4\frac{1}{2}$	$\times\ 27.78 =$	-125.0 kips

Stresses in the diagonals of parallel-chord trusses are usually determined by passing a section perpendicular to the chords and equating the algebraic sum of reaction, loads, and stress components, parallel to this

Courtesy American Bridge Co.

Hetch Hetchy Pipe Line Bridge across Dumbarton Straits near Redwood City, California. Thirty-six Riveted Pratt Truss Spans. Each Span 105 Feet.

section, to zero. The algebraic sum of reaction and load components parallel to such a section is the *transverse shear* and, in a truss with horizontal chords, is the *vertical shear*.

Example 3

Passing a vertical section through panel L_1L_2 of the truss in Fig. 83 and considering the part on the left of this section as in Fig. 85 gives

$$S_v = \text{vertical shear in panel } L_1L_2 = 75 - 30 = 45 \text{ kips}$$

From similar triangles

$$S = S_v \times \frac{h'}{h} = \frac{45 \times 36.8}{27} = +61.3 \text{ kips}$$

It is important to note the kind of shear as this determines the kind of stress, tension, or compression produced in the diagonal. Positive shear (down on right of section, Fig. 86) will cause tension in a diagonal

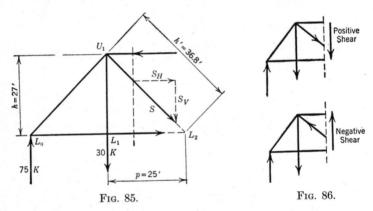

FIG. 85.   FIG. 86.

sloping downward to the right as does U_1L_2. Negative shear will produce stress of the opposite kind. These stresses will be reversed for members sloping in the opposite direction.

Shears produced by vertical loads can be readily computed by starting with the shear in the center panel or the one adjacent to the center of the span and progressing toward the reaction.

Example 4 (Fig. 83)

Panel load, $W = 30$ K

Shears

Panel L_2L_3 $V = +\frac{1}{2}W = +15$ K
Panel L_1L_2 $V = +1\frac{1}{2}W = +45$ K
Panel L_0L_1 $V = +2\frac{1}{2}W = +75$ K

(Shears for a truss having an odd number of panels are shown in Fig. 87.)

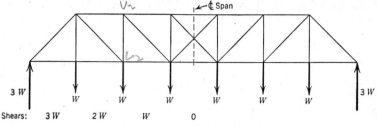

FIG. 87.

Example 5

Since

$$\frac{Wh'}{h} = \frac{30 \times 36.8}{27} = 40.89$$

Stresses

$$L_0U_1 = 2\tfrac{1}{2} \times 40.89 = -102.2 \text{ kips}$$
$$U_1L_2 = 1\tfrac{1}{2} \times 40.89 = +61.3 \text{ kips}$$
$$U_2L_3 = \tfrac{1}{2} \times 40.89 = +20.4 \text{ kips}$$

Stresses in the verticals are best determined by analysis of joints. Thus, considering the forces acting at joint L_1,

$$\text{Stress } U_1L_1 = +30 \text{ kips}$$

If the forces acting at joint U_2 are considered, the magnitude of stress U_2L_2 is the same as the vertical component of U_2L_3, and it acts on U_2 in the opposite direction; hence

$$\text{Stress } U_2L_2 = \tfrac{1}{2} \times 30 = -15.0 \text{ kips}$$

It should be noted that the above stress in U_2L_2 would be increased by the amount of the joint load, if any, at U_2.

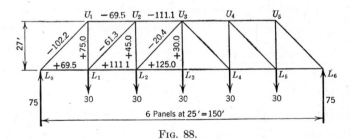

FIG. 88.

For a truss of the Howe type (Fig. 88), the chord stresses would be computed from different moment centers, also the kind of stress in diagonals would be reversed.

66   Parallel-Chord Truss—Dead-Load Stress Coefficients

The *method of coefficients* is particularly useful and rapid for computing dead-load stresses in the members of horizontal-chord trusses when the panels are of equal lengths.   It is essentially one of individual joint analysis, the horizontal and vertical components of stress in each member being equal to the product of a *coefficient* and a *multiplier*.   Its convenience lies in the fact that, for any given stress, the coefficients for its horizontal component, vertical component, and the stress itself are all equal, the different values of these forces being determined by the use of different multipliers. All horizontal forces in the truss will hence have a common multiplier; all vertical forces a common multiplier; and all diagonal forces a common multiplier.

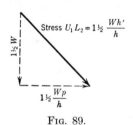

Stress $U_1 L_2 = 1\tfrac{1}{2}\,\dfrac{Wh'}{h}$

$1\tfrac{1}{2}\,\dfrac{Wp}{h}$

$1\tfrac{1}{2}\,W$

FIG. 89.

With reference to the truss in Fig. 83 it will be noted that, since the stress in each chord member equals the bending-moment at a particular joint divided by the height of truss, the quantity Wp/h will appear in each stress computation and hence is a common multiplier for all chord stresses; likewise the quantity Wh'/h appears in all diagonal stress determinations and is a common multiplier for all diagonal stresses; the quantity W is a common multiplier for the stress in all verticals. If a typical diagonal is considered, as, for example, $U_1 L_2$ (Fig. 85), the stress and its components will have the values shown in Fig. 89.   Similar relations will exist between the stress and components of stress for all the other diagonals.   The procedure is illustrated by the following example.

Example

Starting with the diagonal in the center panel (in trusses with an even number of panels, the panel nearest the center), we write the coefficients for stress successively for $U_2 L_3$, $U_1 L_2$, and $L_0 U_1$ (Fig. 90).   The kind of stress, tension or

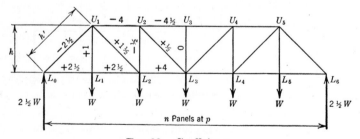

FIG. 90.   Coefficients.

compression, is indicated by the conventional signs $+$ and $-$, respectively, placed before the coefficients. Individual joints are next considered as follows:

Joint L_0

Stress L_0L_1 = horizontal component of stress $L_0U_1 = 2\frac{1}{2}\dfrac{Wp}{h}$

Coefficient $L_0L_1 = +2\frac{1}{2}$

Joint L_1

Stress L_1L_2 = stress $L_0L_1 = 2\frac{1}{2}\dfrac{Wp}{h}$

Coefficient $L_1L_2 = +2\frac{1}{2}$

Stress U_1L_1 = load at $L_1 = W$

Coefficient   = $+1$

Joint U_1 (Fig. 91a)

Stress U_1U_2 = sum of horizontal components of stress in L_0U_1 and

$$U_1L_2 = 2\frac{1}{2}\frac{Wp}{h} + 1\frac{1}{2}\frac{Wp}{h} = 4\frac{Wp}{h}$$

Coefficient $U_1U_2 = 2\frac{1}{2} + 1\frac{1}{2} = -4$

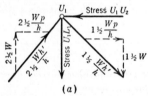

(a)   (b)

Fig. 91.

Joint U_2 (Fig. 91b)

Stress U_2U_3 = stress U_1U_2 plus horizontal component

$$U_2L_3 = 4\frac{Wp}{h} + \frac{1}{2}\frac{Wp}{h} = 4\frac{1}{2}\frac{Wp}{h}$$

Coefficient $U_2U_3 = 4 + \frac{1}{2} = -4\frac{1}{2}$

Stress U_2L_2 = vertical component $U_2L_3 = \frac{1}{2}W$

Coefficient $U_2L_2 = -\frac{1}{2}$

It should be observed that the coefficient for each member is obtained by combining those for the several members meeting at a given joint. Stresses are finally determined by multiplying these coefficients by the following common multipliers:

$$\text{Chords } \frac{Wp}{h}$$

$$\text{Diagonals } \frac{Wh'}{h}$$

$$\text{Verticals } W$$

67   Inclined-Chord Truss—Dead-Load Stresses

Stresses in the members of non-parallel-chord trusses are obtained by cutting the structure and establishing the equilibrium of one of the portions in the manner outlined in Article 59.   Thus, if we consider the truss in Fig. 92 and pass a cutting section through panel L_1L_2, the portion on the left of this section will be acted upon by the reaction, loads,

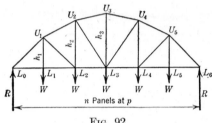

FIG. 92.

and member stresses as shown in Fig. 93.   Since these forces are in equilibrium, the three equations of static equilibrium, $\Sigma H = 0$, $\Sigma V = 0$, and $\Sigma M = 0$, will furnish a solution for the unknown forces S_1, S_2, and S_3.   Instead of these equations, however, it is best to use three separate moment equations, noting that the equilibrium of any system of coplanar forces is established when their moments, with respect to any three separate moment centers, are respectively equal to zero.   If one of these moment centers is chosen at c, the moment of S_2 and S_3 will be zero, and this will provide a direct solution for S_1; with another moment

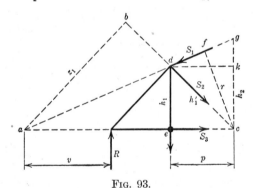

FIG. 93.

center chosen at d, S_1 and S_2 will be eliminated, and this will provide a direct solution for S_3; with the third moment center at a, S_1 and S_3 will be eliminated, and a direct solution will be provided for S_2.   It will be seen that the moment of the reaction and loads about moment center c will be the bending-moment at this point; also the moment of the reaction and loads with respect to moment center d will be the bending-

Inclined Chord Truss.

moment at this point. It therefore follows that the chord stresses will be based on bending-moments at the joints and are determined by dividing the bending-moment by the perpendicular distance from the chord to the joint. Similarly, the stress in the diagonal will be obtained by dividing the moment of the reaction and loads about the point of intersection of the chords by the perpendicular distance from the diagonal to this point. The distances needed for these computations are

$$\text{Length of } dg = \sqrt{p^2 + (h_2 - h_1)^2} \tag{99}$$

From similar triangles gfc and gkd $\quad \dfrac{fc}{dk} = \dfrac{gc}{dg}$

$$r = \frac{ph_2}{\text{length of } dg} \Big) \tag{100}$$

From similar triangles abc and dec $\quad \dfrac{ab}{ed} = \dfrac{ac}{dc}$

$$z_1 = \frac{h_1 \times ac}{h'} \Big) \tag{101}$$

The distance v is computed from the slope of the chord $(h_1 - h_2)$ per panel. Typical dimension computations for a symmetrical truss with inclined top chord are shown in Fig. 94.

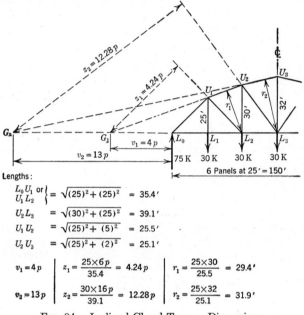

Lengths:

$$\left.\begin{array}{c} L_0U_1 \text{ or} \\ U_1L_2 \end{array}\right\} = \sqrt{(25)^2+(25)^2} = 35.4'$$

$$U_2L_3 = \sqrt{(30)^2+(25)^2} = 39.1'$$

$$U_1U_2 = \sqrt{(25)^2+(5)^2} = 25.5'$$

$$U_2U_3 = \sqrt{(25)^2+(2)^2} = 25.1'$$

$$v_1 = 4p \qquad z_1 = \frac{25\times6p}{35.4} = 4.24p \qquad r_1 = \frac{25\times30}{25.5} = 29.4'$$

$$v_2 = 13p \qquad z_2 = \frac{30\times16p}{39.1} = 12.28p \qquad r_2 = \frac{25\times32}{25.1} = 31.9'$$

FIG. 94.   Inclined Chord Truss.   Dimensions.

Typical dead-load-stress determinations for the truss shown in Fig. 94 are as follows: The truss is symmetrical about center and carries a load of 30 kips at each bottom-chord joint.

Example

Stress L_0U_1

This is computed in the same manner as for the similar member of a parallel-chord truss.

Shear in panel $L_0L_1 = 2\frac{1}{2}W = 75$ kips
Stress $L_0U_1 \qquad = 75 \times 1.414 = -106.0$ kips

Stress U_1U_2

Bending-moment at $L_2 = 4Wp$

Stress $U_1U_2 \qquad = \dfrac{4Wp}{r_1} = \dfrac{4 \times 30 \times 25}{29.4} = -102.0$ kips

Stress L_2L_3

Bending-moment at $U_2 = 4Wp$

Stress $L_2L_3 \qquad = \dfrac{4Wp}{h_2} = \dfrac{4 \times 30 \times 25}{30} = +100.0$ kips

Stress U_1L_2

Section taken through panel L_1L_2: consider forces on left of section as in Fig. 93.

$$\text{Moment about } G_1 = (2\tfrac{1}{2}W \times 4p) - (W \times 5p)$$
$$= 5Wp$$

$$\text{Stress } U_1L_2 \quad = \frac{5Wp}{4.24p} = \frac{5 \times 30}{4.24} = +35.4 \text{ kips}$$

Stress U_2L_2

Section taken through U_1U_2, U_2L_2, and L_2L_3; consider forces on left of section as in Fig. 95.

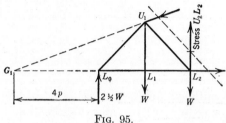

FIG. 95.

$$\text{Moment about } M_G = -(2\tfrac{1}{2}W \times 4p) + (W \times 5p) + (W \times 6p)$$
$$= Wp \text{ (clockwise)}$$

$$\text{Stress } U_2L_2 \quad = \frac{Wp}{6p} = \frac{30}{6} = +5.0 \text{ kips}$$

Stress U_3L_3

Considering joint U_3, it will be seen that the stress in U_3L_3 must equal the sum of the vertical components of stresses in members U_2U_3 and U_3U_4. Since U_2U_3 and U_3U_4 have equal dead-load stress, the stress in U_3L_3 will equal twice the vertical component of U_2U_3 and will be tension.

68 Parallel-Chord Truss—Live-Load Stresses in General

Stresses caused by a given live load are determined by the same fundamental methods that are employed for dead load, when the magnitude and position of the live load have been established. The only new element introduced in the problem is that of locating the live load on the structure. It should always be remembered that the main objective of a stress analysis is the determination of the maximum force which is exerted on each member of the truss due to any rational combination of loads. It is important to note that not only is the numerical magnitude of force essential, but the *kind,* tension or compression, must also be determined, and the *maximum stress of each kind* is therefore the ultimate aim. Some members will always be subjected to the same kind of stress whatever the loading; others may carry tension for a given loading or load position and compression for another loading or load position.

In such cases the maximum numerical value of each kind of stress must be found. These opposite kinds of stress in the same member are commonly called *maximum* and *minimum* stress.

In locating the live load on the structure, consideration must be given to its position laterally with respect to the given truss as well as longitudinally in the span. Obviously, the closer the loading is located to the truss, the greater will be the loads delivered to the truss by the floor system and the greater the effect on the members of the truss. Thus in a highway bridge, the members of one truss will have maximum stress from truck loading when the wheels are against the curb adjacent to that truss. Having located the live loads laterally in order to produce maximum effect on the truss, the proportionate parts of the live loads may be assumed as delivered directly to the truss and these truss loads are then located in the span length of the truss in order to produce the desired maximum effect on a given member.

As previously outlined for dead load, stresses in the members of parallel-chord trusses are derived from the following sources: *chords*—bending-moment at panel points (joints); *web system*—shears in the several panels except particular types of members, such as hangers (U_1L_1) and posts (U_3L_3), where the joint-load or floor-beam reaction determines the stress. It therefore follows that, for maximum stress in a given chord member, the live loading must be placed so as to produce maximum bending-moment at a particular section in the span. For maximum stress in a web member, the loads must generally be placed to produce either maximum positive shear, for one kind of stress, or maximum negative shear, for the opposite kind of stress. For members such as hangers, the loads must be placed to produce maximum joint load at the appropriate panel point. The principles relating to the placing of loads for maximum bending-moment or shear at given sections of a structure have been discussed in Chapter 4.

69   Parallel-Chord Truss—Uniform Live Loading

Consider the highway truss bridge described in Example 1 of Article 65 (Fig. 83), and assume the live load as a uniform load of 100 pounds per square foot distributed over any part or all of the roadway. Obviously, maximum stresses in both trusses will occur when the load covers the entire *width* of roadway. Since every load placed on the span produces positive bending-moment on all sections of the structure, the maximum bending-moments on all sections will occur simultaneously when the uniform load extends over the entire span. This will produce a load condition similar to dead load, and the live-load stresses may be computed in exactly the same manner as for dead load. If the dead-

load stresses have been previously determined, the live-load stress can be most readily found by multiplying the dead-load stress by the ratio of live load per foot of span to the dead load per foot of span, thus

Example 1

$$\text{Width of roadway} = 20 \text{ ft curb to curb}$$

$$\text{Load on each truss} = 100 \times 20 \times \tfrac{1}{2} = 1000 \text{ lb per linear ft}$$

$$\text{Dead load per foot of span} = \tfrac{360}{150} = 2.4 \text{ kips}$$

$$\text{Live load per foot of span} = 100 \times 20 = 2.0 \text{ kips}$$

$$\text{Live load chord stress} = \frac{2.0}{2.4} \times (\text{D.L. stress})$$

$$\text{Live load stress } U_1U_2 = \frac{2 \times 111.1}{2.4} = -92.6 \text{ kips}$$

Live-load stresses in other chord members are determined in a similar manner.

Maximum live-load stress in diagonal U_2L_3 will occur when the shear in panel L_2L_3 is maximum. Since positive shear will produce tension in this member and negative shear compressive stress, both conditions must be investigated. For placing the load, influence lines as discussed in Article 41 offer the best solution, and the influence line for shear in this panel is shown at b in Fig. 96. The zero point in this influence line

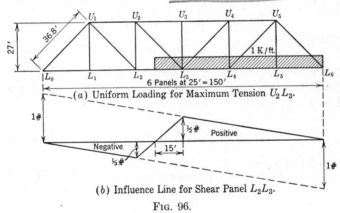

(a) Uniform Loading for Maximum Tension U_2L_3.

(b) Influence Line for Shear Panel L_2L_3.

Fig. 96.

is 15 ft from L_3, and for maximum positive shear the uniform load should extend from this point to L_6 as shown on the truss diagram.

Example 2

$$\text{Maximum positive shear panel } L_2L_3 = 1 \times \tfrac{1}{2} \times 90 \times \tfrac{1}{2} = 22.5 \text{ kips}$$

$$\text{Maximum live-load tension } U_2L_3 = 22.5 \times \frac{36.8}{27} = +30.7 \text{ kips}$$

Maximum negative shear will occur when the other segment of the span is loaded, thus

Maximum negative shear in panel $L_2L_3 = 1 \times \frac{1}{3} \times 60 \times \frac{1}{2} = 10$ kips

Maximum live-load compression $U_2L_3 \ = 10 \times \dfrac{36.8}{27} = -13.6$ kips

When influence lines are used to compute the stress, it is of course unnecessary to determine the individual joint loads. To compute the stress directly from the loading shown at *a* in Fig. 96, it is necessary to determine the truss reaction at L_0 and the joint load at L_2, since these are the only external forces on the left of a section through panel L_2L_3,

Example 3

$$\text{Reaction at } L_0 \ = \ \frac{1 \times 90 \times 45}{150} = 27.0 \text{ kips}$$

$$\text{Joint load at } L_2 = \frac{1 \times 15 \times 7.5}{25} = \ 4.5 \text{ kips}$$

$$\text{Shear in panel } L_2L_3 = 22.5 \text{ kips}$$

Live-load stresses in the other diagonals are found in a similar manner. It may be noted that the end diagonal L_0U_1 will always be in compression and will receive maximum stress when the uniform load extends over the entire span. The stress in this member may therefore be determined from the dead-load stress in the same manner as outlined for the chord stresses.

The stresses in verticals such as U_2L_2 are best derived from the fact that they carry the vertical component of the stress in that diagonal with which they are paired at unloaded chord joints. Thus U_2L_2 carries the vertical component of stress U_2L_3, in this case the shear in panel L_2L_3. Tension in U_2L_3 produces compression in U_2L_2; compression in U_2L_3 produces tension in U_2L_2; therefore

Example 4

$$\text{Maximum compression } U_2L_2 = \ -22.5 \text{ kips}$$

$$\text{Maximum tension } U_2L_2 \qquad = \ +10.0 \text{ kips}$$

The live-load stress in U_1L_1 will always be tension and equal to the joint load or floor beam reaction at L_1.

$$\text{Maximum stress } U_1L_1 = 1 \times 25 = +25.0 \text{ kips}$$

The live-load stress for U_3L_3 of the given truss will be zero.

Maximum and minimum stresses for all the members of this truss are shown on the truss diagram in Fig. 97. It will be observed that,

because of the symmetry of the truss, it is necessary to compute the stress in one-half of the truss only.

A *conventional* method is sometimes employed for computing live-load stress in the web members of comparatively small trusses for uniform loading. In this method *panel loads* are computed for the live load extending over the entire span, and as many of these full panel loads are placed at loaded chord joints as will produce maximum shear of either kind. Thus for maximum positive shear in panel L_2L_3, joints L_3, L_4,

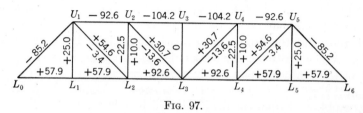

FIG. 97.

and L_5 would be loaded. Since the shear for such a loading will equal the reaction at L_0, the value is most readily found by adding the amounts contributed to this reaction by each of the joint loads;

Example 5

$$W = \text{panel load} = 100 \times 20 \times 25 \times \tfrac{1}{2} = 25 \text{ kips}$$

$$R_L = \tfrac{1}{6}W + \tfrac{2}{6}W + \tfrac{3}{6}W$$

$$= \tfrac{6}{6}W = 25 \text{ kips}$$

The corresponding stress in U_2L_3 would be

$$\text{Stress } U_2L_3 = 25 \times \frac{36.8}{27} = +34.1 \text{ kips}$$

Similarly, the maximum compressive stress would be obtained by placing panel loads at joints L_1 and L_2.

Maximum negative shear = reaction at L_6

$$R_R = (\tfrac{1}{6} + \tfrac{2}{6})W = 12.5 \text{ kips}$$

$$\text{Stress } U_2L_3 = 12.5 \times \frac{36.8}{27} = -17.1 \text{ kips}$$

By comparison with the exact values previously determined, it will be seen that this method produces stresses greater than the true maximum values.

The conventional method lends itself to rapid computation through the use of coefficients similar to those previously explained for dead-load stress (Article 66). In this procedure, a load is placed at L_5 and the

corresponding stress coefficient written for L_4U_5; next a load is added
at L_4 and the coefficient due to both loads obtained for L_3U_4. The
successive coefficients are thus obtained by adding the simple fractions

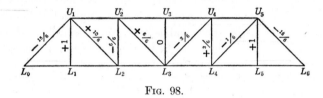

FIG. 98.

which represent the proportionate part of the joint loads transmitted
to L_0. When written clear across the truss, coefficients on members
right of the center of span will be for *minimum* stress; those for members on the left half will be for *maximum* stress. Coefficients for verticals
may be obtained from the diagonals which they meet at the unloaded

Single Track R. R. Bridge
Coopers E60 Engine Loading

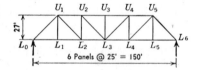

Each truss carries load
on one rail or 1/2 axle
loads.

Stress $U_1 U_2$

Moment center is L_2
Position of load for. Max. B. M. at L_2

Axle at L_2	Loads on Span		W	W_1	$\dfrac{Wa}{L}$	W_1	Check Critical Position
	Axles	Unif. Load	Kips	(max.)		(min.)	
5	1 - 18	14'	468	135	156	105	
7	1 - 18	28'	510	174	170	154.5	✓
8	1 - 18	34'	528	193.5	176	174	✓

B.M. at L_2

Axle 7 at L_2 : $R_L = \dfrac{24546 + (426 \times 28) + (3 \times 28 \times 14)}{150} = 251$ Kips

B.M. $= (251 \times 50) - 3230 = 9320$

Axle 8 at L_2 : $R_L = \dfrac{24546 + (426 \times 34) + (3 \times 34 \times 17)}{150} = 271.8$ Kips

B.M. $= (271.8 \times 50) - 4280 = 9310$

Maximum Stress $U_1 U_2 = \dfrac{9320}{27} = -345.2$ Kips

FIG. 99.

chord (except verticals U_1L_1 and U_3L_3, which are determined as previously noted). Conventional live-load coefficients for the foregoing
truss are written on the truss diagram in Fig. 98.

70 Parallel-Chord Truss—Concentrated-Load Systems

Determination of stresses caused by systems of concentrated loads, such as a train of motor trucks on a highway bridge or locomotive axle loads on a railroad bridge, involve no new principles. Maximum stress

(Same truss as in Fig. 99)

Stress U_2L_3
Length of diagonal = 36.8'
Position of Load for Max. + Shear Panel L_2L_3

Axle at L_3	Loads on Span		W	W_1	$\dfrac{Wp}{L}$	W_1	Check Critical Position
	Axles	Unif. Load	Kips	(max.)		(min.)	
2	1 - 14	0	348	45	58	15	
3	1 - 15	0	367.5	75	61	45	✔

Axle 3 at L_3 : $R_L = \dfrac{16220}{150} = 108.1$ Kips

Joint Load at $L_2 = \dfrac{345}{25} = 13.8$

Shear Panel $L_2L_3 = +94.3$

Stress $U_2L_3 = 94.3 \times \dfrac{36.8}{27} = +128.5$ Kips

Maximum compression U_2L_3 will be produced with engine reversed in direction and will be the same as maximum compression in L_3U_4 with engine headed right to left.

Position of Load for Max. + Shear panel L_3L_4
Try Axle 2 at L_4 — Axles 1 to 10 on span.

$$W = 228 \qquad \dfrac{Wp}{L} = 38 \quad \begin{array}{l} < W_1 \text{ (max.)} = 45 \\ > W_1 \text{ (min.)} = 15 \end{array} \; OK$$

No other position satisfies criterion.

Axle 2 at L_4 : $R_L = \dfrac{6950 + (228 \times 2)}{150} = 49.4$ kips

Joint load at $L_3 = \dfrac{120}{25} = 4.8$

Shear Panel $L_3L_4 = +44.6$

Stress $L_3U_4 = 44.6 \times \dfrac{36.8}{27} = -60.8$ Kips

Summary:
Max. Stress U_2L_3 or L_3U_4: Tension 128.5 Kips
Compression 60.8 Kips

Stress U_2L_2
Stress = Shear Panel L_2L_3
Max. Compression = Max. + Shear Panel $L_2L_3 = -94.3$
Max. Tension = Max. — Shear Panel $L_2L_3 = +44.6$

Fig. 100.

in the chords will occur when the loads are placed to produce maximum bending-moment at particular sections, and the method of placing loads for such effect has been discussed in Chapter 4. A typical stress computation for a chord member of a railroad truss bridge is given in Fig. 99. (For engine loading and use of moment table, see Article 17.) Maximum stresses which are derived from the shear are also determined by methods previously outlined. Typical stress computations for diagonal and vertical members are given in Fig. 100.

71 Inclined-Chord Truss—Uniform Live Load

Since in each case the stress in a chord member is proportional to the bending-moment at a corresponding joint, it follows that, for a uniformly distributed load, maximum stress will occur simultaneously in all chords when the loading extends over the entire span. This produces a condition similar to dead loading, and the live-load stresses may be computed in the same manner as previously outlined for dead load. Chord stresses due to uniform live loading may also be obtained by multiplying the previously computed dead-load stress by the ratio of live to dead load.

The stress in such members as L_0U_1 and U_1L_1 in Fig. 94 is also determined in the same manner as outlined for similar members of parallel-chord trusses.

Determination of the stress in diagonals such as U_1L_2 and U_2L_3 requires a different procedure from that employed for dead-load stress, since the stress in such members is not directly related to the shear in the panel, and for uniform live loading the influence line offers a simple solution. Thus, for the truss represented in Fig. 94, pass a cutting section through panel L_1L_2, and consider the equilibrium of the part of the truss on the left of this section as at a in Fig. 101. When a unit load is

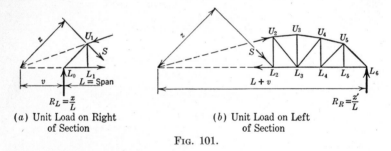

(a) Unit Load on Right (b) Unit Load on Left
of Section of Section

Fig. 101.

placed on the structure at any point between L_2 and L_6, the only force on the left of the section will be the reaction at L_0, and

$$S = +\frac{R_L v}{z} = +\frac{xv}{Lz}$$

where $x =$ distance from L_6 to the unit load.

This is therefore the equation of the portion of the influence line for stress in U_1L_2 corresponding to the distance between L_2 and L_6.

When the unit load is placed on the left of the section, at any point

from L_0 to L_1, the forces on the part of the truss on the right of the section are as represented at b, and

$$S = -\frac{x' \cdot (L + v)}{Lz}$$

where $x' =$ distance from L_0 to unit load.

This, therefore, is the equation for that part of the influence line between L_0 and L_1.

When the unit load moves across the panel from L_1 to L_2, there will be a straight-line transfer of load from one side of the section to the other, and the two lines for which equations have been written must therefore be joined by a straight line.

Example

The complete influence line for stress in U_1L_2 of the given truss is shown at a in Fig. 102.

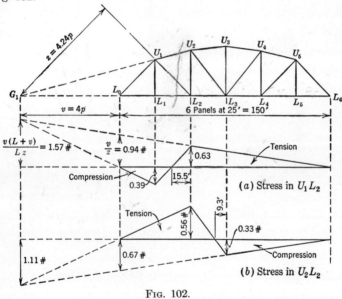

Fig. 102.

The zero point is computed to be 15.5 ft left of L_2, and for maximum tension a uniform load should extend from this point to L_6. For a uniform live load of one kip per lineal foot of truss, the maximum and minimum stresses would be computed as follows:

Maximum tension U_1L_2 $S = 1 \times 0.63 \times 115.5 \times \frac{1}{2} = +36.4$ kips

Maximum compression U_1L_2 $S = 1 \times 0.39 \times 34.5 \times \frac{1}{2} = -6.7$ kips

Maximum and minimum stress in U_2L_2 are obtained in a similar manner, the section being made through U_1U_2 and L_2L_3. The influence line for stress in this member is shown at b.

Maximum stress in U_3L_3 is derived from the chord stresses at U_3 and will equal twice the vertical component of the maximum live-load stress in U_2U_3.

Hammerhead Crane at Fairfield Shipbuilding Co., Clyde, England. Lifting Capacity 240 Tons.

72   Inclined-Chord Truss—Concentrated-Load Systems

The stresses in chord members are derived directly from bending moments at the joints, and the procedure for determining the position of a loading which consists of a series of concentrated loads is identical with that previously discussed for parallel-chord trusses. Maximum stress in such members as L_0U_1 and U_1L_1 (Fig. 102) is also determined in the same manner as for similar members of parallel-chord trusses.

Diagonals of the type of U_2L_3 and verticals such as U_2L_2 require a different procedure from that outlined for parallel-chord trusses.   In

Fig. 102a, the influence line for stress in U_1L_2 indicates that L_2 is the critical joint for loadings producing maximum tension. Following the same procedure as was given in Article 43, and placing one of the concentrated loads at joint L_2,

$$R_L = \frac{Wx}{L}$$

$$\text{Joint load at } L_1 = \frac{W_1x_1}{p}$$

where W = sum of loads on span.

W_1 = sum of loads in panel L_1L_2.

Wx = moment of all loads about L_6.

W_1x_1 = moment of loads in panel L_1L_2 about L_2.

Let t = distance from G_1 to L_1.

$$S = \frac{Wxv}{Lz} - \frac{W_1x_1t}{pz}$$

The stress will therefore be maximum when:

$$\frac{Wp}{L}\left(\frac{v}{t}\right) \genfrac{}{}{0pt}{}{\leq W_1 \text{ (max)}}{> W_1 \text{ (min)}}$$

In a similar manner, it can be shown that, for maximum stress in U_2L_2, the loads must be placed in such position as to fulfill the same criterion.

73 Counters

In all the trusses used in previous examples, the dead load produced tension stress in the diagonals. It was also noted that, should the diagonals be reversed in direction (as in the Howe truss, Fig. 59g), the dead-load stress would also be reversed in kind. It has also been shown that the live load may produce either kind of stress, depending upon its location in the span. Should the live-load compression exceed the dead-load tension, the resultant final stress in the member would be compression, and it would be necessary to design the member to meet this condition. Where rods or diagonals of a type incapable of resisting any appreciable compressive stress are used, it is important to determine if there is any possibility of such stress reversal. If such reversal does occur in trusses having diagonals of this type, it is necessary to introduce *counters* in those panels where such conditions prevail.

A *counter* is a simple tension member placed across the panel in the opposite inclination to the main diagonal. Thus, in the truss shown in

Fig. 96, a reversal of stress in U_2L_3 might indicate the need of a counter L_2U_3; also in the truss shown in Fig. 102, a member L_2U_3 would serve as a counter.

It should be understood that counters are used only when the main diagonals are of a type which is ineffective for compressive stress. Thus, when the live load reverses the stress in such a member, it in effect removes it from the truss, and the counter, if present, will then take its place.

Stresses in main members and in counters will therefore always be tension. Maximum stress in either is obtained by assuming the other removed and placing the loading in position to produce maximum tension in the remaining diagonal. It should be noted that the dead-load stress in a counter is computed as a potential compressive stress for future combination with the live-load tension. If the resulting combination of stresses is compression, the counter simply does not act; otherwise the difference between live- and dead-load stress will represent the maximum tension in the counter.

Example

For the truss shown in Fig. 83, the dead-load stress in U_2L_3 was determined to be $+20.4$ kips. The maximum live-load stress in this member for a load of 1 kip per lineal foot of truss is shown in Fig. 97. For a live loading of two kips per foot, the live-load stresses would be

$$\text{Maximum L.L. tension} \quad = +61.4 \text{ kips}$$

$$\text{Maximum L.L. compression} = -27.2 \text{ kips}$$

The combined dead-load and live-load stress in the diagonal would be

$$20.4 + 61.4 = +81.8 \text{ kips}$$

$$20.4 - 27.2 = -6.8 \text{ kips}$$

Now if U_2L_3 is incapable of resisting this compression stress, a counter L_2U_3 would be needed and U_2L_3 would be assumed to be removed when the counter comes into action in tension. The dead-load stress in the counter (assuming that it will ultimately act in tension and that U_2L_3 is removed from the truss) would be computed as -20.4 kips; the live-load stress is $+27.2$ kips; and the combined live- and dead-load stress, $+6.8$ kips.

For inclined chord trusses, the stress in the counter is also computed with the main member removed both for dead- and live-load stress. It should be noted that, although the moment center is at the same point as for main member stress, the lever arm of the counter stress is different, and the stresses will not be of the same magnitude as those in the main member.

74   Deflection of Truss by Algebraic Summation

Referring to the truss shown in Fig. 103, let it be assumed that the solid lines represent the initial or unstressed form of the truss. Let p represent the magnitude of an infinitesimal force applied at any joint C and acting in the direction of any desired component of such movement of point C as may be produced by the actual loads. Since p is infinitesimal, its contribution to the displacement of point C will also be infinitesimal and may be neglected. This force will, however, induce stresses in the truss members which must be taken into account. With the force p acting, the given loading is now applied to the truss and, owing

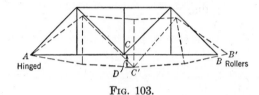

FIG. 103.

to the resulting stress deformations of its members, it will change form as indicated by the dotted lines in the figure with joint C moving to C'.

Let D = Any desired component of the distance CC'.

p = force of infinitesimal magnitude applied at C in the direction of D.

u = stress in any truss member due to the force p.

S = stress in any truss member produced by the given loading.

L, A, and E represent the length, area of cross section, and modulus of elasticity for any member subjected to the stress S.

Since any member with stress S will change in length an amount SL/AE, the force u which was acting on the member during this change will move through this same distance. The internal work in any member on account of the force p acting at C will thus be SuL/AE. When the structure finally attains a position of equilibrium with joint C at C', the force p will have moved through the distance D and will have performed the total work pD. The total internal work is the sum of the amounts determined for each of the several truss members and, since total external work must equal total internal work,

$$pD = \sum \frac{SuL}{AE}$$

and, when p = unity,

$$D = \sum \frac{SuL}{AE} \tag{102}$$

It should be noted that the stresses u are determined from the load p and are directly proportional to this load. The value of D is therefore independent of the value of p, and any convenient value can be used for this load, provided, however, that stresses u are determined therefrom.

To measure downward movement, the unit load p is assumed to act downward; if the movement left to right is desired, it is assumed to act

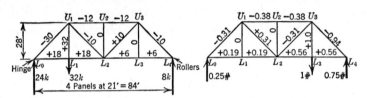

(All members are Structural Steel — $E = 30,000,000$)

Truss Member	L inches	A sq. in.	S kips	u pounds	$\dfrac{SuL}{1000\,A}$
L_0U_1	420	17.5	−30	−0.31	+223.2
L_0L_1	252	10.5	+18	+0.19	+ 82.1
L_1L_2	252	10.5	+18	+0.19	+ 82.1
U_1L_1	336	14.0	+32	0	0
U_1U_2	252	10.5	−12	−0.38	+109.4
U_2U_3	252	10.5	−12	−0.38	+109.4
U_1L_2	420	17.5	−10	+0.31	− 74.4
U_2L_2	336	14.0	0	0	0
L_2U_3	420	17.5	+10	−0.31	− 74.4
L_2L_3	252	10.5	+ 6	+0.56	+ 80.6
L_3L_4	252	10.5	+ 6	+0.56	+ 80.6
U_3L_3	336	14.0	0	+1.00	0
U_3L_4	420	17.5	−10	−0.94	+225.6
Σ					+844.2

$$\text{Deflection } L_3 = \frac{844.2 \times 1000}{30,000,000} = 0.02814 \text{ in.}$$

Fig. 104. Truss Deflection.

from left to right. With the unit load acting in the assumed direction of the movement, the corresponding stresses u are computed for each member of the truss and the value of SuL/AE obtained for all members. The algebraic summation of these values will then give the magnitude

of the joint movement in the direction of the unit load. A negative value of this summation indicates that the movement of the joint is opposite in direction to that assumed. It should be noted that the stresses S in each of the members must be the simultaneous values produced by the given loading in a fixed position on the structure. Particular attention must be given to the relative signs of S and u, since unlike signs (stresses) will produce negative values of corresponding terms in the summation. A typical computation for truss deflection is given in Fig. 104.

Determination of the absolute maximum vertical deflection is a problem involving matters beyond the scope of this book. Considering the general form of the deflection curve of the bottom chord, however, we may observe that the joint nearest the center of the span will either deflect the most or will have a deflection closely approximating the greatest deflection. It will also be observed by reference to the values shown in Fig. 104 that the chord members and end diagonals contribute the major part of the deflection and, since bending-moment is the factor producing stress in chords, the conditions of loading which produce maximum bending-moment will closely approximate that which produces maximum deflection. It is generally sufficiently accurate, therefore, to place the loading on the span in such position as to produce maximum stress in the center chord member (or chord member nearest the center of the span) and determine the stress in all members of the truss for use in computing maximum deflection.

PROBLEMS

6·1 Two trucks as shown have wheels 6 ft apart and axles 14 ft apart and with values of wheel loads $P = 16,000$ lb, and $P' = 4000$ lb. Determine the joint loads

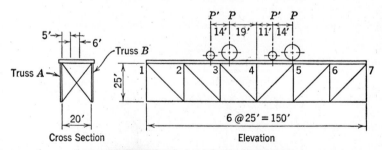

for truss A and truss B, and for joints 1 to 7 inclusive, when trucks are placed as shown.

6·2   *Given:* a through truss bridge with two lines of truck loading as shown.
Determine: (a) The proportion of the two lines of trucks carried by truss A.   (b) The

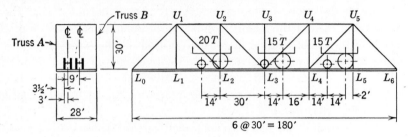

panel loads in tons at L_0 to L_6 inclusive of truss A due to these trucks when placed
as shown.

6·3   Place diagonals in the panels in such a manner that they will be acting in
tension when a dead load of 1000 lb per ft is on the top chord.

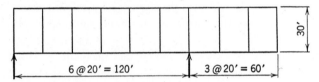

6·4   Determine graphically the forces in the truss members. $P = 4000$ lb.

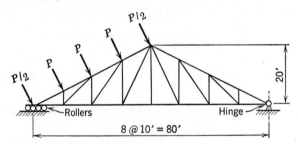

6·5   Determine the forces in the three members cut by section 1-1.

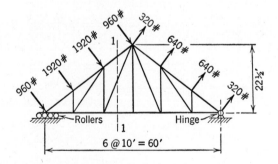

6·6 With the loading as shown, find the force in member L_3U_4.

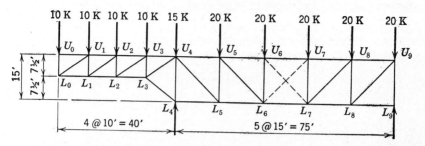

6·7 Compute the forces in members U_2L_2 and L_1L_2.

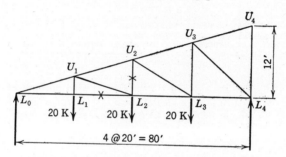

6·8 (*a*) Determine the maximum forces that may be induced in members L_3U_4 and U_4L_4 by a single moving concentrated load of 10,000 lb acting on the lower

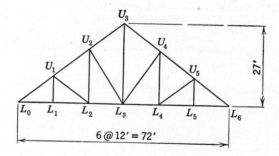

chord. (*b*) Find the force in L_1L_2 due to a load of 10,000 lb acting horizontally to the right at U_2.

6·9 Determine the maximum bending-moment in the left column, the force in the left knee brace, and the forces in the members cut by section 1-1.

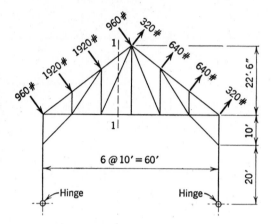

6·10 (*a*) Determine the value of *P* for a normal wind pressure against the roof of 18 lb per sq ft of roof surface for an 18-ft bay. (*b*) Compute the maximum bending-moment in the column *BEF*. (*c*) Calculate the force in member *GK*.

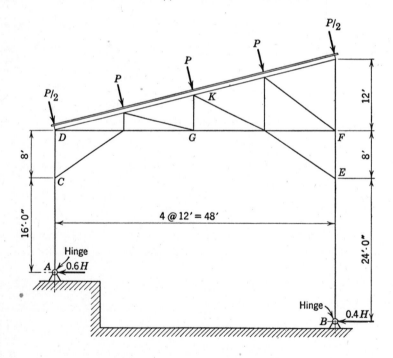

6·11 Draw shear and moment diagrams for the members AB and CD for the wind loads shown. Also find the force in member U_2L_3. Trusses are spaced at 15-ft centers.

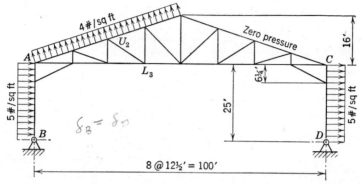

6·12 Assume that the horizontal shear is distributed equally to the two columns and a plane of contraflexure 15 ft above the bases A and D. (a) Determine the reactions at A and D. (b) Draw the shear and bending-moment diagrams for columns

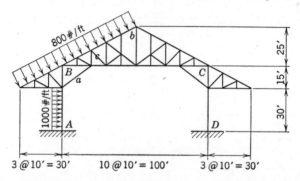

AB and CD. (c) Determine the maximum direct force in column AB. (d) Determine the forces in members marked a, b, and c.

6·13 Based upon the usual assumptions for mill bents, determine the force in knee brace AB due to loads shown.

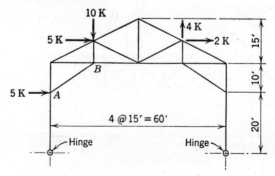

6·14 (a) Find the maximum shear, normal force, and bending moment in the left column. (b) Find the force in members U_0U_1 and L_2L_3.

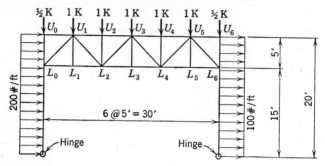

6·15 (a) Find the dead-load force in member U_2U_3 if the dead load is 500 lb per linear ft of truss. (b) Find the maximum live-load tension and compression in member U_2U_3. (c) Find the maximum combined force in the member.

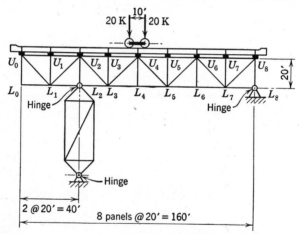

6·16 Assuming columns fixed at the footings and points of contraflexure 10 ft above footings, find the maximum possible live-load tension and compression in member U_2L_3 using vertical loads only.

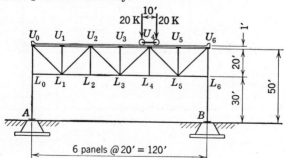

6·17 The general dimensions and arrangement of a highway truss bridge are given in the sketch. *Weights:* trusses and bracing, 225,000 lb; reinforced concrete, 150 lb per cu ft; stringers (each) 50 lb per linear ft; floor beams (each) 152 lb per

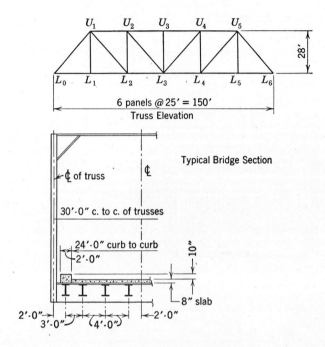

linear ft. Determine dead-load force in all truss members, and indicate values on a diagram of the truss. (*Note.* All loads may be assumed applied at bottom-chord joints.)

6·18 For the highway bridge given in Problem 6·17, determine the maximum live-load force in members U_1U_2 and U_2L_3 using an H20-44 lane loading.

6·19 If the dead load is 2000 lb per ft of truss assumed to act along the bottom chord, what are the dead-load forces in members U_2U_3, U_2L_2, L_2U_3, and U_4L_4?

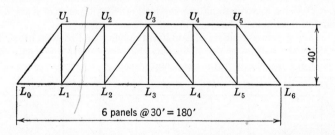

6·20 If the live load on the truss in Problem 6·19 consists of ten concentrated loads of 10,000 lb each spaced at 10-ft intervals, what is the maximum live-load force in U_1U_2, and what is the maximum live-load tension in L_2U_3?

6·21 *Determine:* (a) maximum tension, and (b) maximum compression caused in member U_2L_3 due to one standard H20 truck. The trusses are simply supported, and the truck may be headed in either direction on any part of the roadway.

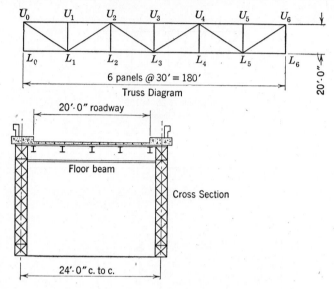

6 panels @ 30' = 180'

Truss Diagram

20'-0" roadway

Floor beam

Cross Section

24'-0" c. to c.

6·22 The Pratt truss shown is to be used for a single-track railroad bridge. (a) Using Cooper's E-60 loading, determine the maximum live-load force in member

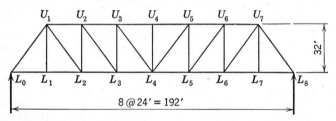

8 @ 24' = 192'

U_2U_3. (b) With a dead load of 1500 lb per ft of truss, determine the dead-load force in U_2L_3. (c) Using a moving uniform live load of 3000 lb per ft of truss, determine the maximum tension in U_2L_3.

6·23 If the live load consists of a uniform moving load of 4000 lb per linear ft applied along the bottom chord, determine the maximum tension and maximum compression in U_1L_1, U_3U_4, U_3L_4, U_7L_7, and U_9L_9.

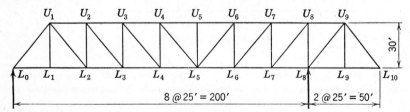

8 @ 25' = 200'

2 @ 25' = 50'

6·24   The following loads are applied at the bottom chord joints: **D.L.** = 1000 lb per linear ft of truss; L.L. = 2000 lb per linear ft of truss.   (a) Compute the dead-load force in U_1L_1, U_1U_2, and U_2L_3.   (b) Determine the maximum live-load force in

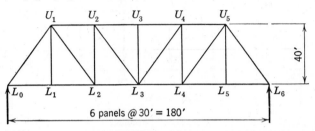

L_0U_1, U_1L_1, and U_1U_2.   (c) Using influence line determine the maximum and minimum live-load force in U_2L_3.   (d) Based on computation in (a) and (c), indicate the force for which U_2L_3 should be designed.

6·25   Use a moving live load consisting of four concentrated loads of 10 kips each spaced 10 ft apart.   Compute the maximum compression in U_2U_3 and the maximum tension in L_2U_3.

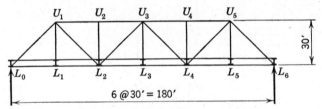

6·26   Determine the maximum tension in member U_1L_2 due to a uniform moving live load of 2 kips per ft per truss.

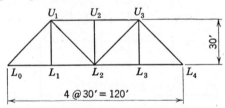

6·27   All loads are applied to truss at upper panel points.   (a) Calculate the dead-load forces in members U_5L_6 and U_2L_2 for a dead load of 1000 lb per ft of truss.

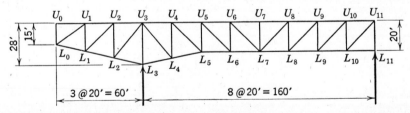

(b) Calculate the maximum live-load tension in member U_5L_6 for a moving uniform live load of 2000 lb per linear ft of truss.

6·28 Find the maximum force in the diagonals L_3U_4 and U_3L_4 for the moving concentrated loads shown.

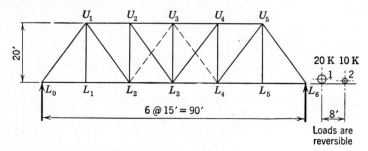

6·29 Find the maximum live-load force in U_2U_3, U_2L_3, and L_2L_3 due to a uniformly distributed live load of 2 kips per ft.

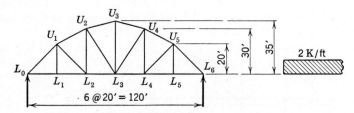

6·30 Calculate the vertical deflection of point L_2 under the loading shown. Gross areas of members are indicated by the figures in parentheses. $E = 29,500,000$.

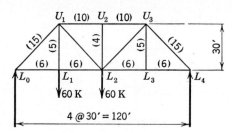

Chapter 7

STABILITY OF MASONRY STRUCTURES AND FOUNDATIONS

75 Definitions

For the purposes of this book, masonry structures are defined to include constructions of brick, stone, concrete, and like materials wherein units of these materials are arranged so as to be supported by other units or upon the earth. Thus a brick wall consists of brick units placed one upon the other to build up the desired form of construction; an ashlar masonry wall consists of squared pieces of stone placed one on another to form the wall; a voussoir arch is a more complex arrangement of stonework held in place by the pressure of each piece or *voussoir* against adjacent pieces. Bridge piers and abutments are generally built as monoliths of concrete or reinforced concrete to support the superstructure and transmit the loads to the foundation soil. Simple footings as placed under the columns of a building are generally masonry units of concrete or reinforced concrete designed to distribute the column load over the bed of the foundation. Retaining walls are masonry structures designed to resist the lateral pressure of a wall of earth. Dams and reservoir walls must resist lateral pressure of water or the liquid held back by the construction.

76 Simple Spread Footings

The purpose of a simple column footing is to receive the load imposed by the superstructure and distribute it over a sufficient area of the supporting soil. Whenever possible, the base area of the footing, in contact with the soil, is made concentric with the axis of the column which is supported on the footing, and equilibrium is obtained when the resultant of the upward pressure against the base of the footing equals the sum of the downward forces (including the weight of the footing). The average intensity of pressure over the base area (Fig. 105) equals the sum of all the loads divided by the base area, and this average pressure is generally used as a basis for determining

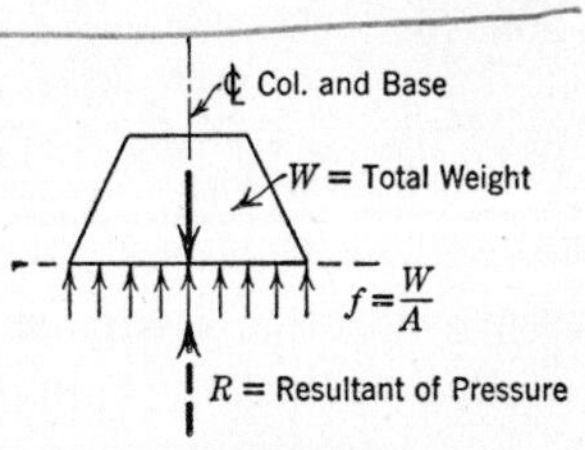

FIG. 105.

the required plan size of the base. Tests [1] of the actual pressures show that in general higher pressures exist at the center of the area, the relative magnitude depending upon the shape of the area and the character of the material supporting the footing (Fig. 106).

When the resultant of the loads acting on the footing does not pass through the centroid of the base area, the footing is said to be eccentrically loaded. This condition may arise either through placing the column off center or because of applied forces or moments which may tend to overturn the footing. Thus in Fig. 107, the force P is the resultant of all superimposed loads, moments, and weight of footing above the plane of the base; the resultant of the resisting forces, R, must equal P and act in the same line of action; the component of R in the plane of the footing, H, represents the resistance to sliding, while the component N is the resultant of the vertical pressure on the footing base.

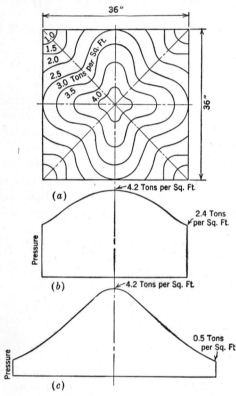

(a)

(b)

(c)

Fig. 106. Distribution of Pressure under a Footing.

(From article by F. J. Converse, *Civil Engg.*, April, 1933.)

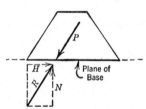

Fig. 107.

When no other means of preventing sliding is provided, friction of the footing against the supporting soil must be depended upon.

For determining the approximate distribution of pressure on the base, it is convenient to move the force N to the centroid of the base area,

[1] Converse, "Distribution of Pressure under a Footing," *Civil Engg.*, April, 1933, p. 207.

adding, in accordance with the principles of statics, the couple Ne to the force system as at a in Fig. 108. The force N will now produce the average uniform pressures $f_1 = N/A$ shown at b, and the pressures induced by the moment Ne are computed in the same manner as stresses in a homogeneous beam, assuming that the foundation material is elastic within the limits of the action. Hence, as shown at c,

$$f_2 = \frac{Nem}{I} \qquad (103)$$

and

$$f_3 = \frac{Nen}{I} \qquad (104)$$

where I = moment of inertia of base area about an axis through its centroid.

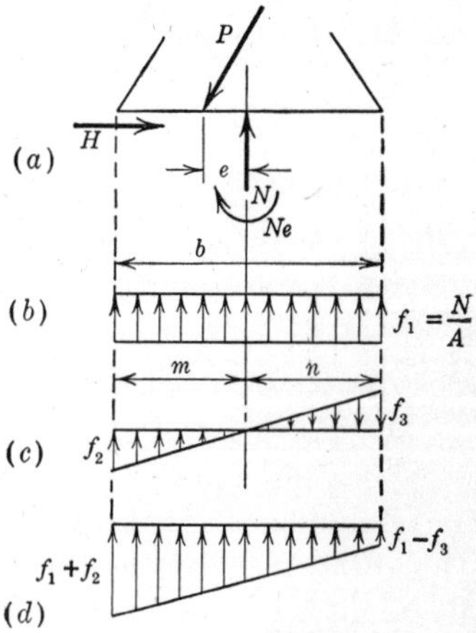

Fig. 108.

The resultant approximate pressure intensities at d are obtained by combining the pressures indicated at b and c. When the base area is rectangular with dimensions l and b,

$$f_2 = \frac{6Ne}{lb^2} = f_3 \qquad (105)$$

This method is limited to those cases where f_3 is equal to or less than f_1, since otherwise tension between the footing and the supporting soil would be indicated by the combination, and this is obviously an absurd result. This limitation can be expressed in terms of the eccentricity e as follows:

$$f_3 \lesseqgtr f_1$$

$$\frac{Nen}{I} \lesseqgtr \frac{N}{A} \qquad (106)$$

$$e \lesseqgtr \frac{I}{nA}$$

For a rectangular footing area

$$e \lesseqgtr \frac{b}{6} \qquad (107)$$

When the resultant P cuts the base within the limiting value of e as shown by Equation 106 (within the middle third of the base width for rectan-

gular footing areas), pressure will be developed over the entire area; when P lies outside this limiting distance the pressure distribution must be determined by another method.

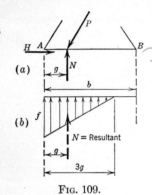

When $e > I/nA$, the approximate pressure distribution for a *rectangular* footing may be computed as follows: Let $g =$ distance from edge of base nearest the resultant to point where the resultant cuts the base (Fig. 109). Assuming a linear distribution of pressures as at b, we have

$$N = \frac{f}{2} \times 3g \times l$$

and

$$f = \frac{2N}{3gl} \qquad (108)$$

Fig. 109.

It is obvious from Equation 108 that the intensity of pressure at A (Fig. 109) increases as the distance g decreases and that a condition of instability results when $g = 0$. Footings are preferably designed so that e is within the limits shown by Equation 106.

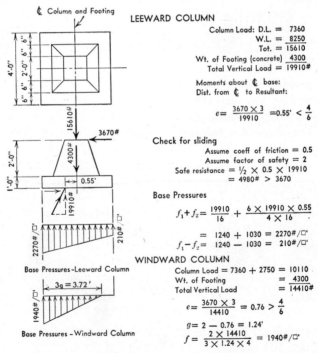

LEEWARD COLUMN

Column Load: D.L. = 7360
W.L. = 8250
Tot. = 15610
Wt. of Footing (concrete) 4300
Total Vertical Load = 19910#

Moments about ℄ base:
Dist. from ℄ to Resultant:

$$e = \frac{3670 \times 3}{19910} = 0.55' < \frac{4}{6}$$

Check for sliding

Assume coeff of friction = 0.5
Assume factor of safety = 2
Safe resistance = $\frac{1}{2} \times 0.5 \times 19910$
= 4980# > 3670

Base Pressures

$$f_1 + f_2 = \frac{19910}{16} + \frac{6 \times 19910 \times 0.55}{4 \times 16}$$

$$= 1240 + 1030 = 2270\#/\square'$$
$$f_1 - f_2 = 1240 - 1030 = 210\#/\square'$$

WINDWARD COLUMN

Column Load = 7360 + 2750 = 10110
Wt. of Footing = 4300
Total Vertical Load = 14410#

$$e = \frac{3670 \times 3}{14410} = 0.76 > \frac{4}{6}$$

$$g = 2 - 0.76 = 1.24'$$
$$f = \frac{2 \times 14410}{3 \times 1.24 \times 4} = 1940\#/\square'$$

Base Pressures -Leeward Column

$3g = 3.72'$

Base Pressures - Windward Column

Fig. 110. Mill Bent Column Footing. Hinged-Column Base.

Typical computations of base pressures under the footings of a mill bent are shown in Figs. 110 and 111.

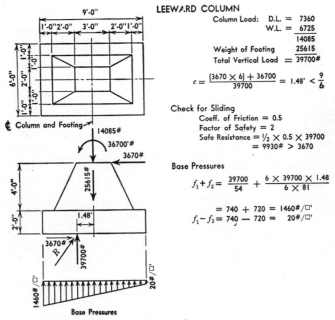

LEEWARD COLUMN

Column Load: D.L. = 7360
               W.L. = 6725
                     14085

Weight of Footing   25615
Total Vertical Load = 39700#

$$e = \frac{(3670 \times 6) + 36700}{39700} = 1.48' < \frac{9}{6}$$

Check for Sliding
  Coeff. of Friction = 0.5
  Factor of Safety = 2
  Safe Resistance = $\frac{1}{2} \times 0.5 \times 39700$
              = 9930# > 3670

Base Pressures

$$f_1 + f_2 = \frac{39700}{54} + \frac{6 \times 39700 \times 1.48}{6 \times 81}$$

$$= 740 + 720 = 1460\#/\square'$$
$$f_1 - f_3 = 740 - 720 = 20\#/\square'$$

Fig. 111.   Mill Bent Column Footing.   Fixed-Column Base.

77 Pile Foundations

When the subsoil material under a footing is unstable or will not develop the required resistance to pressure without excessive settlement, the load may be transmitted to a lower strata by means of piling. Piles may consist of wooden poles or timbers, concrete, or structural steel rolled sections. They are generally driven into the ground by means of a mechanical hammer or pile driver until they reach the desired penetration or resistance to driving; piles may also be jetted into place by forcing water under pressure through pipes placed alongside the pile. The safe load that may be placed on a pile is based upon the resistance it offers to being forced further downward into the subsoil. This resistance may be furnished by friction of the soil on the surface of the pile, by the resistance the point offers to being forced into a hard stratum, or by a combination of these two factors.

Piles are preferably placed in a direction parallel to the resultant load as their resistance to lateral component of forces is relatively low and somewhat unreliable. Thus, to resist an inclined force most effectively, *batter piles* or piles driven at an inclination to the vertical might be used.

The extra expense of driving batter piles precludes their use except in unusual cases.

To produce uniformity of loading, piles are preferably arranged symmetrically with respect to axes intersecting at the position of the resultant load. Driving conditions ordinarily require a minimum spacing of at least $2\frac{1}{2}$ feet for wood or steel piles and 3 feet for concrete piles.

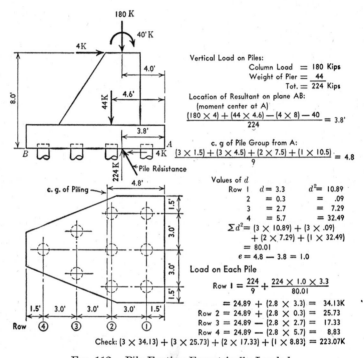

FIG. 112. Pile Footing Eccentrically Loaded.

When the resultant vertical load passes through the center of gravity of the pile group, the load on each pile will equal the total load divided by the number of piles. For eccentric loads or moments tending to overturn the footing, pile loads are determined in the same manner as noted in Article 76 for simple spread footings under similar conditions.

$$P = \frac{N}{n} \pm \frac{Ned}{\Sigma d^2} \qquad (109)$$

where N = total vertical load on tops of piles.

e = eccentricity of resultant load with respect to center of gravity of pile group.

d = normal distance from center of any pile to center of gravity of pile group.

P = total load on any pile.

n = number of piles in group.

It should be noted that Equation 109 would indicate an uplift on piles when

$$\frac{Ned}{\Sigma d^2} > \frac{N}{n}$$

Therefore the limiting effective distance of any pile on the negative (heel) side of the center of the group is

$$d \gtreqless \frac{\Sigma d^2}{en} \tag{110}$$

A typical computation of loads on a group of piles carrying an eccentric loading is given in Fig. 112.

78 Stability of Retaining Walls for Earth

Retaining walls for earth must resist the lateral pressure of the retained material in addition to supporting the weight of masonry composing the wall and such other forces as may be imposed on it. Determination of the stability of a retaining wall embodies the application of the same principles as were outlined for a rectangular footing in Article 76.

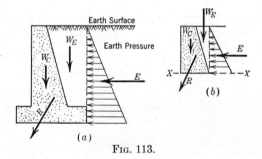

Fig. 113.

For such a wall as is shown in Fig. 113, the earth pressure is determined on a vertical plane through the heel of the footing as at a. The earth between this imaginary plane and the wall is regarded as inert filling which adds to the vertical load. The resultant pressure R on the foundation soil is determined as the resultant of the force system above the plane of the foundation. The vertical component N of this resultant is resisted by earth pressures acting upward against the base of the wall.

The horizontal component must be resisted by friction between the base of the wall and the supporting earth, unless other means of resisting the tendency of the wall to slide laterally are provided.

Typical Gravity Retaining Wall.

When the resultant cuts the base within the middle third of its width ($e \gtrless b/6$), the pressure at the edge nearest the resultant may be determined from the equation

$$f = \frac{N}{b} + \frac{6Ne}{b^2} = \frac{N}{b}\left(1 + \frac{6e}{b}\right) \tag{111}$$

and for the pressure at the edge farthest from the resultant

$$f = \frac{N}{b} - \frac{6Ne}{b^2} = \frac{N}{b}\left(1 - \frac{6e}{b}\right) \tag{112}$$

When R falls outside the middle third, $e > b/6$, and

$$f = \frac{2N}{3g} \quad \text{(see Fig. 109)} \tag{113}$$

For stability against overturning, the wall must be so proportioned that R falls within the limits of the base width, and, in order to provide a suitable factor of safety, it is preferable for it to pass within the middle third of the base.

The stability of any section such as xx in Fig. 113 is determined in the same manner as above, for that part of the construction (Fig. 113b) above such section. A *gravity* type wall is one where no tension can be resisted on such a section, and such walls must be so formed that the resultant on any such section will remain within the wall, preferably within the middle third, to furnish an additional factor of safety against overturning of the upper section and to furnish pressure over the entire joint to prevent water seepage. Reinforced concrete walls are designed to resist tension on such sections and are hence rendered internally stable.

Example

For the plain concrete gravity wall shown in Fig. 114, the computation for stability would be as follows:

Data: Weight of concrete: 150 lb per cu ft
      Weight of earth fill: 100 lb per cu ft
      Angle of internal friction of earth fill: 30 degrees
      Lateral earth pressure at base of wall (see Article 21, Equation 15)

$$q = 100 \times 15 \times \left(\frac{1 - 0.5}{1 + 0.5}\right) = 500 \text{ lb per sq ft}$$

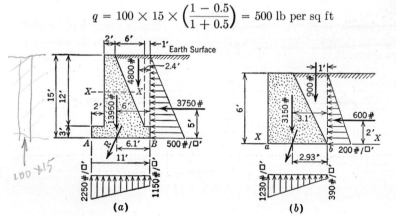

Fig. 114.

For 1 lineal ft of wall

Weight of wall	= 13,950 lb
Weight of earth fill on back of wall	= 4,800 lb
Total vertical load = N	= 18,750 lb
Total horizontal earth pressure = $500 \times 15 \times \frac{1}{2}$ =	3,750 lb

Moments about center of base

(clockwise moment indicated by +)

$$3,750 \times 5 \quad = -18,750$$
$$13,950 \times 0.5 = \quad -6,975$$

$$-25,725$$
$$4,800 \times 3.1 = +14,880$$

$$\text{Resultant moment} = -10,845 \text{ ft-lb}$$

Since the resultant moment is negative, the resultant will cut the base to the left of the center, and

$$e = \frac{10,845}{18,750} = 0.6 < \frac{11}{6}$$

$$\text{Toe pressure (at } A) = \frac{18,750}{11}\left[1 + \frac{6 \times 0.6}{11}\right] = 2250 \text{ lb per sq ft}$$

$$\text{Heel pressure (at } B) = \frac{18,750}{11}\left[1 - \frac{6 \times 0.6}{11}\right] = 1150 \text{ lb per sq ft}$$

If the wall is founded upon a clay subsoil and it is assumed that the coefficient of friction of the wall masonry on moist clay is about 0.3, the factor of safety against sliding would be

$$\frac{18,750 \times 0.3}{3750} = 1.5$$

The stability of the portion above any given plane is determined by similar procedure. Considering a section 6 ft below the top of the wall, the forces acting are as shown at b.

$$N = 4050 \text{ lb}$$

$$e = \frac{(600 \times 2) + (3150 \times 0.6) - (900 \times 1.5)}{4050} = 0.43 < \frac{5}{6}$$

The resultant therefore passes within the middle third of the section and

$$\text{Pressure at } a = \frac{4050}{5}\left[1 + \frac{6 \times 0.43}{5}\right] = 1230 \text{ lb per sq ft}$$

$$\text{Pressure at } b = \frac{4050}{5}\left[1 - \frac{6 \times 0.43}{5}\right] = 390 \text{ lb per sq ft}$$

79 Reinforced Concrete Retaining Walls

Reinforced concrete retaining walls (Fig. 115) are generally either of the *cantilever* type as at *a* or of the *counterfort* type as at *b*. For either

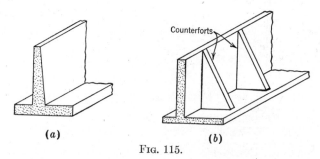

(*a*)   (*b*)

Fig. 115.

type, the stability of the wall as a whole and the pressures on the foundations are determined in the same manner as outlined in Article 78. For the counterfort-type wall, it is generally convenient to make the analysis for a length of wall corresponding to the spacing of counterforts. Since such walls are designed to resist internal bending-moment and shear, the

Counterfort-Type Reinforced Concrete Retaining Wall.

stability of sections is based upon the internal strength of the materials composing the wall.

Computations for the stability of a typical cantilever-type wall are shown in Fig. 116. Bending-moments and shears on various sections are computed in the usual manner. Thus the bending-moments carried by

the vertical wall or *stem* are produced by the lateral earth pressure and
(Fig. 117) are computed as if this portion of the wall were a cantilever
beam fixed at the top of the base slab. The portion of the base extending

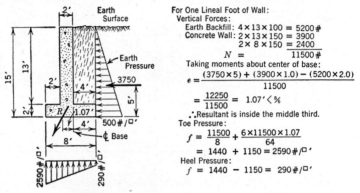

For One Lineal Foot of Wall:
Vertical Forces:
Earth Backfill: $4 \times 13 \times 100 = 5200\,\#$
Concrete Wall: $2 \times 13 \times 150 = 3900$
$ 2 \times 8 \times 150 = 2400$
$$N = \overline{11500\,\#}$$
Taking moments about center of base:
$$e = \frac{(3750 \times 5) + (3900 \times 1.0) - (5200 \times 2.0)}{11500}$$
$$= \frac{12250}{11500} = 1.07' < \%$$
∴ Resultant is inside the middle third.
Toe Pressure:
$$f = \frac{11500}{8} + \frac{6 \times 11500 \times 1.07}{64}$$
$$= 1440 + 1150 = 2590\,\#/\square'$$
Heel Pressure:
$$f = 1440 - 1150 = 290\,\#/\square'$$

FIG. 116.   Stability of Cantilever Type Wall.

in front of the stem is called the *toe*, and this is also assumed to be a
cantilever fixed at the face of the vertical wall (Fig. 118). The weight
of earth which may be applied on top of the toe is omitted since it may
not always be present. Similarly, the portion of the base extending to
the rear of the stem, known as the *heel*, is computed as a cantilever fixed
at the rear face of the vertical
wall (Fig. 118). The upward
pressure against the lower surface of the heel is frequently
omitted.

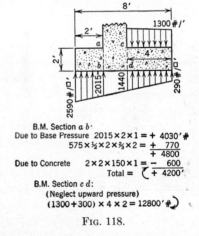

B.M. Section $a\,b$:
Due to Base Pressure $2015 \times 2 \times 1 = + 4030'\#$
$ 575 \times \tfrac{1}{2} \times 2 \times \tfrac{2}{3} \times 2 = + \underline{770}$
$ + 4800$
Due to Concrete $ 2 \times 2 \times 150 \times 1 = - \underline{600}$
$ \text{Total} = + 4200'$

B.M. Section $c\,d$:
(Neglect upward pressure)
$(1300 + 300) \times 4 \times 2 = 12800'\#$

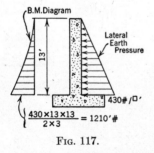

B.M. Diagram

Lateral
Earth
Pressure

$430\,\#/\square'$

$$\frac{430 \times 13 \times 13}{2 \times 3} = 1210'\#$$

FIG. 117.   FIG. 118.

80   Masonry Dams

Masonry dams have the same essential characteristics as the retaining
walls previously discussed. Since it is their function to retain water, it is
important that they be impervious at all sections, and they should there-

fore be so proportioned that pressure will exist over all portions of joints in the construction. To meet this condition, the line of resultant pressure under any condition of loading must lie within the middle third of

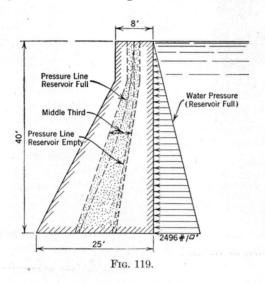

Fig. 119.

the wall section. Thus, in Fig. 119, the middle-third zone has been outlined for a typical dam section and resultant pressure lines indicated for two cases of loading.

81 Voussoir Arches

The stability of masonry arches of stone or brickwork, not reinforced to resist internal tensile stress, is determined by application of the foregoing principles and methods. The voussoir stone arch is the most common example of this type of construction and generally consists of individual stone blocks or *voussoirs* properly shaped and placed to form the arch. The stability of each individual voussoir is dependent upon the resisting pressure furnished by the voussoirs on either side, and the stability of the entire arch depends upon the resisting pressure of the abutments.

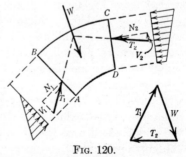

Fig. 120.

For an individual voussoir, the conditions will be as represented in Fig. 120, where W represents the force on the voussoir and T_1 and T_2 the resultant thrusts on faces AB and CD,

respectively. The stability of the voussoir requires that the following conditions be fulfilled:

(a) *Rotation.* For stability against rotation, the resultant thrusts T_1 and T_2 must lie within the limits of sections AB and CD, respectively. It is generally preferable that these forces pass within the middle third of the respective sections in order to provide a suitable factor of safety; to provide pressure over the entire section and thus deter entry of water into the joint; and to reduce the intensity of pressure on the masonry or mortar forming the joint.

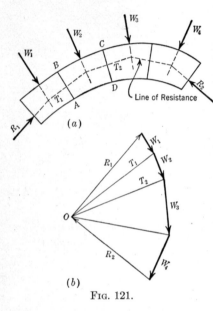

(b) *Crushing.* The intensity of pressure must not exceed the safe resistance to crushing of the masonry or mortar in the joint.

(c) *Sliding.* Components V_1 and V_2 in the plane of the respective sections must not exceed the safe shear resistance of the joint.

Since the resisting thrusts T_1 and T_2 are furnished by the adjoining voussoirs, their values and locations must be consistent with the equilibrium of the entire assemblage in the given construction. Thus Fig. 121a represents such an assembly where the line of resistance and location of any such thrusts as T_1 and T_2 are seen to conform with the equilibrium polygon, drawn from the force polygon at b. In the force polygon at b, the pole O was chosen at random, and it will be noted that an infinite number of such equilibrium polygons representing lines of resistance for the entire assembly could therefore be drawn. It therefore remains to determine the most probable or *true* line of resistance. The most generally accepted hypothesis for the true line of resistance is that it will be represented by the equilibrium polygon drawn with minimum thrust values consistent with equilibrium of the arch. Thus the middle-third zone would be outlined throughout the arch and a pole chosen to pass a polygon inside this zone maintaining at the same time minimum values of the forces R_1, T_1, T_2, etc. Such a polygon would pass through the lower middle-third limits at the supports and would

touch the outer-third point at or near the crown, and the problem thus is reduced to passing an equilibrium polygon through these points as discussed in Article 28.

PROBLEMS

7·1 Calculate the base pressures under the concrete column footing, and draw the pressure-distribution diagram.

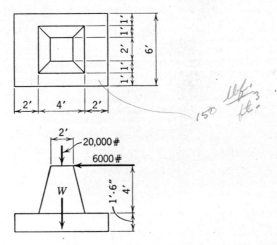

7·2 The weight of the retained earth is 100 lb per cu ft, and the assumed lateral pressure is $0.3wh$. Each 8 ft length of concrete retaining wall is supported on six piles as shown. Determine the maximum and minimum load per pile.

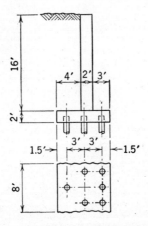

7·3   (*a*) Find the intensities of earth pressure beneath the heel and toe, and draw the pressure-distribution diagram for the reaction beneath the base.   (*b*) Compute bending-moments on sections *a-b*, *a-d*, *b-c*.

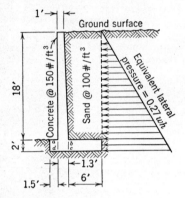

7·4   The angle of internal friction, $\phi = 30°$.   The weight of earth is taken as 100 lb per cu ft and of concrete 150 lb per cu ft.   (*a*) According to the Rankine theory, what

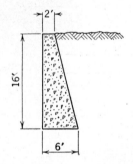

is the pressure distribution on a vertical surface through the retained earth?   (*b*) Determine the magnitude and direction of the resultant pressure on the back of the wall.   (*c*) Find the distribution of pressures on the base.

Part II

DESIGN OF SIMPLE STRUCTURES

FOREWORD

The design of a structure involves the selection of suitable materials, the determination of the dimension of individual parts, and the arranging of the component elements of the construction into an assembly which will be structurally sound and which will provide properly for the intended usage of the completed work. The designer must not only be competent to analyze the behavior of a structure in accordance with the principles of mechanics and to perform the necessary mathematical solutions incidental to this work, but he must also have knowledge of materials of construction, their physical properties, cost, utility for service under various conditions, and methods of construction and erection. Ability to visualize the completed structure in advance of its technical design is imperative, for all structures have their inception in the imagination of their designer.

The design of a structure starts with the determination of its need and the utility which must be provided. With these established, the designer evolves from his imagination, backed by his knowledge of the elements previously noted, a structural arrangement which he hopes will be satisfactory. He then makes an analysis of this arrangement and determines the forces to be resisted and finally computes the necessary dimensions of the component parts so that sufficient material will be provided in all parts to meet the computed stress conditions. The final results of this work are recorded in the form of drawings and written specifications which show the work to be done, materials to be provided, and arrangement of parts. Frequently several structural arrangements may be considered, and the best arrangement from the standpoint of cost, appearance, or other considerations may be selected after tentative or preliminary designs and estimates have been prepared.

It should be observed that designing a structure is essentially a process of trial and error. The first step is invariably the assumption of the material, general arrangement of parts, and probable dimensions. The second step is the determination of dead load and the structural analysis of the assumed arrangement under all loading conditions. The third step involves the determination of sizes and dimensions in accordance with the results of the second operation. When the results of the third step are at variance with the original assumptions, the original assumptions are accordingly revised, and the process is repeated until the final design is evolved.

Chapter 8

STRUCTURAL FASTENINGS AND CONNECTIONS

82 Nails and Screws

Wire nails are formed from steel wire which is cut to the desired length and a head and point formed on opposite ends. In size they are designated as ten-penny (10d), twenty-penny (20d), etc., the designation determining the diameter of the wire and the length of the nail. The sizes of common wire nails is given in Table 3.

Nails are generally used to resist transverse shearing force between two pieces of wood, and the force on the nail is thus applied in a direction normal to the length of the nail. When used in this manner in seasoned wood, the safe lateral load in pounds per nail may be determined by the following formula recommended by the U. S. Forest Products Laboratory:

$$P = KD^{3/2} \tag{114}$$

where P = safe lateral load in pounds per nail.

D = diameter of nail in inches.

K = a constant depending upon the species of wood.

Values recommended by the Forest Products Laboratory for use in Equation 114 are as follows:

Eastern hemlock, spruce, white pine	$K = 900$
Cypress, western hemlock, Norway pine	$K = 1125$
Douglas fir (coast), southern yellow pine	$K = 1375$
White ash, hickory, maple, oak	$K = 1700$

Nails should be driven so that the penetration of the point into the base timber is not less than one-half the length of the nail for dense hardwoods to two-thirds the length of the nail for the softer woods. When nails are driven parallel to the grain of the wood, that is, into the end grain, the safe lateral load for softwoods should be taken not more than 60 per cent of the value obtained by Equation 114.

The Forest Products Laboratory recommends that the safe resistance of nails to withdrawal be computed from the following formula:

$$P_1 = 1150 \, G^2 D \tag{115}$$

where P_1 = safe longitudinal load in pounds per lineal inch of penetration.

G = specific gravity of timber based on oven dry weight and
   volume.

D = diameter of nail.

When nails are driven into green wood and seasoning takes place, most
types of nails lose a large part of their holding power and safe values are
practically impossible of determination.

A *boat spike* is made from square steel or wrought-iron bars with a
head forged on one end and a point on the other. They may be of any
desired size and are used when larger and stronger fastenings, than can
be provided by means of wire nails, are required. They are obtainable
commercially in sizes varying from $\frac{1}{4}$ inch × 3 inches to $\frac{1}{2}$ inch × 12
inches long.

A *drift pin* or *drift bolt* is made from round metal with a head forged
on one end and a point on the other. They may be made any desired
length or diameter and are used in fastening together large timbers.

When the applied forces are parallel to the length of the screw, *wood
screws* are generally used in place of nails, since the resistance of nails to
a pulling-out force is exceedingly unreliable.

A *lag screw* is essentially a large wood screw made with a square head
and a gimlet point. They are obtainable commercially in sizes as shown
in Table 4.

83 Special Devices for Connecting Timbers

Modern connections [1] for timber construction have been extensively
used abroad and were introduced into the United States in 1933.

The Teco Toothed-Ring [2] (Fig. 122) is made of sheet steel with four
sizes commercially available, 2 inches, $2\frac{5}{8}$ inches, $3\frac{3}{8}$ inches, and 4 inches
in diameter adapted to use in 3-, 4-, 5-, and 6-inch nominal widths of tim-
ber. In making the connection, holes are bored through the timbers to
be joined, the timbers are separated and the toothed ring connector
placed between them. High-strength alloy steel bolts, with ball-bearing
washers and double-depth nuts, are then placed through the holes and
the timbers drawn tightly together, forcing the connector one-half its
width into each adjoining timber. The special bolts are then replaced
by ordinary machine bolts.

[1] "Modern Connections for Timber Construction," Bulletin prepared jointly by
National Committee on Wood Utilization and U. S. Forest Products Laboratory,
published by U. S. Government Printing Office.

[2] Manufactured under patents controlled by Timber Engineering Co., Washington, D. C.

FIG. 122.   Teco Toothed Ring.

190

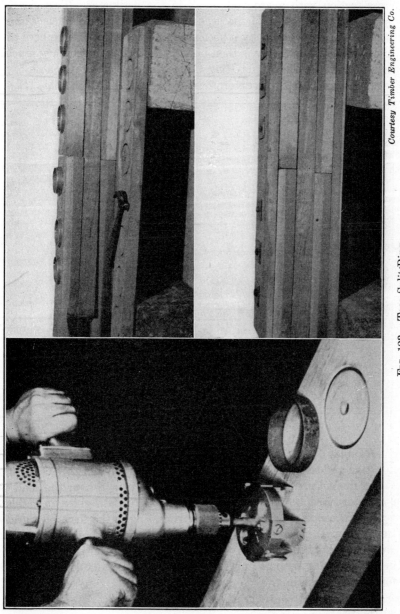

Fig. 123. Teco Split-Ring.

Courtesy Timber Engineering Co.

The Teco Split-Ring [3] is a plain steel ring (Fig. 123) of rectangular cross section with a grooved break in the perimeter. Two sizes, $2\frac{1}{2}$ inches and 4 inches, in diameter, are commercially available. The ring is placed in grooves cut by a special grooving tool in the timbers to be joined, and the assembly is then bolted together with ordinary machine bolts. Data for Teco Split-Ring Connectors are given in Table 5, and required spacing may be determined from Design Charts I, II, III, and

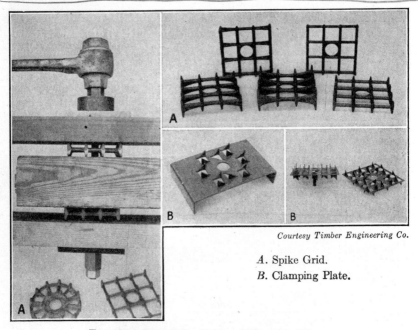

Courtesy Timber Engineering Co.

A. Spike Grid.
B. Clamping Plate.

FIG. 124.   Teco Spike Grid and Clamping Plates.

IV. Tables 6 and 7 show permissible increases of load based upon load duration and required decreases in load based upon moisture conditions. When more than three connectors are used in a group, the load per connector must be reduced in accordance with data given in Table 8.

The Teco Spike-Grid [4] is a malleable casting in the form of a grid or frame (Fig. 124) with sharp spikes projecting from both faces. Grids are placed between timbers to be connected and the points imbedded in the adjoining timbers in substantially the same manner as employed for the Toothed-Ring.

[3] Manufactured and distributed under patents controlled by the Timber Engineering Co., Washington, D. C.

[4] Manufactured and distributed under patents controlled by the Timber Engineering Co., Washington, D. C.

The Teco Claw-Plate Connector [5] is used either in pairs for timber to timber connections or singly for connections between wood and steel. It is a circular, malleable cast-iron plate with teeth on one face (Fig. 125) and is installed by forcing the teeth into the wood beyond the depth of the circular notch cut to receive the rim and plate portions.

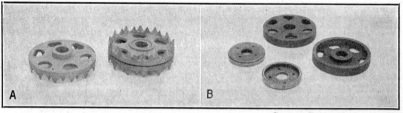

A. Teco Claw Plate.   *B.* Teco Shear Plate.

Fig. 125. Teco Claw and Shear Plates.

84 Bolts in Timber Construction

Bolts are manufactured from round bars of structural steel or wrought iron with threads formed on one end and a head upset on the other. The length is measured from the inside face of the head to the extreme end of the threaded portion. Bolts are usually furnished with square heads and square nuts, but hexagonal heads or nuts can be obtained on special order. Standard dimensions of bolt heads and nuts are shown in Table 9; standards for screw threads are shown in Table 10. The threaded portion will ordinarily be furnished to lengths specified in Table 11, but it can be made any specified length. The threaded portion of *cut-thread* bolts is formed by machine cutting, and the net area at the root of the thread is therefore less than that of the shank or unthreaded portion. *Rolled-thread* or *pressed-thread* bolts have the threaded portion formed by squeezing or pressing the form of the thread on the end of the bolt; the rolling or pressing process upsets the end of the bar so that the outside diameter of the threaded portion is slightly larger than the shank of the bolt, and the net area at the root of the thread is the same as the original bar. It is apparent that rolled-thread bolts cannot be inserted in holes of the nominal size of the bolt and should not be used where tight-fit bolts are required.

Bolts are generally regarded as more reliable than nails when shearing force between two pieces of timber is to be resisted, as at *b* in Fig. 126.

[5] Manufactured and distributed under patents controlled by the Timber Engineering Co., Washington, D. C.

Tests made by the U. S. Forest Products Laboratory and reported in Technical Bulletin 332 of the United States Department of Agriculture show that the safe load on a bolt can be determined in the following manner:

A. Force on bolt in direction parallel to grain

f = basic unit stress on projected area of bolt parallel to grain.
L = length of bolt (thickness of main member).
D = diameter of bolt.
K = percentage factor determined by test.
p = safe unit bearing stress on projected bolt bearing area.
  = fK for metal side plates.
  = $0.8 \, fK$ for wood side plates.
S = safe load on one bolt = pLD (116)

 Use one-half this value for arrangement as at c or d in Fig. 126.

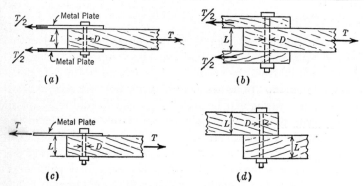

Fig. 126.   Bolts in Timber.

B. Force on bolt in direction normal to grain

f = basic unit stress on projected area of bolt perpendicular to grain.
L = length of bolt (thickness of main member).
D = diameter of bolt.
m = percentage factor determined by test.
n = diameter factor determined by test.
q = safe unit bearing stress on projected bolt bearing area.
  = fmn (for either metal or wood side plates).
S = safe load on one bolt = qLD (117)

Use one-half this value for arrangement as at c or d in Fig. 126.

Values of the basic stresses p and q for various species of wood are given in Table 12; percentage factors K and m are given in Table 13;

diameter factors n are given in Table 14. With these tables, assuming the arrangement at a in Fig. 126 (two-end load with metal side plates), the safe load T for a $\frac{7}{8}$-inch diameter common bolt through a $5\frac{1}{2}$-inch thick southern yellow pine timber would be computed as follows:

Example 1

Basic stress f (Group 3, Table 12) = 1300 psi.

$$L/D = \frac{5.5}{0.875} = 6.3$$

Percentage factor K from Table 13 = 64.1

$p = 1300 \times 0.641 = 835$ lb per sq in.

$S = 835 \times 5\frac{1}{2} \times \frac{7}{8} = 4020$ lb

Example 2

For the arrangement shown at b in Fig. 126, the value of S would be 80% of that computed above, or 3220 lb. For the arrangement at c, a value of 2010 lb would be used; for the arrangement at d, the value is 1610 lb.

For each bolt in member B of the arrangement at c in Fig. 127, assuming western hemlock, $L = 5\frac{1}{2}$ in., $D = \frac{3}{4}$ in., using common bolts and either metal or wood side plates.

Basic stress f (Group 2, Table 12) = 200 lb per sq in. $L/D = \dfrac{5.5}{0\,75} = 7.3$

Percentage factor m (Table 14) = 99.5

Diameter factor n (Table 14)   = 1.41

$q = 200 \times 0.995 \times 1.41 = 280$ lb per sq in.

$S = 280 \times 5\frac{1}{2} \times \frac{3}{4}$ = 1150 lb

When the applied force on a bolt is at an angle to the grain, the allowed stress on the projected area of bearing of bolt on timber may be determined from the Hankinson formula,

$$n = \frac{pq}{p \sin^2 \theta + q \cos^2 \theta} \tag{118}$$

where n = allowed unit stress in a direction θ with the grain.

p = allowed unit stress in compression parallel to grain.

q = allowed unit stress in compression normal to grain.

θ = angle of inclination (less than 90 degrees) of applied force to the direction of grain.

For the arrangement at c in Fig. 127, assuming timber to be coast type Douglas fir, wood side plates, $\frac{3}{4}$ inch diameter common bolts, member B

$5\frac{1}{2}$ inches thick (parallel to length of bolt), the safe load on each bolt in member B when θ is 20 degrees would be computed as follows:

Example 3

  Basic stress (Table 12)

   Parallel to grain, $f = 1300$ lb per sq in.
   Normal to grain, $f = 275$ lb per sq in.

$L/D = 5\frac{1}{2} \div \frac{3}{4} = 7.3$
Percentage factor K (Table 13) $= 55.3$
For wood side plates $p = 0.8 \times 1300 \times 0.553 = 575$ lb per sq in.
Percentage factor m (Table 14) $= 94.9$
Diameter factor n (Table 14) $= 1.41$

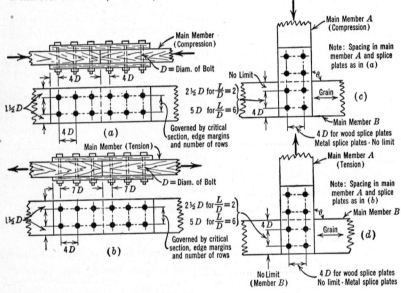

FIG. 127. Bolted Joints in Timber Construction.

$$q = 275 \times 0.949 \times 1.41 = 370 \text{ lb per sq in.}$$

$$\sin \theta = 0.342 \qquad\qquad \sin^2 \theta = 0.117$$

$$\cos \theta = 0.94 \qquad\qquad \cos^2 \theta = 0.9$$

$$n = \frac{575 \times 370}{(575 \times 0.117) + (370 \times 0.9)} = 530 \text{ lb per sq in.}$$

$$S = 530 \times 5\frac{1}{2} \times \frac{3}{4} = 2190 \text{ lb per bolt}$$

  In choosing the bolt diameter for a given design, it is recommended that the diameter be made such that L/D is 6 or more. Recommenda-

tions for spacing of bolts under various conditions are illustrated in Fig. 127. For splices of the types shown at *a* and *b* in Fig. 127, it is recommended that bolts be arranged in rows and not staggered. In tension splices (Fig. 127*b*), the area of the net section of timber should be not less than 80 per cent of the combined bearing area of all the bolts in the particular timber for softwoods and 100 per cent of the combined bolt bearing area for hardwoods. The use of cross bolts to prevent splitting of the timber is also recommended, especially when the *L/D* ratio is small.

85 Structural Rivets and Bolts

Steel rivets are generally used for fastening together steel members. Rivets are forged from round steel bars with a round or button head on one end and are sufficiently long to pass through the parts to be connected and allow excess length to be upset to form a head on the end originally left blank. Dimensions of structural rivets are given in Table 15. When rivet heads may interfere with adjoining construction they may be flattened, countersunk, or countersunk and chipped (see Fig. 132).

Rivets are placed red hot in the holes provided and are then squeezed by presses or hammered by riveters to form the head on the blank end and force the metal to fill the hole completely. Owing to erection and assembly requirements some rivets are driven in the field and are termed *field rivets*; those placed in the fabricating shop are termed *shop rivets*. Shearing and bearing values of power-driven rivets and turned bolts in reamed holes are given in Table 16. Similar values for unfinished bolts are given in Table 17.

In order to provide entry of the rivet the holes in the parts to be fastened must be made $\frac{1}{16}$ inch larger than the nominal diameter of the rivet. After driving, therefore, the rivet is actually increased in size by this amount, but this is not taken into account in computing the cross section of the rivet, the nominal diameter being regarded as the final rivet size. Where rivet holes are punched, severe local stresses are developed around the periphery of the hole resulting in damage to the metal. On this account the holes are computed as if they were $\frac{1}{8}$ inch larger than the nominal size of the rivet. To reduce the amount of this damage and provide better work, holes may be drilled to the required size or may be subpunched to a size smaller than the rivet and reamed to a diameter $\frac{1}{16}$ inch larger.

The strength of a rivet is based on (*a*) its resistance to shear, and (*b*) its resistance to the bearing pressure on the contact area between the rivet and the parts fastened. The action of a rivet in *single shear* is illus-

trated at a in Fig. 128, and its resistance to this action equals the product of the unit shearing resistance of the rivet material and the cross-sectional area of the rivet shank. The action of a rivet in *double shear* is illustrated at b in Fig. 128, where it is noted that the rivet is sheared on two planes simultaneously; hence the double shear value is twice the single shear value. The *bearing value* of a rivet is measured as the product of the allowed unit bearing stress and the projected contact area (nominal rivet diameter $\times$ thickness of plate) of rivet and plate. Thus at a in Fig. 128 the bearing area for plate A is t_1d. This type is termed

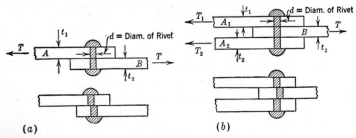

(a)   (b)

FIG. 128.   Rivets in Single and Double Shear.

single shear bearing. Double shear bearing is the type which occurs on plate B in Fig. 128b. For the arrangement shown at a, the safe value of one rivet would be computed as follows:

$$u = \text{allowed intensity of bearing stress}$$

$$d = \text{nominal diameter or rivet}$$

$$R = \text{value of rivet}$$

As determined by plate A, $R = ut_1d$
As determined by plate B, $R = ut_2d$

The smaller of these values of R would control.

For the arrangement shown at b, the value of one rivet in bearing would be as follows:

As determined by plate A_1, $R_1 = ut_1d$
As determined by plate A_2, $R_2 = ut_2d$
$$R = R_1 + R_2 = ud\,(t_1 + t_2)$$
As determined by plate B, $R = ut_3d$

The smaller of these values of R controls. (Note that double shear bearing is considered on plate B.)

When rivets are used in a group, as for example to splice a tension member or to fasten the end of a tension or compression number, it is

assumed that the force is equally divided among the rivets in the group. For small rivet groups, little error is introduced by this assumption, but in large groups there may be considerable variance in the force distribution. Rivets in any group should be as compactly arranged as possible and preferably with the center of gravity of the rivet group on the line of action of the applied force. As between the arrangements shown in Fig. 129, the rivets in *a* will not be equally stressed, the end rivets receiving substantially more load than the ones between; the rivets shown at *b*

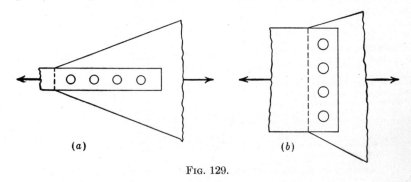

(*a*)   (*b*)

Fig. 129.

will, on the other hand, be practically equally stressed. The arrangement at *a* is, however, more economical of plate material since only one hole is deducted to obtain the net section whereas four holes must be deducted from the plate section in *b*. As a result, the adopted arrangement of rivets in such a connection is usually a compromise of these conditions.

The following is an example of the computations for a tension splice.

Example

Main plates, 9 in. $\times \frac{7}{8}$ in.
Total stress in plates, 94 kips
Rivets, $\frac{7}{8}$ in. diam.

If the rivets are arranged in three lines (see Fig. 130), three holes 1 in. in diameter will be taken out of the main plate to obtain the net section.

Gross section main plate = $9 \times \frac{7}{8}$ = 7.875 sq in.
Deduct 3 rivet holes $1 \times \frac{7}{8} \times 3$ = 2.625 sq in.

Net area main plate   5.25 sq in.

Unit stress main plate = $\dfrac{94,000}{5.25}$ = 17,900 psi

This is regarded as satisfactory, and the splice plates will be made $\frac{7}{16}$ in. thick.

Value of one rivet

Double shear (Table 16) = 18,040 lb

Bearing on $\frac{7}{16}$-in. splice plate = $2 \times \frac{7}{16} \times \frac{7}{8} \times 32,000 = 24,500$

Bearing on main plate = $\frac{7}{8} \times \frac{7}{8} \times 40,000 = 30,600$

Double shear controls and $R = 18,040$

Number rivets required each side of splice = $\dfrac{94,000}{18,040} = 6$

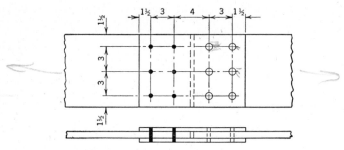

FIG. 130.   Riveted Tension Splice.

In arranging rivets, consideration must be given to the necessary clearances for placing and driving. Standard driving clearances are indicated in Table 18. For convenience, standard location lines called *gage lines* are adopted for rolled sections, and, unless specifically indicated otherwise, rivet holes are located on these lines. Standard gages for angles are shown in Fig. 131. Standard gages for I-beams, channels,

	USUAL GAGES FOR ANGLES, INCHES														CRIMPS
Leg	8	7	6	5	4	3½	3	2½	2	1¾	1½	1⅜	1¼	1	$b = t + 1\frac{1}{2}''$ Min $= 2''$
g	4½	4	3½	3	2½	2	1¾	1⅜	1⅛	1	⅞	⅞	¾	⅝	
g_1	3		2½	2¼	2										
g_2	3		3	2½	1¾										

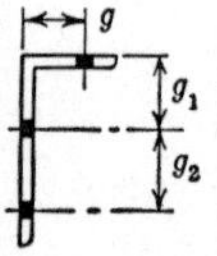

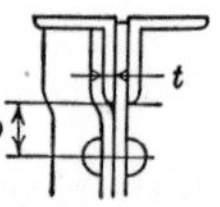

FIG. 131.   Standard Gages for Angles.

(From "Steel Construction," by courtesy of the American Institute of Steel Construction.)

and other rolled sections will be found in structural-steel handbooks. Conventional signs used on structural drawings are shown in Fig. 132.

Rivets are preferably not used where tension is developed in the rivet, and, when this is unavoidable, relatively low unit stresses are allowed. Bolts are generally preferred to rivets for carrying tensile stress.

Structural bolts (see Tables 9, 10, and 11) are made of structural steel and act in the same manner as rivets. Unfinished bolts are generally assigned the same values as rivets of the same size. Turned bolts made to a driving fit in reamed holes are assigned the same values as power-driven rivets.

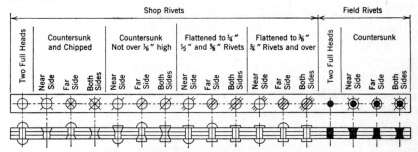

FIG. 132. Conventional Signs for Riveting.

(From "Steel Construction," by courtesy of the American Institute of Steel Construction.)

86 Eccentric Riveted Connections

When the applied force does not pass through the center of gravity of the rivet group, the rivets must resist the torsional effect as well as the direct force. Such a riveted joint is said to be eccentric, and the eccentricity is measured as the distance from the line of action of the resultant force to the center of gravity of the rivet group. The moment acting on the rivet group is the product of the resultant force and the eccentricity, and each rivet must contribute its share to the resisting moment.

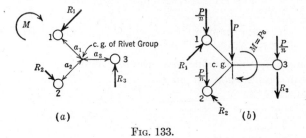

FIG. 133.

The force on each rivet in an eccentric joint is the resultant of the moment stress on the rivet and the direct force (total force divided by the number of rivets).

In the analyses of such rivet groups, it is commonly assumed that the center of rotation (corresponding to the neutral axis of a beam section) coincides with the center of gravity of the rivet group and that each rivet

acts as an elastic unit. The moment of resistance of the rivet group is therefore (see Fig. 133a)

$$M = \frac{R\Sigma a^2}{a} \tag{119}$$

where R = moment force on any rivet acting normal to a line from the center of the rivet to the center of gravity of the group.

a = distance of any rivet from the center gravity of the group.

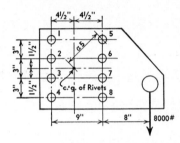

Rivet	a^2	a	$a/{\Sigma a^2}$
1	40.50	6.36	0.0252
2	22.50	4.74	0.0188
3	22.50	4.74	0.0188
4	40.50	6.36	0.0252
5	40.50	6.36	0.0252
6	22.50	4.74	0.0188
7	22.50	4.74	0.0188
8	40.50	6.36	0.0252
Σ	252.00		

Moment = 8000 × 12.5 = 100000"#

Moment Stress:

    Rivets, 1, 4, 5 and 8; 0.0252 × 100 000 = 2520#

    Rivets, 2, 3, 6 and 7; 0.0188 × 100 000 = 1880#

Direct Stress (All rivets) = 1/8 × 8000 = 1000#

Rivets 5 and 8 will receive maximum force

$$\text{Vertical Component} = 1000 + \left(\frac{2520 \times 4.5}{6.36} \right) = 2780\#$$

$$\text{Horizontal Component} = \frac{2520 \times 4.5}{6.36} = 1780$$

$$R = \sqrt{(2780)^2 + (1780)^2} = 3300\#$$

FIG. 134.   Eccentric Riveted Connection.

In addition to the moment force which is computed from Equation 119, each rivet must carry its share of the direct force, and these two forces (Fig. 133) are components of the resultant force on the rivet.

A typical computation for an eccentric riveted connection is shown in Fig. 134.

87 Pins

Short heavy pins are sometimes used to fasten steel members together. Pins are computed as beams, and consideration must be given to the bearing of the parts fastened on the pin as well as the shears and bending-moments developed in the pin.

Figure 135 shows a typical arrangement of pieces bearing on a pin, connecting the members of a truss bridge. The forces are resolved into horizontal and vertical components, and, with the pin acting as a beam, as in Fig. 136, the bending-moments and shears in each direction are

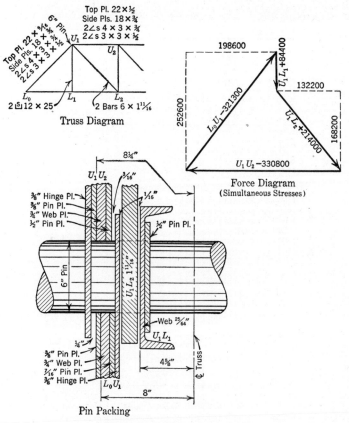

Truss Diagram

Force Diagram
(Simultaneous Stresses)

Pin Packing

Forces in members connected.

FIG. 135. Stress Analysis of Pin Connection.

determined. These bending-moments and shears are then combined to obtain the resultant effects. The unit stresses are as follows:

Example

Bearing on pin of

$$\text{Member } L_0 U_1 = \frac{321{,}300}{2 \times \frac{3}{16} \times 6} = 13{,}850 \text{ lb per sq in.}$$

$$\text{Member } U_1 U_2 = \frac{330{,}800}{2 \times \frac{1}{8} \times 6} = 13{,}750 \text{ lb per sq in.}$$

$$\text{Member } U_1 L_2 = \frac{214{,}000}{2 \times 1\frac{11}{16} \times 6} = 10{,}550 \text{ lb per sq in.}$$

$$\text{Member } U_1 L_1 = \frac{84{,}400}{2 \times \frac{57}{64} \times 6} = 7900 \text{ lb per sq in.}$$

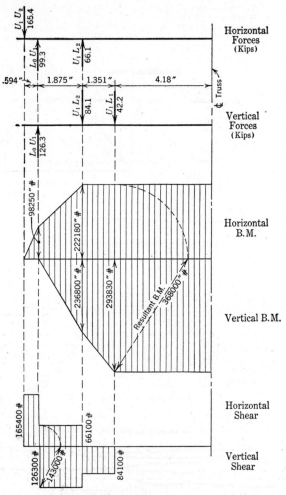

B.M. and shear diagram.

Fig. 136.   Stress Analysis of Pin Connection.

Bending in pin

Max B.M.   = 368,000 in.-lb

$$f = \frac{368,000}{216 \times 0.0982} = 17,350 \text{ lb per sq in.}$$

Shear in pin

Max shear   = 165,400 lb

$$\text{Average shear} = \frac{165,400}{36 \times 0.7854} = 5850 \text{ lb per sq in.}$$

Field House and Gymnasium,   Michigan State College.
(Completed in 1940.)
205

88   Welded Connections

Although extensively used for machine work, automobile construction, and miscellaneous purposes, welding is not so freely employed for making connections in bridge and building work. This is due in part to the necessity of providing temporary fastenings to hold the work together during assembly, which necessitates such shop handling and punching as to obviate most of the economic advantage which might otherwise accrue through the use of welded connections. Welding is, however, extensively used in the shop for minor details and fastenings and also in the field where noise elimination during construction is essential and for repairs and alterations to existing structures.

For structural purposes the electric-arc welding method is generally preferred to others. In this method, the pieces to be welded are brought

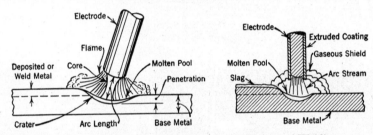

Fig. 137.   Diagrammatic Sketch of Arc in Process of Welding.

(Reprinted from the "Procedure Handbook of Arc Welding Design and Practice," published by the Lincoln Electric Co., Cleveland, Ohio.)

to the proper temperature by heat liberated at the terminals and in the stream of an electric arc so that the metals are completely fused. The arc is formed between the work to be welded and an electrode held in a suitable holder (Fig. 137). The electrode may be either metal or carbon depending upon the work to be done, the metallic electrode generally being employed for structural welding. Metallic electrodes commonly used vary from $\frac{1}{8}$ inch to $\frac{3}{8}$ inch in diameter and are 14 inches or 18 inches long. They may be bare wire of the specified size and composition or they may be coated with chemicals which form gases to protect the molten metal during the welding process (Fig. 137). The use of coated electrodes is generally preferred as producing more uniform and reliable welds.

Welds are classified according to location as *flat, vertical, overhead,* and *horizontal;* and according to type as *butt* welds, *fillet* welds, *lap* welds, *edge* welds, and *plug* welds. These are illustrated in Fig. 138.

A *flat weld* is one in a plane inclined at an angle of 45 degrees or less to the horizontal, the weld being made from the top side of the plane.

A *vertical weld* has its linear direction inclined at an angle of less than 45 degrees to the vertical.

An *overhead weld* is the same as a flat weld except that the weld is made from beneath the plane of the weld.

A *horizontal weld* has its linear direction inclined at an angle less than 45 degrees to the horizontal in planes which are inclined less than 45 degrees to the vertical.

An *intermittent weld* is one of broken continuity and generally consists of relatively short lengths of bead spaced at uniform distances along the length of the pieces welded.

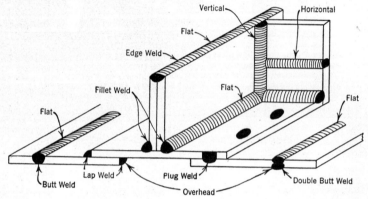

FIG. 138.   Examples of Welds and Locations.

(Reprinted from the "Procedure Handbook of Arc Welding Design and Practice," published by the Lincoln Electric Company, Cleveland, Ohio.)

A *tack weld* is an intermittent weld used to hold parts together for assembly purposes.

In order to promote uniformity of practice in the conveying of information by means of drawings, the American Welding Society has proposed the use of conventional symbols (Fig. 139) to indicate needed information to construct welds of various types. For more detailed information relative to the use of these symbols the reader is referred to publications of the American Welding Society.

The American Welding Society Code for Fusion Welding in Building Construction (1937) defines the elements and dimensions of the section of a weld as indicated in Fig. 140. The *effective length* of a fillet weld is under this code $\frac{1}{4}$ inch less than the overall length of the weld.

The internal stress in a weld is determined from its size and length and depends upon the magnitude and manner of application of the external load. The cross-sectional area of weld metal under stress is always considered as the product of the *throat dimension* and the *effective*

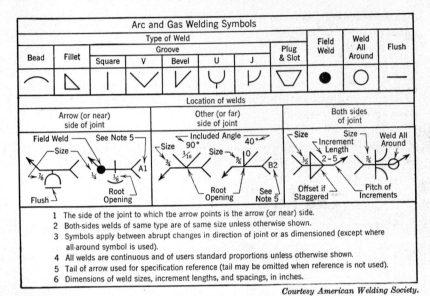

Courtesy American Welding Society.

FIG. 139.   Symbols Used to Indicate Welds.

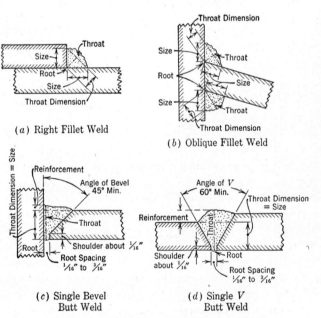

(a) Right Fillet Weld

(b) Oblique Fillet Weld

(c) Single Bevel Butt Weld

(d) Single V Butt Weld

FIG. 140.   Elements and Dimensions of Welds.

length. Formulae for unit stress in typical welds may be expressed as follows,[6]

where P = external load in pounds (tension or compression).

f = unit stress in weld (tension or compression)

V = external shear on weld.

v = unit stress in shear.

t = size of weld in inches.

L = effective length of weld.

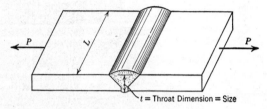

t = Throat Dimension = Size

Fɪɢ. 141.   Butt Weld.

Butt Welds

For a simple butt weld, as in Figs. 140c, 140d. or 141, either in tension or compression,

$$f = \frac{P}{tL}$$ (120)

With the external forces applied to produce transverse shear (either vertical or longitudinal),

$$v = \frac{V}{tL}$$ (121)

Transverse Fillet Welds

It is the generally accepted practice to assume that the stress on the throat section of a transverse fillet weld is a normal tensile or compressive stress.   For the arrangement as shown at a or b in Fig. 142,

$$\text{Throat dimension of weld} = 0.707t$$ (122)

$$f = \frac{\frac{1}{2}P}{0.707tL} = \frac{P}{1.414tL}$$ (123)

[6] For a more complete discussion of stresses in a weld, see paper, "Welding Design" by Chas. H. Jennings, *A.S.M.E. Transactions*, October, 1936.

When two plates of unequal thickness are welded, as shown at Fig. 142*c*, assuming welds of the same dimensions,

$$\text{for the top weld,} \qquad f = \left(\frac{b}{a+b}\right)\frac{P}{0.707tL} \qquad (124)$$

$$\text{for the bottom weld,} \quad f = \left(\frac{a}{a+b}\right)\frac{P}{0.707tL} \qquad (125)$$

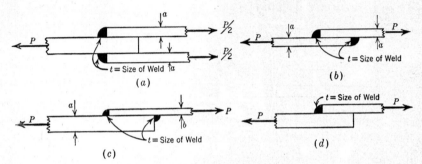

Fig. 142.   Transverse Fillet Welds.

The arrangement shown at Fig. 142*d* is non-symmetrical with the result that bending stresses are induced in the weld. The stress at the root of the weld is in this case critical and

$$f = \frac{3.414P}{tL} \qquad (126)$$

Transverse fillet welds of the type shown at *c* in Fig. 143 are most often found in machines and

$$f = \frac{P}{tL(d+t)}[2e^2 + \tfrac{1}{2}(d+t)^2]^{1/2} \qquad (127)$$

Longitudinal Fillet Welds

Referring to Fig. 143 we see that, for parallel or transverse fillet welds of the types shown at *a* or *b*, the stress on the throat section is shear and

$$v = \frac{\tfrac{1}{2}P}{0.707tL} = \frac{P}{1.414tL} \qquad (128)$$

For longitudinal fillet welds in bending as at d

$$f = \frac{4.24Pe}{tL^2} \tag{129}$$

The safe working stress depends upon the quality of the weld metal and the characteristics of the loading. Typical physical properties of metal deposited in welds by bare and coated electrodes are shown in Table 19.

Permissible unit stresses as given in the American Welding Society Committee Code for Fusion Welding in Building Construction (1937) are given in Table 20. Working stresses recommended by Jennings for

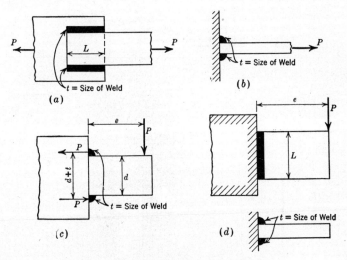

FIG. 143. Miscellaneous Fillet Welds.

bare and coated electrodes are given in Table 21; also stress concentration factors to be used where dynamic loads are encountered.

For a more complete discussion of the design of welded joints the reader is referred to a paper by H. M. Priest, "The Practical Design of Welded Steel Structures," published in the August, 1933, issue of the *Journal of the American Welding Society*. Typical stress and design computations as presented in this paper are reproduced in Figs. 144, 145, 146, and 147.

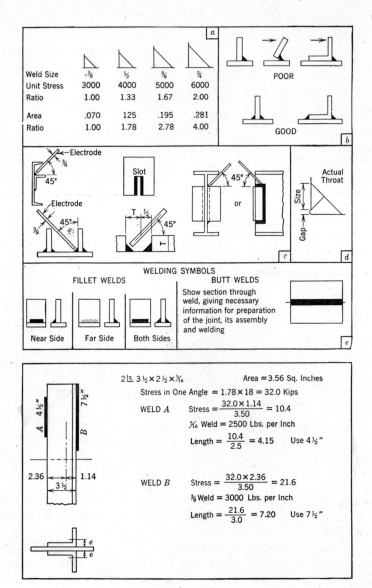

FIG. 144.

(From "The Practical Design of Welded Steel Structures," by H. M. Priest, *J. Am. Welding Soc.*, August, 1933.)

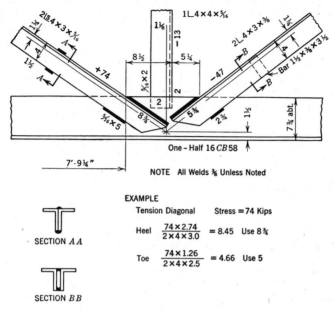

FIG. 145. Typical Welded Truss Joint.

(Reprinted from "The Practical Design of Welded Steel Structures," by H. M. Priest, *J. Am. Welding Soc.*, August, 1933.)

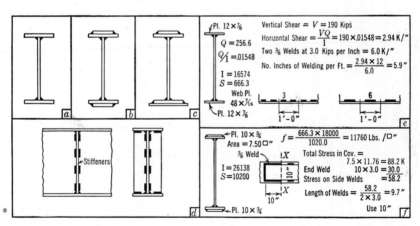

FIG. 146.

(From "The Practical Design of Welded Steel Structures," by H. M. Priest, *J. Am. Welding Soc.*, August, 1933.)

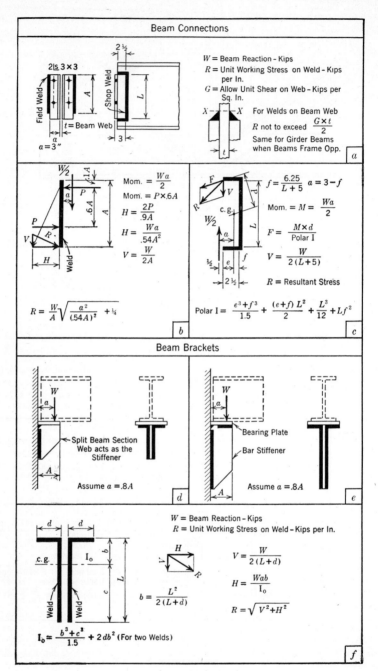

$$\text{F{\small IG}. 147.}$$

(From "The Practical Design of Welded Steel Structures," by H. M. Priest, *J. Am. Welding Soc.*,
August, 1933.)

PROBLEMS

8·1 All members are 2-in.×10-in. (nominal size) southern yellow pine. How many 16d nails are required for the adequate design of this splice if the total force transmitted is 1500 lb compression?

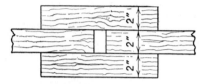

8·2 If the material is southern yellow pine, how many Teco No. 1 Split-Ring Connectors are required to transmit the force of 10,000 lb into the horizontal member?

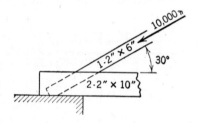

8·3 (*a*) Two pieces of Rocky Mountain Douglas fir, 3-in.×10-in. nominal size, are fastened together by bolts as in Fig. 126*d*. The pull on each piece is 30,000 lb. How many 1-in. diam. bolts will be required? (*b*) How many Teco Split-Ring Connectors No. 3 will be required if the angle of load with grain is 10°

8·4 Two yellow pine pieces, each 2 in. x 6 in., are to be fastened together as in Fig. 126*d*. The pull on the pieces is 10,000 lb. How many $\frac{3}{4}$-in. bolts will be required? How many Teco Split-Rings No. 2 would be required if the grain makes an angle of 20° with the load?

8·5 Find the unit shearing stress in each rivet.

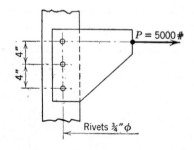

8·6 Determine the magnitude and direction of the maximum shearing force per rivet for each rivet group.

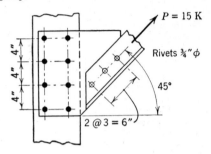

8·7 Using the allowable rivet stresses in Table 16 and assuming the allowable tension in the plates to be 20,000 psi, find the allowable load, P, on the tension splice.

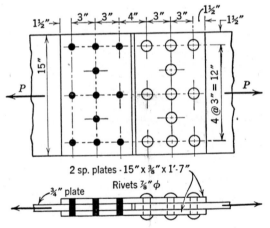

8·8 Check the adequacy of the rivets in the connection shown according to A.I.S.C. Specifications.

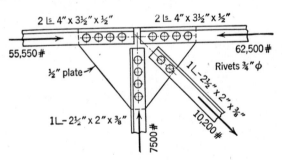

8·9 What is the shearing stress and the bearing stress in psi on these rivets at a point in the span where the transverse shearing force is 100,000 lb?

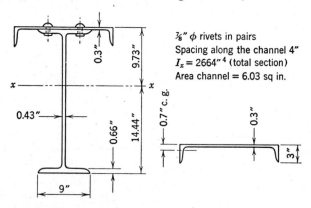

⅞" φ rivets in pairs
Spacing along the channel 4"
$I_x = 2664"^4$ (total section)
Area channel = 6.03 sq in.

8·10 Two 8-in. × ½-in. steel plates are welded together as shown in Fig. 142*b*, using ½-in. welds. The allowable unit stress on the weld is 13,600 psi, and the allowable tension in the plates is 18,000 psi. What is the safe tensile strength of splice?

Chapter 9

TIMBER BEAMS AND COLUMNS

89 Grades and Sizes of Timber

Differing from most structural materials, wood is of organic origin and is used in its natural state. It is cut to specific shapes and sizes and is properly seasoned before use, and under particular conditions it may be impregnated with preservative material. Trees made into lumber and timbers are broadly divided into two groups, *softwoods* and *hardwoods*. The coniferous evergreen trees are customarily called softwoods and the broad-leaved or deciduous trees hardwoods.

As a result of its natural growth, wood may contain many defects [1] when considered for structural purposes. When manufactured into the ordinary commercial sizes, these defects will remain in the finished pieces, and the quality of a given piece will depend upon their extent, size, and location. In order to standardize material in classes for various usages, manufacturers have established grading rules [2] which limit these defects in various types of wood products.

Lumber is defined as the product of the saw and planing mill not further manufactured than by sawing, resawing, and passing lengthwise through a standard planing machine, crosscut to length, and matched. Softwood lumber is classified into three main groups, *yard lumber*, *structural timbers* (often referred to under the general term *timbers*), and *factory and shop lumber*. The general classification shown in Fig. 148 gives the grade names used by lumber manufacturers' associations for the various classes of material.

Softwood *yard lumber* is lumber less than 5 inches in thickness and is intended for general building purposes. *Strips* are yard lumber less than 2 inches thick and under 8 inches wide. *Boards* are yard lumber less than 2 inches thick and 8 inches or over in width. *Dimension* is all yard lumber except strips, boards, and timbers; that is, yard lumber over 2 inches and under 5 inches in thickness and of any width. *Planks*

---

[1] See "Wood Handbook," published by United States Department of Agriculture; also Standard Definition D9–30, American Society for Testing Materials.

[2] See "Wood Structural Design Data," published by the Natural Lumber Manufacturers' Assoc.; also Basic Laws for Structural Grades in "Douglas Fir Use Book," published by West Coast Lumberman's Assoc.

are dimension lumber over 2 inches, and under 4 inches, in thickness and 8 inches or more in width. *Scantlings* are dimension lumber over 2 inches and under 5 inches thick and under 8 inches in width. *Heavy joists* are dimension lumber 4 inches thick and 8 inches or over in width. The grading of yard lumber is based upon the use of the entire piece except

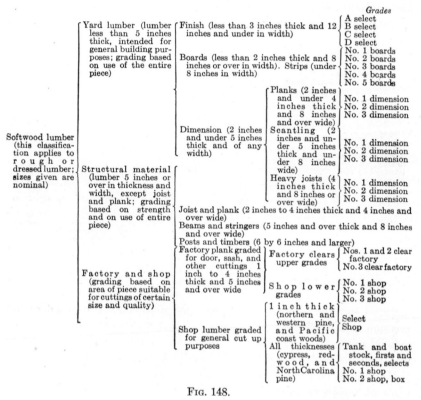

Fig. 148.

(From "Wood Handbook," published by U. S. Dept. of Agriculture.)

that dimension planks and joists to be used where working stresses are required should be graded as structural material. Standard nominal dimensions of yard lumber are given in Table 22.

Softwood yard lumber is graded on the basis of quality into two main classes: (*a*) *select* lumber, and (*b*) *common* lumber; these are again subdivided into classes or grades depending upon the size, extent, and character of defects (see Fig. 149).

Structural timbers are softwood lumber 5 inches or larger in least dimension. This material is intended for use in carrying calculated stress and is graded with regard both to the strength and to the use of

the entire piece. Structural timbers, including dimension yard lumber intended for structural use, are further classified as *joists and planks, beams and stringers,* and *posts and timbers.*

Structural timbers are graded for quality in accordance with their safe principal working stress. Thus *1600f joist and plank* indicates material suitable for carrying up to 1600 pounds per square inch tension or extreme fiber in bending; *1200c posts and timbers* would indicate

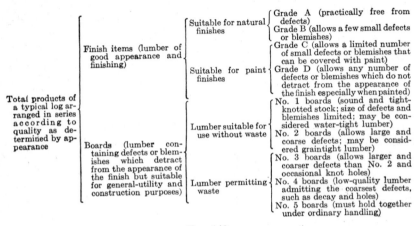

Fig. 149.

(From "Wood Handbook," published by U. S. Dept. of Agriculture.)

material suitable for carrying up to 1200 pounds per square inch compression as a short column. Lumber grades are specified by their commercial grade names as given in Table 25. The basis of stress grading for structural timbers was developed by the Forest Products Laboratory.[3]

Manufactured lumber is classified as *rough, surfaced,* or *worked.*

Rough lumber is undressed material as it comes from the saw, where it is cut to the nominal dimensions in green condition. Errors in sawing and the shrinkage due to seasoning may produce variations in the actual size of rough material from the nominal dimensions.

Surfaced lumber is that which has been dressed by passing it through a standard planing machine. It may be surfaced on one side (S1S), two sides (S2S), one edge (S1E), or combinations of side and edges (S1S1E), (S2S1E), etc.

[3] "Guide to the Grading of Structural Timbers and the Determination of Working Stresses," Miscellaneous Publication 185 of the U. S. Dept. Agriculture. See also, "Douglas Fir Use Book," published by West Coast Lumberman's Assoc.; "Wood Structural Design Data," publication of National Lumber Manufacturers' Assoc.; Specifications for Structural Timbers (1936), "American Ry. Engg. Assoc. Manual."

Standard nominal dimensions for rough and surfaced yard lumber and structural timbers are given in Tables 22, 23, and 24. Lumber is indicated by its nominal dimensions, and its quantity is determined in *board feet*. A board foot is a piece 1 inch thick by 12 inches wide by 1 foot long, and the number of board feet in any piece will be one-twelfth the product of its cross-sectional dimensions (in inches) with its length

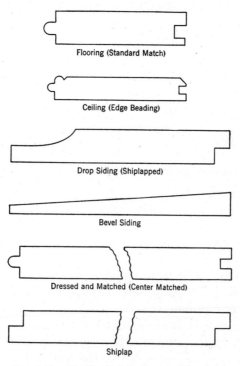

Flooring (Standard Match)

Ceiling (Edge Beading)

Drop Siding (Shiplapped)

Bevel Siding

Dressed and Matched (Center Matched)

Shiplap

Fig. 150.   Six Typical Patterns of Lumber.

(From "Wood Handbook," published by U. S. Dept. of Agriculture.)

(in feet).   Actual minimum dimensions must be used in computations for strength.   Lumber is cut to standard lengths, which are multiples of 2 feet, except for the following odd lengths which are allowed.

2×4, and 2×6	9 and 11 feet
2×8	9, 11, and 13 feet
2×10	13 and 15 feet
8×8, 10×10, and 12×12 14×14, 16×16, and 18×18	11 and 13 feet
6×6, 6×18, 8×16, and 8×18	15 and 17 feet

Worked lumber is that which has been run through a machine to produce a particular form of cross section and may be matched, shiplapped, or patterned. *Matched lumber* is edge dressed and shaped to make a close tongue and groove joint at the edges or ends when laid edge to edge or end to end. *Shiplapped lumber* is edge dressed to make a close rabbeted or lapped joint when laid edge to edge. *Patterned lumber* is worked lumber that is shaped to a pattern or mold form. Standard shapes of worked lumber may be obtained from various manufacturers' associations upon request. Typical forms of standard workings are shown in Fig. 150.

For more complete information relative to grades and sizes of lumber the reader is referred to the "Wood Handbook" published by the United States Department of Agriculture, the "Manual of the American Railway Engineering Association," and the publications of various lumber manufacturers' associations.

90   Working Stresses for Structural Timbers

Determination of a safe working stress for material of such variable qualities as wood requires consideration of many factors. Defects inherent in the material will, in accordance with their size and extent, tend to decrease its strength; conditions of exposure and particularly the presence of moisture will reduce further the capacity of the material to resist stress safely. The basis for determination of allowed working stress is the basic unit stress permissible on clear material under ideal or dry conditions of exposure; these are then reduced in accordance with effect of defects permissible in material of the given class and further reduced to allow for the effect of adverse conditions of exposure.[4] Allowable working stresses recommended by the National Lumber Manufacturers' Association are given in Table 25.

Limitation of defects in material of a given stress grade is in accordance with specification [5] standards; no material having defects in excess of these limitations is permitted in a given grade. For material continuously dry and covered, Table 25 indicates directly the safe working stress for such material, and the amount by which these stresses must be reduced,[6] or the size of timbers increased to allow for adverse condition of exposure, is dependent upon the judgment of the engineer.

[4] See Miscellaneous Publication 185, U. S. Dept. Agriculture.
[5] See Specifications for Structural Timbers, 1941, "American Railway Engg. Assoc.," Manual A.A.S.H.O. Standard Specifications for Highway Bridges, 1944.
[6] See Specifications for Structural Timbers, 1941, "A.R.E.A. Manual."

91 Wood Beams and Joists

The safe load-carrying capacity of a rectangular wood beam is determined by (1) the stress on the extreme fiber due to flexure; (2) the maximum horizontal shear stress; (3) the stress in compression across the grain at end bearings and under concentrated loads; and (4) the deflection permitted in the finished construction.

The stress f on the extreme fiber in flexure is obtained from the flexure formula for homogeneous beams, $f = Mc/I$, and

$$f = \frac{6M}{bh^2} = \frac{M}{S} \tag{130}$$

where h = depth of section (actual size).
  b = width of section (actual size).

$$S = \text{section modulus} = \frac{I}{\frac{1}{2}h} = \frac{2I}{h}.$$

Properties for designing rectangular timber sections are given in Table 26.

The total shear per inch of span length on any horizontal plane in a homogeneous beam is given by the equation

$$vb = \frac{VQ}{I} \qquad S_s = \frac{V\,\overline{q}A}{bI} \tag{131}$$

where V = change in bending-moment per inch of span at the given point in the span = total vertical shear at this point.
  I = moment of inertia of a vertical cross section taken at the given point in the span.
  Q = statical moment of that part of the cross section on one side of the horizontal plane with respect to the neutral axis.
  b = width of beam cut by the horizontal plane.
  v = intensity of shearing stress.

For a rectangular section, the intensity of horizontal shear stress at any depth y from the top of the beam (where $y \gtrless h/2$) is, therefore,

$$v = \frac{6Vy(h - y)}{bh^3} \tag{132}$$

For a rectangular section, Equation 132 indicates a parabolic variation of the intensity of shear stress from 0 at $y = 0$ to a maximum, when $y = h/2$, at the midpoint of the depth where

$$v = \frac{3V}{2bd} \tag{133}$$

For sections at the support, Equation 132 will produce results greatly in error, owing to the fact that timber checking will produce essentially a two-beam action,[7] and the reaction will be carried by the upper and lower parts of the beam acting as two independent beams. For such a condition, the following solution has been recommended:

(a) Use the equation

$$v = \frac{3R}{2bh} \tag{134}$$

where R = reaction in pounds.

(b) Use the customary allowable shear stress.

(c) In calculating the reaction for use in the formula:

(1) Take into account any relief to the beam as a result of load distribution to adjacent parallel beams by flooring or other parts of the construction;

(2) Neglect all loads within a distance equal to the height of beam from both supports;

(3) If there are moving loads, place the largest at a distance three times the height of the beam, from the support;

(4) Treat all other loads in the usual manner.

(d) If a timber does not qualify under the above recommendation, which under certain conditions may be overconservative, the reactions for the concentrated loads should be determined by the following equation:

$$R = \sum \frac{10P(L - a)\left(\frac{a}{h}\right)^2}{9L\left[2 + \left(\frac{a}{h}\right)^2\right]} \tag{135}$$

where P = any concentrated load on span.

L = span in inches.

a = distance from reaction to load P in inches.

h = height of beam in inches.

The intensity of bearing stress across the grain at the support is equal to the reaction divided by the bearing area. No account is taken of the fact that the intensity is higher at the edge of the support due to the

---

[7] "Wood Beam Design Method Promises Economies," by J. A. Newlin, G. E. Heck, and H. W. March, *Engg. News-Record*, May 11, 1933; "Shear in Checked Beams," by J. A. Newlin, *Bulletins of A.R.E.A.*, February, 1934; "Wood Handbook," U. S. Dept. Agriculture.

deflection of the beam. Similar computations apply to concentrated loads which may occur at intermediate points.

Deflection computations are made using formulae and methods applicable to homogeneous beams and a modulus of elasticity corresponding with the given quality and species of wood. Deflection limitations usually depend upon the usage of the completed structure. For plastered ceilings, deflection is usually limited to $\frac{1}{360}$ of the span. Wood beams acquire a permanent set or sag, under long-continued loading, which is approximately equal to the dead-load deflection using the modulus given in Table 25. In order to make allowance for this it is customary to double the dead load but not the live load in computing deflection.

Typical computations of critical stress in a wood-floor construction are shown in Fig. 151. The data given in Table 26 are useful in making such computations. The joist computations show that the maximum stresses are well within the safe capacity of the grade specified. The deflection, computed on the basis of twice the dead load plus the live load, is slightly in excess of the customary limit for plastered ceilings but not sufficiently so to require a change in the design. The beams are seen to be satisfactory as regards horizontal shear and bearing but will have excessive deflection. This condition cannot be corrected by specifying a higher grade timber and hence, to hold deflection to not more than $\frac{1}{360}$ of the span, the beam must be increased in size. Computation of a 10×12 beam will show a deflection of

$$\frac{165}{209} \times 0.56 = 0.45 \text{ inch} = \frac{L}{360}$$

and hence would be satisfactory in this respect. An 8×14 timber, having a still larger I, will give still less deflection.

Typical design computations are shown in Fig. 152. Such problems start with the assumption of the proposed layout and arrangement of members including estimated sizes. These assumptions are then revised as the design proceeds in case changes are necessary. It should be observed that many alternative arrangements and selections will be available, and the final design should select the best and most economical construction labor and material. It is frequently necessary to determine several possible arrangements and base the choice on estimates of cost. In the example shown in Fig. 152 no attempt has been made to select the most economical design. In the computation relating to the laminated floor it will be observed that the thickness used would permit a beam spacing of 5 feet. The 4-foot spacing chosen was selected because it would provide a regular and uniform spacing of beams with respect to the column centers. Further design study should be made for a $2\frac{1}{2}$-inch

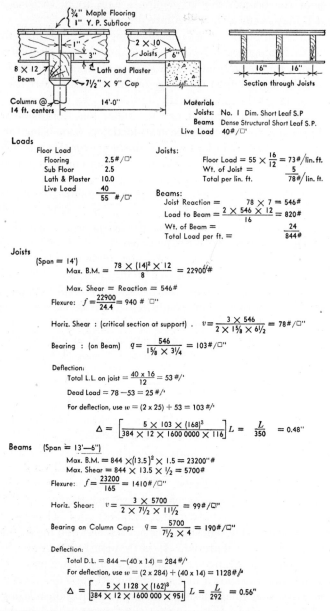

Loads

Floor Load		Joists:

Floor Load

Flooring	2.5 #/□'
Sub Floor	2.5
Lath & Plaster	10.0
Live Load	40
	55 #/□'

Joists:

Floor Load = $55 \times \dfrac{16}{12} = 73$ #/lin. ft.

Wt. of Joist = 5

Total per lin. ft. = 78 #/lin. ft.

Beams:

Joist Reaction = $78 \times 7 = 546$ #

Load to Beam = $\dfrac{2 \times 546 \times 12}{16} = 820$ #

Wt. of Beam = 24

Total Load per ft. = 844 #

Joists

(Span = 14')

Max. B.M. = $\dfrac{78 \times (14)^2 \times 12}{8} = 22900$ ''#

Max. Shear = Reaction = 546#

Flexure: $f = \dfrac{22900}{24.4} = 940$ # □''

Horiz. Shear : (critical section at support) . $v = \dfrac{3 \times 546}{2 \times 1\frac{5}{8} \times 6\frac{1}{2}} = 78$ #/□''

Bearing : (on Beam) $q = \dfrac{546}{1\frac{5}{8} \times 3\frac{1}{4}} = 103$ #/□''

Deflection:

Total L.L. on joist = $\dfrac{40 \times 16}{12} = 53$ #/'

Dead Load = $78 - 53 = 25$ #/'

For deflection, use $w = (2 \times 25) + 53 = 103$ #/'

$$\Delta = \left[\dfrac{5 \times 103 \times (168)^3}{384 \times 12 \times 1600\ 0000 \times 116}\right] L = \dfrac{L}{350} = 0.48''$$

Beams   (Span = 13'—6'')

Max. B.M. = $844 \times (13.5)^2 \times 1.5 = 23200$ ''#

Max. Shear = $844 \times 13.5 \times \frac{1}{2} = 5700$ #

Flexure: $f = \dfrac{23200}{165} = 1410$ #/□''

Horiz. Shear: $v = \dfrac{3 \times 5700}{2 \times 7\frac{1}{2} \times 11\frac{1}{2}} = 99$ #/□''

Bearing on Column Cap: $q = \dfrac{5700}{7\frac{1}{2} \times 4} = 190$ #/□''

Deflection:

Total D.L. = $844 - (40 \times 14) = 284$ #/'

For deflection, use $w = (2 \times 284) + (40 \times 14) = 1128$ #/'

$$\Delta = \left[\dfrac{5 \times 1128 \times (162)^3}{384 \times 12 \times 1600\ 000 \times 95}\right] L = \dfrac{L}{292} = 0.56''$$

FIG. 151.   Typical Stress Computations for Wood Floor Construction.

floor to determine if this could be used on the smaller span. If the deflection must be limited to $\frac{1}{360}$ of the span, an 8×14 size beam is required.

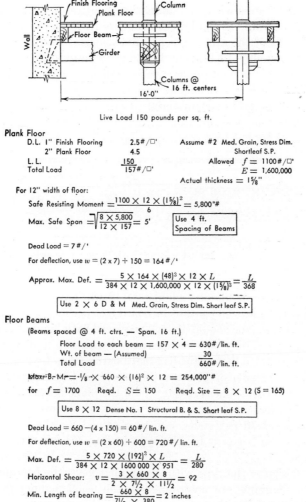

Live Load 150 pounds per sq. ft.

Plank Floor

D.L.	1" Finish Flooring	2.5#/□'	Assume #2 Med. Grain, Stress Dim.
	2" Plank Floor	4.5	Shortleaf S.P.
L. L.		150	Allowed $f = 1100\#/□'$
Total Load		157#/□'	$E = 1,600,000$
			Actual thickness $= 1\frac{5}{8}"$

For 12" width of floor:

Safe Resisting Moment $= \dfrac{1100 \times 12 \times (1\frac{5}{8})^2}{6} = 5,800\#$

Max. Safe Span $= \sqrt{\dfrac{8 \times 5,800}{12 \times 157}} = 5'$ | Use 4 ft. Spacing of Beams |

Dead Load $= 7 \#/'$

For deflection, use $w = (2 \times 7) + 150 = 164 \#/'$

Approx. Max. Def. $= \dfrac{5 \times 164 \times (48)^3 \times 12 \times L}{384 \times 12 \times 1,600,000 \times 12 \times (1\frac{5}{8})^3} = \dfrac{L}{368}$

| Use 2 × 6 D & M Med. Grain, Stress Dim. Short leaf S.P. |

Floor Beams

(Beams spaced @ 4 ft. ctrs. — Span. 16 ft.)

Floor Load to each beam $= 157 \times 4 = 630\#/$lin. ft.
Wt. of beam — (Assumed) $\underline{30}$
Total Load $660\#/$lin. ft.

Max. B. M. $= \frac{1}{8} \times 660 \times (16)^2 \times 12 = 254,000"\#$

for $f = 1700$ Reqd. $S = 150$ Reqd. Size $= 8 \times 12$ ($S = 165$)

| Use 8 × 12 Dense No. 1 Structural B. & S. Short leaf S.P. |

Dead Load $= 660 - (4 \times 150) = 60\#/$ lin. ft.

For deflection, use $w = (2 \times 60) + 600 = 720 \#/$ lin. ft.

Max. Def. $= \dfrac{5 \times 720 \times (192)^3 \times L}{384 \times 12 \times 1600\,000 \times 951} = \dfrac{L}{280}$

Horizontal Shear: $v = \dfrac{3 \times 660 \times 8}{2 \times 7\frac{1}{2} \times 11\frac{1}{2}} = 92$

Min. Length of bearing $= \dfrac{660 \times 8}{7\frac{1}{2} \times 380} = 2$ inches

Fɪɢ. 152. Typical Design Computations for a Timber Floor.

Tables published by various manufacturers' associations are useful in the design of timber beam and joist construction.[8]

[8] "Wood Structural Design Data," Natural Lumber Manufacturers' Assoc.; "Douglas Fir Use Book," West Coast Lumberman's Assoc.; "Maximum Spans for Joists and Rafters," Natural Lumber Manufacturers' Assoc.

92 Built-Up Beams and Girders

When solid timber of the required size is not available, wood beams and girders may be built up of smaller sections.

Laminated beams with the laminations vertical and bolted together were found in tests [9] at the Forest Products Laboratory to be as strong as solid beams of the same external dimensions. The pieces should be fastened thoroughly to prevent buckling of individual planks, and if spikes are used it is good practice to provide also some through bolts or bolts and connectors. It should be observed that a built-up beam of this type will contain more material (measured in board feet) than one of equivalent solid section; thus a solid 12×12 beam will have actual dimensions $11\frac{1}{2}$×$11\frac{1}{2}$ and contain 12 board feet per foot of length; an

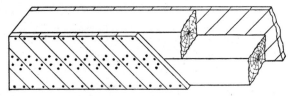

FIG. 153.   Built-Up Beam with Diagonal Boards.
(From "Wood Handbook," published by U. S. Dept. of Agriculture.)

equivalent section made of 7 planks 2×12 will have the actual dimensions $11\frac{3}{8}$×$11\frac{1}{2}$ and will contain 14 board feet per foot of length. Built-up beams of this type should always be placed with laminations vertical.

Built-up beams may also be constructed with two timbers placed one on the other and either with diagonal boards (Fig. 153) spiked to the sides of the timbers, or else the timbers should be bolted and keyed (Fig. 154) to provide shear resistance on the plane between the timbers. Tests [10] have indicated that, as compared with beams of solid section, an efficiency of 70 per cent may be obtained for the type shown in Fig. 153 and 80 per cent for the type in Fig. 154 when cast-iron keys are used.

In the design of the type with rectangular keys, the bending-moment and shear diagrams are determined in the usual manner for the prescribed loading. The designing moment is then found by dividing the maximum bending-moment by the assumed efficiency percentage (80 for cast-iron keys and 75 for white oak keys), and the theoretical size of required solid timber is determined in the usual way. Two equal tim-

[9] "Built-Up Southern Yellow Pine Timbers Tested for Strength," Natural Lumber Manufacturers' Assoc., Wood Construction Information Service, Ser. E2b.

[10] Tests by Edward Kidwell, *Trans. Am. Soc. Mining Engineers*, Vol. 27; "Resistance of Timber Joints," by Alvarez, *Engg. Record*, Vol. 70, No. 5.

bers are then selected whose actual dimension, when placed one on the other, will correspond with the theoretical size. The number and size of keys to be used are determined by trial. The forces acting on a key are shown in Fig. 155, and it will be noted that P_1 represents the total

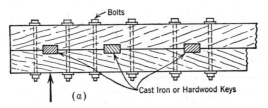

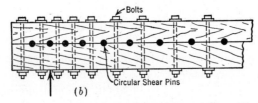

Fɪɢ. 154. Built-Up Beam with Keys or Shear-Pins.

horizontal shear over a length of beam corresponding to the spacing of keys; therefore

$$P_1 = \left(\frac{3V}{2h}\right) s \tag{136}$$

$$P_2 = \frac{3P_1 t}{4l} \tag{137}$$

where V = total vertical shear on beam section at center of key.
  h = overall depth of beam.
  s = spacing of keys.
  t = vertical thickness of key.
  l = length of key in direction of span of beam.
  b = breadth of beam.

$$f_1 = \frac{2P_1}{tb} = \text{compression unit stress on end of grain} \tag{138}$$

$$f_2 = \frac{4P_2}{lb} = \text{compressive stress normal to grain} \tag{139}$$

Bolts on either side of the key must be provided to resist the forces P_2 in tension. Consideration must also be given to the horizontal shear parallel to the grain of timber on the section between keys (Fig. 156).

The size and spacing of keys are adjusted until unit stresses are within prescribed limits for the materials. More complete information on the design of this type of construction may be found in various treatises [11] on timber designing.

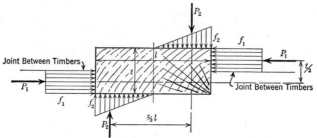

Fig. 155. Forces Acting on Rectangular Key.

Deflections in built-up beams are likely to be excessive unless great care is used in their construction. Deflections of beams of the type shown in Fig. 153 are reported to be about double those of solid beams of the same size. Special care must be employed in framing keyed beams to obtain tight keys, and only thoroughly seasoned timber should be

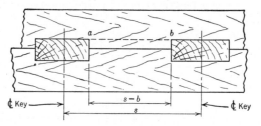

Fig. 156. Spacing of Rectangular Keys.

used. Keys are sometimes made in two parts and are tapered like wedges so that a driving fit may be obtained.

93 Trussed Beams

When spans are too great for a single timber section and the headroom permits, a *trussed beam* (Fig. 157) may be used.

In the approximate design of such a structure, joint loads are computed for joints A, C, D, and B as for a truss of like form and using center line dimensions. Stresses in the members of this truss are assumed to constitute the direct stress in the several parts of the assembly. A

---

[11] Henry D. Dewell, *Timber Framing*, Dewey Publishing Co., 1918; Hool and Johnson, "Handbook of Building Construction," McGraw-Hill Book Co., 1929.

metal rod is selected to resist the direct stress in members AD and DB, and a timber or metal post or strut is provided for the direct stress in member CD. The force on the post will equal two times the vertical component of the stress in the rod, and a saddle must be provided to distribute this over the bottom of the post. The bending moment in the beam is computed as if it were simply supported at A and B and a section selected using a reduced allowable stress to allow for the average direct stress from truss action. The foregoing computation for the beam assumes that it acts as two individual beams of length AC and CB,

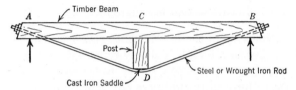

Fig. 157.   Trussed Timber Beam.

respectively; actually there will be some continuous action which will tend to increase the stiffness of the construction and reduce the unit stress. To take this into account, however, requires a solution using methods applicable to statically indeterminate structures.

94   Timber Columns—Axial Loads

Solid wood columns are classified into three groups: *short* columns, *intermediate* columns, and *long* columns. Short columns are those whose strength is dependent upon the crushing or compressive resistance of the material only. Intermediate columns are those of such proportion of length to cross section that resistance to both crushing and lateral buckling determines their strength. Long columns are those of relatively slender proportions whose strength depends almost entirely upon their resistance to lateral deflection or buckling.

It is customary to measure the slenderness of a rectangular timber column by the ratio of its length to its least transverse dimension, thus

$$L/d = \text{slenderness ratio}$$

where L = unsupported length in inches.

   d = dimension in inches normal to axis of bending.

It should be noted that L represents the length over which bending may occur. The *slenderness ratio* is an inverse measure of the resistance to lateral buckling; hence the maximum value of L/d for a given column should be used. This will usually be obtained when d represents the dimension of the least side.

Tests [12] made by the Forest Products Laboratory on Douglas fir and southern yellow pine timbers indicate that, when the slenderness ratio does not exceed 11, the strength of the column is measured entirely by the resistance of the material to compressive stress parallel to the grain. Thus

$$P = fA \qquad (140)$$

where P = safe total axial load on column.

f = allowed stress in compression parallel to grain for short columns (indicated by stress grade).

A = area of cross section in square inches.

For timber columns in the intermediate classification, the tests indicated that the law of strength is closely represented by a fourth power parabola which becomes tangent to the Euler curve at a point corresponding to two-thirds of the ultimate crushing strength. The equation of this parabola, known as the Forest Products Laboratory Fourth-Power Parabolic Formula, is as follows:

When

$$L/d > 11$$

$$< K$$

$$\frac{P}{A} = f\left[1 - \frac{1}{3}\left(\frac{L}{Kd}\right)^4\right] \qquad (141)$$

The value of K, which is the value of L/d corresponding to the point of tangency with the Euler curve, is obtained from the Euler formula (Equation 143) as follows:

Let $f = \frac{1}{3}$ of ultimate crushing strength.
Then, when

$$\frac{P}{A} = \frac{2}{3} \times 3f = 2f$$

$$K = \frac{L}{d} = \frac{\pi}{2}\sqrt{\frac{E}{6f}} \qquad (142)$$

The value of K is thus seen to be a constant for any species and grade of timber.

Long columns are those where the value of L/d equals or exceeds the value of K as expressed in Equation 142. When $L/d = K$, the allowable axial unit stress in the column section is $P/A = \frac{2}{3}f$. The Timber

[12] Technical Bulletin 167, U. S. Dept. Agriculture.

Products Laboratory found that within the elastic limit of the material the best interpretation of the behavior of long columns is the Euler formula.

$$f = \frac{P}{A} = \frac{\pi^2 E}{\left(\dfrac{L}{r}\right)^2} = \frac{\pi^2 E}{12\left(\dfrac{L}{d}\right)^2} \tag{143}$$

Based on a safety factor of 3 and with pin ends assumed, the safe axial load as determined by this formula is as follows:

$$P = \left[\frac{0.274E}{\left(\dfrac{L}{d}\right)^2}\right] A \tag{144}$$

It is generally recommended that no column be used in structural work with a slenderness ratio in excess of 50. The majority of columns used in actual construction are included in the short and intermediate classes. Design Chart V can be used for obtaining values of the allowed unit stress on the column, based on Equation 141.

Round columns will carry the same loads in both bending and compression [13] as square columns of the same sectional area. The procedure in the design of a round column is first to obtain the size required for a square column and then to use a diameter of round column which will give the same sectional area, thus

$$D = \frac{2d}{\sqrt{\pi}} \tag{145}$$

where D = required diameter (actual) of round column.

d = required side (actual) of square column.

For tapered round columns the diameter should be measured at a section one-third of the column length from the small end, and the stress on the small end must not exceed that permitted on a short column.

95 Timber Columns—Bending and Direct Stress

Columns are sometimes subjected to lateral loads or known eccentricities of longitudinal loading which produce determinable bending-moments and corresponding stresses in addition to those incident to column action. It should be observed that this additional bending

[13] Newlin and Grayer, "The Influence of the Form of a Wooden Beam on Its Stiffness and Strength," National Advisory Committee for Aeronautics; Annual Reprint 9, Technical Report 181, pp. 377–393; Annual Report 10, Technical Report 188, pp. 95–105.

action imposed on the column will tend to emphasize its tendency to buckle laterally under the axial or direct load, and the column will therefore be more critical in its behavior. Neglecting the secondary bending-moment induced by the lateral deflection, the fiber stress on the extreme fiber of the column section will be given by the equation

$$ f = \frac{P}{A} \pm \frac{Md}{2I} \tag{146} $$

where P = longitudinal or axial load.

   A = area of cross section.

   M = bending-moment at the midlength of column.

   d = dimension of section normal to axis of bending (diameter of round column).

   I = moment of inertia of section.

(Note that the bending stress given by the second term will be tension on one side and compression on the other side of the section.)

There appears to be no uniformity of opinion as to what unit stress should be permitted on columns subject to such action. It is considered conservative practice to limit the value of the unit stress as obtained from Equation 146 to the value obtained for P/A in Equation 141 or 144.

96   Timber Tension Members

Timber is rarely used for tension members, as better and cheaper construction usually can be obtained by using structural steel shapes or rods. When wood members are designed for tension, the details of connections will usually control the design. Tensile stress computations are made on the basis of the net section of timber obtained by deducting the area removed from the gross section by bolt holes and cuts necessary for the connection of the end of the member, or for splicing. Allowable working stresses in tension are taken as the same values as allowed for flexural stress on the extreme fiber.

97   Timber Trusses

Since a truss is in general an assemblage of tension and compression members, the design of the individual members embodies the principles and methods which have previously been stated. The determination of joint details involves the exercise of ingenuity and understanding of the mechanics involved and an appreciation of the limitations of workmanship. Typical joint details for timber roof trusses are shown in Fig. 158. A typical truss assembly is shown in Fig. 159. For further details the reader is referred to standard textbooks on timber design.

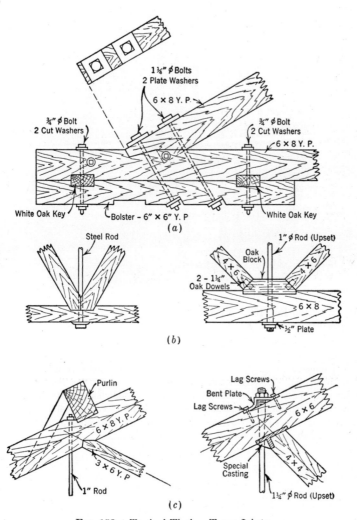

Fig. 158. Typical Timber Truss Joints.

Fig. 159.   Typical Timber Truss Construction.

PROBLEMS

9·1   The elements of the wood beam shown are fastened together by nails driven at 2-in. intervals.   Determine the maximum shear and the maximum bending-moment that the section can safely resist if the following conditions are imposed: (a) Maximum tensile or compressive stresses shall not exceed 1400 psi.   (b) Maximum shearing stress shall not exceed 200 psi.   (c) Maximum horizontal shearing force on one nail shall not exceed 400 lb.

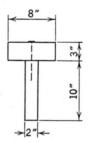

9·2   (a) A 3-in. ×12-in. wood joist (actual size $2\frac{3}{4} \times 11\frac{1}{2}$) of 12-ft span, simply supported, must carry a uniform dead load of 200 lb per ft (including its own weight) and a concentrated movable live load, P.   What is the maximum safe value of P

for the following allowable unit stresses: tension and compression 1600 psi and horizontal shear 140 psi? (*b*) Check deflection conditions to see whether maximum deflection is more than $\frac{1}{360}$ of the span.

9·3 Find the depth of the Douglas fir beam required to support the traveling hoist shown. Check shear stress. Dead load = 25 lb per linear ft including the track. Use Paragraph 218a grade Douglas fir, Coast Region.

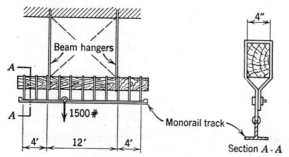

9·4 A timber beam 12 in. × 20 in. in cross section is formed from two 10-in. × 12-in. sections by passing the horizontal shear through hardwood keys whose horizontal resistance H = 5000 lb. If the beam is subjected to two concentrated loads, P, as

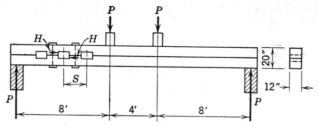

shown, what spacing S of the horizontal keys is required to develop a maximum normal fiber stress due to bending of 1600 psi? Base calculation on sizes given and neglect dead weight of beam.

9·5 Nails and friction between the two elements of the timber beam shown can develop a horizontal shear of 40 psi. The allowable extreme fiber stress in tension

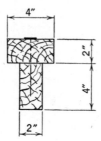

or compression is 1000 psi. Neglecting the weight of the beam, calculate the maximum allowable concentrated load which the beam will carry at the center of (*a*) an 8-ft span, and (*b*) a 6-ft span.

9·6 A timber beam is to be designed to carry a total uniform load (includes weight of beam) of 2500 lb per ft over a simple span of 20 ft. It has been decided to use longleaf southern pine, of Select Structural grade (B and S). Determine the minimum standard size timber required and the length of bearing at the ends.

9·7 A timber beam, 3 in. ×14. in nominal size, carries a total uniform load of 175 lb per linear ft over a simple span of 20 ft. The allowable stresses are: in bending, 1800 psi; in shear, 150 psi; in bearing on support, 350 psi; and deflection, $\frac{1}{360}$ of span. Is the beam safe?

9·8 A square timber column 24 ft long is required to carry an axial load of 90,000 lb. Using No. 1 Structural, P and T, long-leaf southern pine, what size timber is required?

9·9 Find the maximum load P which can be raised by the boom under its worst condition of operation. Assume that the lines of force are concurrent at a point 20 ft from the bottom pin. Assume that all pulleys are frictionless.

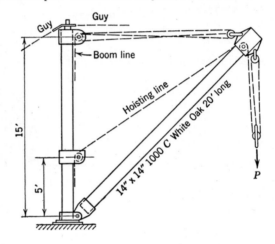

Chapter 10

STEEL TENSION MEMBERS, COLUMNS, BEAMS, AND GIRDERS

98 Physical and Chemical Properties of Steel

Steel is manufactured from scrap and pig iron in either an open-hearth furnace, a Bessemer converter, or an electric furnace. Practically all steel intended for structural use is made by either the open-hearth or the Bessemer methods. Open-hearth steel is generally preferred to the Bessemer, as the method of manufacturing affords better control of such injurious elements as phosphorus and sulphur. The electric furnace is used in making alloy steels. Steel is also generally classified as *carbon steel* or *alloy steel*. Carbon steel is steel which owes its distinctive properties to the carbon rather than to the other elements which it contains. Alloy steel is steel which owes its particular qualities to some element or elements other than carbon.

Practically all steel used in general construction is carbon steel, which is further divided into three classes or grades, *structural grade*,[1] *intermediate grade*,[2] and *hard grade*. The carbon content of structural grade steel is generally less than 0.25 per cent, for intermediate grade 0.25 to 0.50 per cent, and for the hard grade more than 0.50 per cent. Increasing the carbon content tends to increase the tensile strength, hardness, and brittleness and to decrease the ductility.

The specifications of the American Society for Testing Materials require that steel intended for bridges or buildings [3] shall be made by either or both the open-hearth or electric-furnace processes, except that steel for plates and sections $\frac{7}{16}$ in. and under in thickness, intended for use in buildings and other structures subject to static loads only, may be

---

[1] Also referred to as *soft* or *mild* steel.

[2] Also referred to as *medium* steel.

[3] Standard Specifications for Steel for Bridges and Buildings, A.S.T.M., Serial Designation A7–39.

made by the acid-Bessemer process. These specifications also limit the chemical composition of such steel as follows:

Phosphorus, maximum percentage
    Open hearth or electric furnace
        Acid   0.06
        Basic   0.04
        Acid Bessemer   0.10
Sulphur, maximum percentage (open hearth or electric
    furnace)   0.05
Copper, when copper steel is specified, minimum per-
    centage   0.20

Specified Physical Properties of Steel for Bridges and Buildings, Structural Rivet Steel, and Structural Silicon Steel, according to Standard A.S.T.M. Specifications, are given in Table 27.

The A.S.T.M. Specifications [4] require that structural silicon steel be made by either or both the open hearth or the electric furnace. The chemical composition of such steel is limited as follows:

	Ladle Analysis	Check Analysis
Carbon, maximum percentage	0.40	0.44
Phosphorus, maximum percentage		
Acid	0.06	0.075
Basic	0.04	0.05
Sulphur, maximum percentage	0.05	0.063
Silicon, minimum percentage	0.20	0.18

For structural rivet steel, the A.S.T.M. Specifications [5] require that it be made by either or both the open-hearth or electric-furnace processes. The chemical composition is limited in the same amounts as specified for steel intended for bridges and buildings. The physical properties specified are also given in Table 30.

A small percentage of copper is sometimes added to structural steel to increase its resistance to corrosion.[6] Such material is known as

---

[4] Standard Specifications for Structural Silicon Steel, A.S.T.M., Serial Designation A 94–39.

[5] Standard Specifications for Structural Rivet Steel, A.S.T.M., Serial Designation A 141–39.

[6] "Copper in Steel, Its Influence on Corrosion," by D. M. Buck, *J. of Ind. Engg. Chem.*, 1913, p. 447; "Symposium on the Outdoor Weathering of Metals and Metallic Coatings," *Proceedings A.S.T.M.*, March 7, 1934; "A Critical Study of the A.S.T.M Corrosion Data on Uncoated Commercial Iron and Steel Sheets," *Proceedings*

copper steel or *copper bearing steel*. Its principal use is for steel structures serving under extreme conditions of exposure and where the construction will be inaccessible after erection. The addition of less than 2 per cent of copper does not materially change the physical properties of the steel as regards its strength and elastic behavior.

Alloy steels are seldom used in ordinary structural work since their higher cost renders such use uneconomical. For structures of great magnitude, where dead weight plays an important part, and for other situations where high strength is necessary, such steels may be desirable.[7] The alloy steels most frequently used in such structures are silicon steel [8] and nickel steel.

The physical properties of steel which are of primary concern to the engineer engaged in the design of a steel structure are its strength in tension, compression or shear, its elasticity, and its ductility. As noted in Table 27, structural steel used in bridge and building construction has a yield point strength in tension of not less than 33,000 pounds per square inch. Within this unit-stress limit, the material has almost perfect elasticity, that is, the ability to regain its original form when the stress is released. For unit stresses less than the yield point (proportional limit), the material obeys Hooke's law, and the ratio of unit stress to corresponding unit strain (elongation in inches per inch) is constant. This ratio measures the elasticity of the material or *modulus of elasticity* and is denoted by the symbol E. The value of E for all types of steel varies within relatively narrow limits and is usually taken at 29,500,000 pounds per square inch. Comparative stress-strain curves for several types of steel and other metals are shown in Fig. 160. It will be noted that, for unit stress beyond the proportional limit, the value of E has no significance since the material no longer follows Hooke's law and, when stressed beyond the yield point it will retain a permanent deformation or set. Compression and shear behavior are similar to tensile behavior for stresses within the magnitude of the proportional limit in tension. Ductility of the material used for structures is an important quality since it measures the ability of the material to adjust itself to changes in form, without rupture. Local stress concentrations which have a magnitude beyond the elastic limit will cause the material to flow away

---

A.S.T.M., 1929; British Iron and Steel Institute, Report of the Corrosion Committee, First Report, 1931, Second Report, 1934; "Durability of Light Weight Steel Construction," J. H. Cissel, and W. E. Quinsey, University of Michigan, *Engineering Research Bulletin* 30, 1942.

[7] See "Structural Application of Steel and Light Weight Alloys, A Symposium," *Transactions Am. Soc. C. E.*, 1937, p. 1179.

[8] See American Society for Testing Materials Standards, A94–36.

from such points of concentration, and with ductile material this may be accomplished, to a limited degree, without destruction of the parts.

Fatigue strength is not as a rule important in structures such as buildings and bridges since maximum load conditions are not frequently

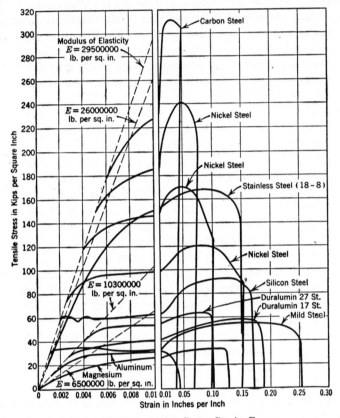

Fig. 160.   Comparative Stress-Strain Curves.

(From "Modern Stress Theories," by A. V. Karpov, *Trans. Am. Soc. Civ. Eng.*, 1937, p. 1192.)

repeated. Fatigue properties must of course be considered when a structural element must resist frequent applications of loadings as in machinery or movable structures.

Working stresses are determined from a consideration of the elastic limit and ultimate strength of the material, the refinements possible in the calculation of stresses, and the probability of load combinations producing maximum effects, with allowance of reasonable margins or factors of safety to provide for errors in assumptions, calculations, and construction.

99   Rolled-Steel Structural Sections

For use in construction, structural steel is rolled into *shapes, plates,* and *bars.* Shapes are made by passing steel ingots through rolls which squeeze the metal into the desired form. Shapes most commonly used in structures, illustrated in Fig. 161, are called wide-flange sections, I-beams, channels, angles, zees, tees, etc. The American Institute of Steel Construction publishes a manual [9] containing data on steel shapes

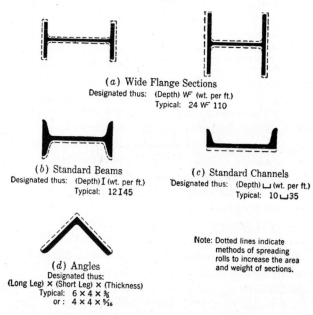

(*a*) Wide Flange Sections
Designated thus: (Depth) W⁻ (wt. per ft.)
Typical: 24 W⁻ 110

(*b*) Standard Beams
Designated thus: (Depth) I (wt. per ft.)
Typical: 12 I 45

(*c*) Standard Channels
Designated thus: (Depth) ⊔ (wt. per ft.)
Typical: 10 ⊔ 35

(*d*) Angles
Designated thus:
(Long Leg) × (Short Leg) × (Thickness)
Typical: 6 × 4 × ⅜
or :   4 × 4 × 5⁄16

Note: Dotted lines indicate methods of spreading rolls to increase the area and weight of sections.

Fig. 161.   Typical Rolled-Steel Sections.

and plates indispensable to the user of such steel products. This manual also contains other data and information of value to engineers. Tables 28 to 34 inclusive have been extracted from this manual with the permission of the Institute.

Wide-flange sections, American standard I-beams, and American standard channels are the section types most commonly employed for ordinary beam construction. Other shapes may be used for special purposes. For example, angles may be employed as lintels over windows or door openings, and zees may be used for purlins or girts in light steel framing.

[9] Obtainable from the American Institute of Steel Construction at a nominal charge.

100   Structural-Steel Tension Members

Steel may be fashioned into a variety of forms for use in carrying tensile stress. The nature and purpose of the construction and requirements to be met in fastening the member to adjacent construction will determine the most suitable form. To avoid undesirable stress concentrations and to insure uniform stress distribution over the sections of a tension member, it is preferable to provide as compact a section as possible. Since the strength is controlled by the area of the net section, the design of the connection will generally determine the arrangement and dimensions of the member.

The simplest form of tension member is a round or square bar. When threaded at the ends to provide attachment to adjacent construction, the area of cross section at the root of the thread constitutes the net area available to resist tension, and the ends are sometimes upset so that the area at the root of the thread is the same as that of the main body of the bar. Standard clevises are available to fit the threaded end of the bar and thus transfer the force to pins passing through the holes provided in the clevis. *Loop rods* are formed by bending and forging one end into a loop which can engage a pin connection. Bars to be used with a clevis and also loop rods are usually made in two sections with a turnbuckle which may be adjusted to tighten the member after it is in place. Standard dimensions and details of plain and upset screw ends, clevises, and loop rods may be obtained from the "Steel Manual." Members of this type are most frequently used in temporary construction, for bracing and tie rods, and in small roof trusses.

Eye-bars are relatively thick plates with heads forged on each end and the heads drilled to provide for a pin connection. They are principally used in pin-connected trusses of relatively large size. In large work, eye-bars are frequently made of alloy steel or are specially heat-treated to provide high strength. Standard dimensions for eye-bar heads are given in the "Steel Manual."

Rolled-steel angles are frequently used for carrying tension stresses in riveted trusses and similar construction. They may be used singly or in pairs and are fastened at their ends by rivets or bolts to gusset plates which form a common connector for all members meeting at a joint. When used in pairs, angles are usually fastened together by stitch rivets at intervals of 2 or 3 feet. In using angles for tension members, difficulty is encountered in providing a concentric connection and a uniform distribution of stress over the entire cross section of the angle. Usually the angle is connected to the gusset plate by rivets in one leg only, thus developing eccentricity and producing stress concentration in the attached leg. For this reason, the American Railway Engineering

Association specifications [10] for railway bridges require that, when angles are connected on one side to a gusset plate, the effective section shall be the net section of the connected leg plus one-half the section of the unconnected leg. Therefore, unequal leg angles with the longer leg contacting the gusset plate are generally preferred.

Built-up sections consisting of plates and angles or other rolled sections may also be employed as tension members where such use is eco-

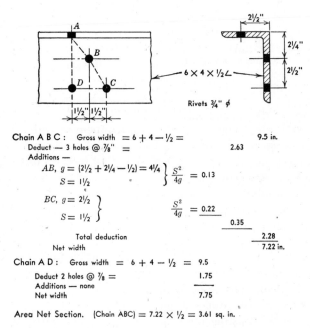

Chain A B C : Gross width $= 6 + 4 - \frac{1}{2} =$ 9.5 in.
Deduct — 3 holes @ $\frac{7}{8}$" $=$ 2.63
Additions —

$AB,\ g = (2\frac{1}{2} + 2\frac{1}{4} - \frac{1}{2}) = 4\frac{1}{4}$ } $\dfrac{S^2}{4g} = 0.13$
$S = 1\frac{1}{2}$

$BC,\ g = 2\frac{1}{2}$ } $\dfrac{S^2}{4g} = 0.22$
$S = 1\frac{1}{2}$ 0.35

       Total deduction   2.28
       Net width   7.22 in.

Chain A D : Gross width $= 6 + 4 - \frac{1}{2} =$ 9.5
Deduct 2 holes @ $\frac{7}{8} =$ 1.75
Additions — none
Net width   7.75

Area Net Section. (Chain ABC) $= 7.22 \times \frac{1}{2} = 3.61$ sq. in.

Fig. 162. Determination of Net Section.

nomic or otherwise desirable. In the design of such members, consideration must be given to the reduction in section by the holes required for the rivets used to fasten the parts together. Standard rules for determining the net section of a riveted tension member are as follows:

(*a*) The net section of a built-up riveted tension member is obtained by adding the net section of the parts composing the member.

(*b*) The net section of any part is the product of its thickness and its least net width.

(*c*) The gross width of a part is the width of a right section. The net width is obtained from the gross width by deducting the sum of diame-

[10] A.R.E.A. Specifications (1944) for Steel Railway Bridges.

ters of all rivet holes in any chain across the section and adding for
each gage space in such chain the quantity

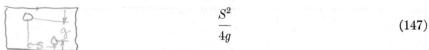

$$\frac{S^2}{4g} \tag{147}$$

where S = pitch of any two successive holes in the chain.

g = gage of the same holes.

(*d*) The gross width of an angle is the sum of the widths of the legs
less the thickness. For holes in opposite legs, the gage is considered to
be the sum of the gages from the back of the angle less the thickness.
A typical example of the application of the foregoing rules is given in
Fig. 162.

101   Steel Columns—Safe Axial Loading

A member is said to be *axially loaded* when the resultant of the applied
external loading acts in the direction of the longitudinal axis of the
member and passes through the centroid of all sections of the member.
Under such an ideal condition, no bending could occur on any section
and all parts would be subject to purely compressive stress. It is, however, physically impossible to apply external loading with such theoretical accuracy; moreover, the variations in straightness of the elements of
the column, inaccuracies in cross-sectional dimensions, variation in the
material and other factors will produce unintentional eccentricities with
the result that bending-moments will actually develop, and the member
will deflect accordingly. If unbraced against lateral deflection, the
column must resist the resultant tendency to deflect through the development of internal resisting stresses which will combine with the axial
stresses. For relatively short heavy sections, the magnitude of such
deflection as may be induced by bending is relatively small, and the
strength of the column will be limited by the compressive resistance or
crushing strength of the material. For extremely long slender columns
which have small resistance to bending, the lack of stiffness may permit comparatively large lateral deflections with correspondingly high
flexural stresses so that the ultimate failure of the column would be the
result of flexural action instead of crushing of the material. Between
these two extremes lies a range of conditions wherein failure may be due
to a combination of crushing and flexural action and the determination of
safe load requires an accurate appraisal of the probable magnitudes of
these actions.

In accordance with the foregoing conception of column behavior and
to provide a convenient classification for column analysis and design,

columns are classified in three groups, *short* columns, *intermediate* columns, and *long* columns. Short columns include those whose proportions are such that their load capacity is dependent solely upon the crushing resistance of the material. Intermediate columns are those whose safe capacity depends upon a combination of crushing and bending resistance. Long columns are those whose capacity depends almost entirely upon their resistance to bending.

The comparative stiffness of a column is measured by its slenderness ratio, which for steel columns is defined as the ratio of the unsupported length to the radius of gyration of the column section; hence

$$L/r = \text{slenderness ratio}$$

where L = unsupported length of column or length over which bending
        must be resisted by the column section.
    r = radius of gyration of cross section = $\sqrt{I/A}$.
    I = moment of inertia of cross section.
    A = area of cross section.

In computing the value of L/r, such axis of the cross section is chosen as will produce the maximum value of this ratio and r is therefore usually the *least* radius of gyration of the section. Approximate limiting values of the slenderness ratio which define the three classes of columns are as follows:

    Short columns $L/r = 0$ to 40

    Intermediate columns $L/r = 40$ to 170

    Long columns $L/r = $ greater than 170

The axial load which will produce failure of a long column is expressed by the Euler [11] formula as follows:

Columns with pin ends $P = fA = \dfrac{\pi^2 EA}{(L/r)^2}$ (148)

Columns with fixed ends $P = fA = \dfrac{4\pi^2 EA}{(L/r)^2}$ (149)

where A = area of cross section.
    f = average unit stress on section.
    E = modulus of elasticity.
    L/r = slenderness ratio.

It should be noted that the Euler formula is applicable only to stresses within the elastic limit of the material. Therefore, since the elastic

[11] For derivation, see any standard text on strength of materials.

limit stress and modulus of elasticity of structural steel are about 33,000 and 29,000,000 pounds per square inch, respectively, Equation 148 is not applicable to steel sections whose L/r ratio is less than 93 since, for smaller values, a breaking unit stress greater than the elastic limit would be indicated. The Euler formula takes no account of the crushing strength of the material and will therefore give inaccurate values of the breaking strength of the column when L/r is less than a value of about 170. When used for columns having an L/r greater than about 170, tests indicate that the Euler formula accurately determines the breaking strength. Safe working strengths for long columns can therefore be obtained by dividing the value of f as given by the Euler formula by a suitable factor of safety, usually not less than 2.

The theoretical expression or formula which at present appears to best represent the behavior of columns in the *intermediate* and *short* classifications is the so-called secant formula,[12]

$$f = \frac{P}{A}\left[1 + \frac{ec}{r^2}\sec\left(\frac{L}{2r}\sqrt{\frac{P}{EA}}\right)\right] \tag{150}$$

where P = load on column (parallel to longitudinal axis of column).

A = area of cross section.

e = eccentricity of load P from the neutral axis of the column section at the ends of the column.

c = distance from neutral axis of section to extreme fiber.

r = radius of gyration of column section.

L = unsupported length of column.

E = modulus of elasticity of material.

f = maximum compressive unit stress developed on the section.

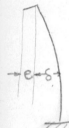

In the derivation of Equation 150, the load P is assumed to have a small, even if unintended, eccentricity, and the final unit stress on the extreme fiber is computed as the sum of the average direct stress P/A and the stress due to a bending-moment $P(e + \Delta)$, where Δ is the resultant final deflection of the column. Equation 150 expresses the sum of these unit stresses. It should also be noted that the term $L/2r\sqrt{(P/EA)}$ is expressed in radians (one radian = 57.2958 degrees). The term ec/r^2 is a constant for a given cross section and can be used as a measure of the actual or unintentional eccentricity of axial loading, crookedness of the column, and other conditions which may promote lateral deflection. In

---

[12] For complete derivation, the reader is referred to current textbooks on strength of materials; also *Proceedings Am. Soc. C. E.*, February, 1929, p. 416; also *Transactions Am. Soc. C. E.*, 1936, pp. 422–500, for discussions of column theories.

the Final Report of the Steel Column Research Committee of the American Society of Civil Engineers,[13] a value of $ec/r^2 = 0.25$ is recommended as a rational allowance for this term. This committee also proposed the following general formula for the working stress to be used for all classes of steel columns:

$$p = \frac{\dfrac{S_y}{m}}{1 + a \sec\left[\dfrac{l'}{2r}\sqrt{\dfrac{pm}{E}}\right]}$$ (151)

where p = working stress.
S_y = yield point of material.
m = factor of safety.
a = eccentric ratio assumed.
l' = assumed free length of column.

In addition to recommending that the eccentric ratio be taken equal to 0.25, the committee proposed that for riveted-connected members, as in the case of compression members in riveted trusses, the value of l' be

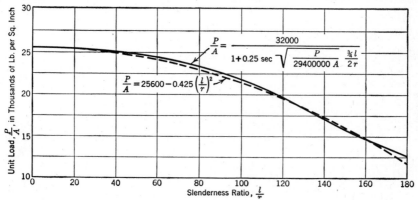

Fig. 163.   Comparison of Secant and Parabolic Formulas for $\dfrac{ec}{r^2} = 0.25$.

(From Final Report of Special Committee on Steel Column Research, *Trans. A. S. C. E.*, 1933, p. 1455.)

taken as three-fourths the full length of member. In view of objections to the secant formula on the grounds of its complexity for practical use, the studies of the committee showed that a formula of the parabolic type gave practically the same values as the secant formula for all values

[13] *Transactions Am. Soc. C. E.*, 1933, pp. 1376–1462.

of L/r up to 160 (Fig. 163). In view of this fact, the following formulae were proposed:

Members with riveted ends	$p = 15,000 - \frac{1}{4}(L/r)^2$	(152)
Members with pin ends	$p = 15,000 - \frac{1}{3}(L/r)^2$	(153)

These formulae provide a factor of safety of about 1.7 when results are
compared with those obtained from Equation 151 using $S_y = 32,000$,
$a = 0.25$, and $l' = \frac{3}{4}L$.

The A.A.S.H.O. Specifications (1944) for highway bridges and the
A.R.E.A. Specifications (1944) for steel railway bridges require the use
of Equations 152 and 153 for designing compression members up to
values of $L/r = 140$. For larger values of L/r, the A.R.E.A. Specifications require the use of Equation 151 with the following values:

$$S_y = 33,000 \text{ for structural steel}$$

$$= 45,000 \text{ for silicon steel}$$

$$= 50,000 \text{ for nickel steel}$$

$$m = 1.76 \text{ for structural steel}$$

$$= 1.80 \text{ for silicon steel}$$

$$= 1.78 \text{ for nickel steel}$$

$$a = 0.25$$

$$l' = \frac{3}{4}L \text{ for riveted ends}$$

$$= \frac{7}{8}L \text{ for pin ends}$$

$$E = 29,400,000$$

For practical use with columns of structural-grade steel, Equation 151
can be more conveniently arranged as follows:

$$p = \frac{18,700}{[1 + \frac{1}{4}K]} \qquad (154)$$

where $K = \sec (0.007L/r.\sqrt{p})$(in degrees)   (155)
$L = \frac{3}{4}$ total length for riveted ends.
$\quad = \frac{7}{8}$ total length for pin ends.

The value of p can be obtained from Equation 155 by successive approximations, and the chart given in Fig. 164 is useful in estimating values of $(\frac{1}{4}K)$ for substitutions in the formula. Note that, since p must not

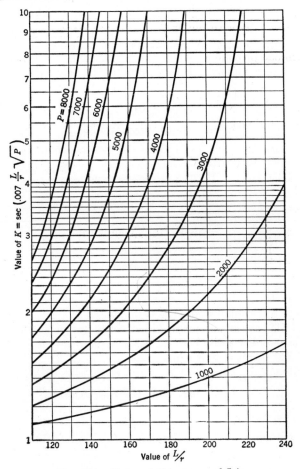

FIG. 164. Value of K in terms of L/r.

exceed $33{,}000/m = 18{,}700$, the value of $\frac{1}{4}K$ must always be positive; hence the formula can be used only when

$$0.007 \frac{L}{r} \sqrt{p} < 90 \tag{156}$$

The A.I.S.C. Specifications (1946) for steel buildings require the following formulae for determining the working stress on the gross section of steel columns.

For axially loaded columns

L/r not greater than 120	$p = 17,000 - 0.485(L/r)^2$	(157)
L/r greater than 120	$p = \dfrac{18,000}{1 + \dfrac{1}{18,000}(L/r)^2}$	(158)

Examples of computations to determine the safe load on a compression member are as follows:

Example 1

Determine the safe axial load on the following column:

Column section 10 × 10 wide-flange rolled section 60 lb per ft.
Unsupported length 12 ft.
From Table 28, $A = 17.66$ sq in., least $r = 2.57$ in.

$$L/r = \frac{144}{2.57} = 56 \quad \text{and} \quad (L/r)^2 = 3136$$

A.I.S.C. Specifications (Equation 157), safe $p = 17,000 - (0.485 \times 3136)$
$$= 15,480 \text{ psi.}$$
Safe axial load $= 15,480 \times 17.66 = 273,000$ lb

Example 2

A 4 × 4 × $\frac{3}{8}$ structural-steel angle is to be used as a column to carry axial loading and will have an unsupported length of 10 ft, 6 in. Determine the safe axial load in accordance with both the A.I.S.C. and A.R.E.A. Specifications.

Unsupported length $= 10$ ft 6 in. $= 126$ in.
Least r (from Table 33) $= 0.79$ in., $A = 2.86$ sq in.

$$L/r = 160 \quad \text{and} \quad (L/r)^2 = 25,600$$

A.I.S.C. Specifications:

Allowed unit stress (Equation 158) $= \dfrac{18,000}{1 + \dfrac{25,600}{18,000}} = 7420$ psi

Safe axial load $= 7420 \times 2.86 = 21,200$ lb

A.R.E.A. Specifications:

$L/r = 160 > 140$ (use Equation 151 modified as shown by Equation 154)

Try $p = 5000$

From Fig. 164,
$$K = 5.5$$

$$p = \frac{18,700}{2.37} = 7900$$

Since the computed value of p does not agree with the assumed value, further trials must be made.

$$\text{Try } p = 5500,$$

$$K = 8$$

$$p = \frac{18,700}{3} = 6200$$

$$\text{Try } p = 5700,$$

$$K = 9$$

$$p = \frac{18,700}{3.25} = 5750$$

Therefore, since the assumed and computed values of p are in substantial agreement, the allowable $p = 5750$ psi and safe axial load $= 5750 \times 2.86 = 16,500$ lb.

102   Shear in Built-Up Steel Columns

Built-up columns are composed of shapes and plates so fastened together that the composite section may be considered to act as a unit. Unless the fastening is adequate, the strength of the column will be merely the sum of the column strengths of the individual parts used in its make-up. The bending or buckling of the column under axial loading induces shearing forces [14] which tend to separate the elements making up the section. For solid column sections, such as H-beams, these shear stresses are of neglibile magnitude, but built-up columns must be designed to resist such stresses.

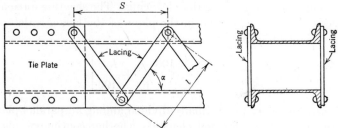

Fig. 165.   Lacing for Steel Columns.

The A.I.S.C. Specifications (1946) for steel buildings require *lacing bars* to be placed on the open sides of all compression members with *tie* or *batten plates* at each end of the member and at intermediate points if lacing is interrupted (Fig. 165). The spacing of lacing bars should be

[14] For a more complete discussion, see "Rational Design of Steel Columns," by Young, *Transactions Am. Soc. C. E.*, 1936, p. 440.

such that the L/r ratio of the flange between connections is not more than three-fourths that of the member as a whole, and the inclination to the axis of the member should be not less than 45 degrees for double lacing and 60 degrees for single lacing. These specifications require further that the lacing be proportioned to resist a shearing stress, normal to the axis of the member, equal to 2 per cent of the total compressive stress in the member. The lacing acts as a truss in resisting this total shear, and the force in an individual bar is therefore given by the following expression:

$$F = \frac{1}{N} [0.02P \sec (90 - \alpha)] \qquad (159)$$

where F = force in lacing bar (compression).
$\quad\quad P$ = axial column load.
$\quad\quad \alpha$ = inclination of bar to axis of member.
$\quad\quad N$ = number of planes of lacing.

The bar is designed as a column to resist the axial force F, and the L/r of the bar is limited to a maximum of 140 for single lacing and 200 for double lacing. For further details, the reader should consult the specifications referred to.

The A.R.E.A. Specifications (1944) for steel railway bridges require that the spacing be such that the slenderness ratio of the flange between connections shall not be more than 40 or more than two-thirds the slenderness ratio of the whole member. The angle of inclination of lacing bars to the axis of the member should be approximately 60 degrees for single lacing and 45 degrees for double lacing. The shearing force normal to the axis of the member and in the plane of the lacing is determined from the following formula:

$$V = \frac{P}{100} \left[\frac{100}{L/r + 10} + \frac{L/r}{100} \right] \qquad (160)$$

This shear is assumed to be equally divided among all parallel planes in which there are shear resisting elements whether continuous plates or lacing and the force in individual lacing bars computed as for the diagonal of a parallel chord truss. Further details of construction may be obtained by reference to the specifications.

103   Selection and Design of Steel Columns

In common with previously discussed problems of structural design, columns are designed by successive approximations. The load delivered to the top of the column is estimated from the previously established

design of the construction to be supported, and the estimated weight of the column itself is generally added to this load. The choice of type of section to be used is a matter of judgment with due consideration for the details of connections to adjacent or supported construction and economy of material and labor in the construction of the column itself. Since the buckling resistance is a function of the least radius of gyration, it follows that an ideal column section would be one which had equal radii of gyration with respect to all axes through the centroid of the section, and a hollow cylindrical section such as a pipe would therefore furnish such an ideal section. The difficulty of making connections to such a member, however, usually prevents its use. A hollow square section could be regarded as an approximation of the cylinder and, while a section of this type might present difficulties in fabrication, it will be observed that most column sections tend toward such a form. Typical arrangements used for compression members are shown in Fig. 166.

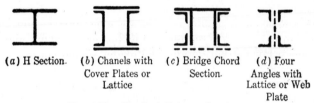

(*a*) H Section.   (*b*) Chanels with   (*c*) Bridge Chord   (*d*) Four
              Cover Plates or   Section.   Angles with
                 Lattice   Lattice or Web
                                                    Plate

Fig. 166.   Typical Column Sections.

Several such arrangements are generally available for use in any particular situation, and the designer should choose the one which best meets the requirement of overall economy. Usually alternate designs are prepared and their advantages compared before a final selection is made.

Tables such as those given in the "Steel Manual" are necessary for the selection of column sections of standard types. For column sections built-up of plates and shapes, the design is started by assuming the probable unit stress which will be allowed on the final column. Then a tentative required area is determined and a section is arranged to furnish this area. The least radius of gyration (maximum L/r) of this section determines the allowed working stress and with this working stress, the required area is again computed and the section revised accordingly. This process is repeated until the section and allowable unit stress are in complete agreement.

In the typical design problem solved in Fig. 167 two sections have been selected which will meet the given requirements. Type A weighs 100 pounds per linear foot, whereas the weight of Type B is computed to be 93.94 pounds per linear foot. Thus about 6 pounds per foot or

90 pounds for each column could be saved by using Type B. It is probable, however, that this saving would be more than offset by the additional cost of fabricating column Type B.

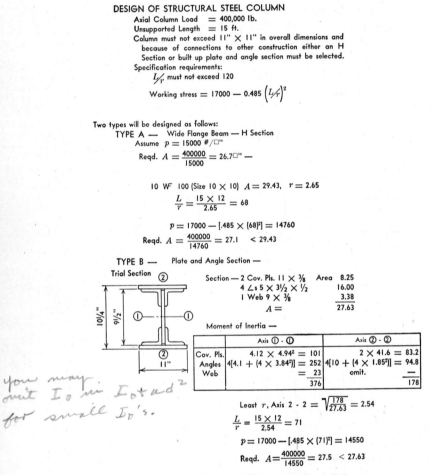

DESIGN OF STRUCTURAL STEEL COLUMN

Axial Column Load   = 400,000 lb.
Unsupported Length   = 15 ft.
Column must not exceed 11" × 11" in overall dimensions and because of connections to other construction either an H Section or built up plate and angle section must be selected.

Specification requirements:

L/r must not exceed 120

Working stress $= 17000 - 0.485 \left(L/r\right)^2$

Two types will be designed as follows:

TYPE A —   Wide Flange Beam — H Section
Assume $p = 15000 \,\#/\square"$

Reqd. $A = \dfrac{400000}{15000} = 26.7\square"$ —

10 WF 100 (Size 10 × 10) $A = 29.43$, $r = 2.65$

$$\frac{L}{r} = \frac{15 \times 12}{2.65} = 68$$

$$p = 17000 - [.485 \times (68)^2] = 14760$$

Reqd. $A = \dfrac{400000}{14760} = 27.1$ < 29.43

TYPE B —   Plate and Angle Section —

Trial Section

Section — 2 Cov. Pls. 11 × ⅜   Area 8.25
4 ∟s 5 × 3½ × ½   16.00
1 Web 9 × ⅜   3.38
$A =$ 27.63

Moment of Inertia —

	Axis ① - ①	Axis ② - ②
Cov. Pls.	4.12 × 4.94² = 101	2 × 41.6 = 83.2
Angles	4[4.1 + (4 × 3.84²)] = 252	4[10 + (4 × 1.85²)] = 94.8
Web	= 23	omit. —
	376	178

you may omit I_0 in $I_0 + ad^2$ for small I_0's.

Least r, Axis 2 - 2 $= \sqrt{\dfrac{178}{27.63}} = 2.54$

$$\frac{L}{r} = \frac{15 \times 12}{2.54} = 71$$

$$p = 17000 - [.485 \times (71)^2] = 14550$$

Reqd. $A = \dfrac{400000}{14550} = 27.5$ < 27.63

Fig. 167.   Design of Structural Steel Column.

104   Eccentric Loads—Bending and Direct Stress

When columns are subject to a known eccentricity of loading, the stress on the extreme fiber can be computed from the secant formula (Equation 150), which is derived for such a condition of loading. It should be noted that the term $\left[\dfrac{ec}{r^2} \sec \left(\dfrac{L}{2r} \sqrt{\dfrac{P}{EA}}\right)\right]$ represents the bending stress which is, of course, tension on the side opposite the eccentricity

and compression on the other side. The allowable working stress for such columns should be determined from Equation 151, using the following value for a:

$$a = \frac{ec}{r_2} + 0.001L/r \qquad (161)$$

When columns are subjected to transverse loading or bending-moments, including those produced by a known eccentricity of axial load,

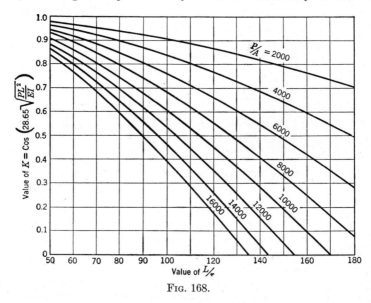

FIG. 168.

Equation 150 may be expressed in the following form by substituting M for Pe, where M is the bending-moment on a section at the middle of the column length due to all external forces including eccentricity of axial loading.

$$f = \left[\frac{P}{A} \pm \frac{Pec}{Ar^2} \sec \frac{1}{2} \sqrt{\frac{PL^2}{EI}} \right]$$

$$= \frac{P}{A} \pm \frac{Mc}{I} \sec \frac{1}{2} \sqrt{\frac{PL^2}{EI}}$$

$$= \frac{P}{A} \pm \frac{Mc}{KI} \qquad (162)$$

where

$$K = \cos \left(28.65 \sqrt{\frac{PL^2}{EI}} \right) \qquad (163)$$

(units for term in parentheses are degrees)

Values of K may be taken from Fig. 168. It should be noted that K = unity when $L/r = 0$; hence for relatively short stiff members this factor can be omitted. Equation 162 is also sometimes written in the form

$$f = \frac{P}{A} \pm \frac{Mc}{I \pm \dfrac{PL^2}{CE}} \tag{164}$$

where C = a constant based upon the condition of end restraint and nature of loading.

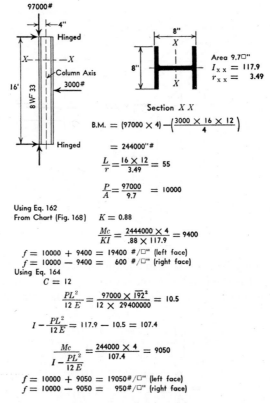

$$\text{B.M.} = (97000 \times 4) - \left(\frac{3000 \times 16 \times 12}{4}\right)$$

$$= 244000''\#$$

$$\frac{L}{r} = \frac{16 \times 12}{3.49} = 55$$

$$\frac{P}{A} = \frac{97000}{9.7} = 10000$$

Using Eq. 162
From Chart (Fig. 168) $K = 0.88$

$$\frac{Mc}{KI} = \frac{2444000 \times 4}{.88 \times 117.9} = 9400$$

$$f = 10000 + 9400 = 19400 \ \#/\square'' \ \text{(left face)}$$
$$f = 10000 - 9400 = 600 \ \#/\square'' \ \text{(right face)}$$

Using Eq. 164
$$C = 12$$

$$\frac{PL^2}{12\,E} = \frac{97000 \times \overline{192}^2}{12 \times 29400000} = 10.5$$

$$I - \frac{PL^2}{12\,E} = 117.9 - 10.5 = 107.4$$

$$\frac{Mc}{I - \dfrac{PL^2}{12\,E}} = \frac{244000 \times 4}{107.4} = 9050$$

$$f = 10000 + 9050 = 19050\#/\square'' \ \text{(left face)}$$
$$f = 10000 - 9050 = 950\#/\square'' \ \text{(right face)}$$

Fig. 169.   Structural Steel Column—Eccentric Load.

For a concentrated transverse load acting at the middle of the column length

Column with hinged ends $C = 12$

Column with fixed ends $C = 24$

For a uniform transverse load over the length of the column

Column with hinged ends $\quad C = 10$
Column with fixed ends $\quad\quad C = 32$

The $+$ sign is applied to the second term in Equations 162 and 164 to determine the maximum compressive stress in the extreme fiber on one

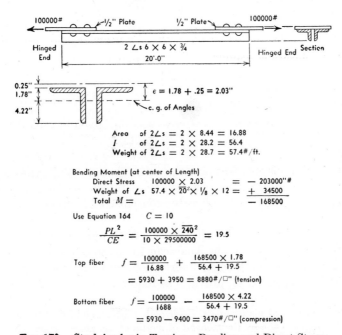

Area of $2\angle\mathrm{s} = 2 \times 8.44 = 16.88$
I of $2\angle\mathrm{s} = 2 \times 28.2 = 56.4$
Weight of $2\angle\mathrm{s} = 2 \times 28.7 = 57.4\#/\mathrm{ft.}$

Bending Moment (at center of Length)
Direct Stress $\quad 100000 \times 2.03 \quad\quad = -203000''\#$
Weight of $\angle$s $\quad 57.4 \times \overline{20^2} \times \frac{1}{8} \times 12 = +\ 34500$
Total $M = \quad\quad\quad\quad\quad\quad\quad\quad\quad\quad -168500$

Use Equation 164 $\quad C = 10$

$$\frac{PL^2}{CE} = \frac{100000 \times \overline{240}^2}{10 \times 29500000} = 19.5$$

Top fiber $\quad f = \dfrac{100000}{16.88} + \dfrac{168500 \times 1.78}{56.4 + 19.5}$

$= 5930 + 3950 = 8880\#/\square''$ (tension)

Bottom fiber $\quad f = \dfrac{100000}{1688} - \dfrac{168500 \times 4.22}{56.4 + 19.5}$

$= 5930 - 9400 = 3470\#/\square''$ (compression)

FIG. 170. Steel Angles in Tension—Bending and Direct Stress.

side of the section, and the $-$ sign is used to determine the unit stress on the opposite face of the column. The $-$ sign applies to the term PL^2/CE in Equation 164 when P is a compressive force. When Equation 164 is used for tension members subject to bending and direct stress, the signs noted above are reversed.

Typical solutions of problems in bending and direct stress are shown in Figs. 169 and 170.

105 Rolled-Steel Beams—Safe Loads

The load-carrying capacity of a rolled-steel beam is determined by its ability to resist bending-moment, shear, crippling of the web, and deflection. Unit stresses developed in all parts of the beam must not exceed commonly accepted safe working values. Bending-moments and shears

are computed in the usual manner, based upon the given loading with proper allowance for the weight of the beam. Tables in the "Steel Manual" (see Appendix) give the physical dimensions and other data used in strength computations.

The stress on the extreme fiber due to bending is obtained from the formula for homogeneous beams:

$$f = \frac{Mc}{I} = \frac{M}{S}$$

where M = bending-moment on a given section.
f = unit stress at extreme fiber.
c = distance from neutral axis to f.
d = overall depth of beam.
I = moment of inertia of cross section (given in tables).
S = section modulus (given in tables).

When the section is constant over the entire span, the unit stress is computed from the greatest bending-moment. When holes are punched in the flanges or web for connections to adjacent construction or where the section may be altered for any purpose, consideration must be given to a possible critical strength at such points. With respect to the necessary deductions for rivet holes, the American Institute of Steel Construction "Specifications for the Design, Fabrication, and Erection of Structural Steel for Buildings," 1946, provides as follows:

> Riveted and welded plate girders, cover plated beams and rolled beams shall in general be proportioned by the moment of inertia of the gross section. No deduction shall be made for standard shop or field rivet holes in either flange; except that in special cases where the reduction of the area of either flange by such rivet holes . . . exceeds 15% of the gross flange area, the excess shall be deducted. If such members contain other holes, as for bolts, pins, countersunk rivets, or plug or slot-welds, the full deduction for such holes shall be made. The deductions thus applicable to either flange shall be made also for the opposite flange if the corresponding holes are there present.

The A.A.S.H.O. Specifications (1944) for the design and construction of steel railway bridges provide that plate girders, I-beams, and other members subject to bending that produces tension on one face shall be proportioned by the moment-of-inertia method. The neutral axis is taken along the center of gravity of the gross section; tensile stress is computed from the moment of inertia of the entire net section; and the compressive stress is computed from the moment of inertia of the entire gross section.

For design of building construction, the A.I.S.C. Specifications (1946) permit unit stresses on rolled I-beams as follows:

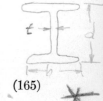

Tension on extreme fiber	20,000 psi
Compression on extreme fiber	
with Ld/bt not in excess of 600	20,000 psi
with Ld/bt in excess of 600	$\dfrac{12,000,000}{Ld/bt}$ psi

$$(165)$$

L is the unsupported length and d the depth of the member; b is the width and t the thickness of its compression flange; all are in inches, except that L shall be taken as twice the length of the compression flange of a cantilever beam not fully stayed at its outer end against translation or rotation.

For railway bridges, the A.R.E.A. Specifications (1944) permit the following unit stresses on rolled I-beams:

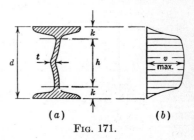

Tension on extreme fiber	18,000 psi
Compression on extreme fiber	
when L/b is less than 40	$18,000 - 5(L/b)^2$

$$(166)$$

L is the unsupported length, and b is the width of the compression flange.

For highway bridges, the A.A.S.H.O. Specifications (1944) provide the same allowable stresses as noted above for railway bridges.

Vertical shear is seldom critical in rolled-beam sections except for very short spans with heavy loading. Even for such sections, the chief danger is the probability of the web buckling (Fig. 171a) rather than of the material failing in shear. The intensity of shear stress at any point in the depth may be determined from the general equation for homogeneous beams (see Equation 131), and a typical distribution for an I-section is shown at Fig. 171b. It is seen that the flange areas contribute little to the total shear resistance and that the intensity of stress is fairly uniform over the depth of the web proper. For practical purposes, therefore,

(a) (b)

FIG. 171.

$$v = \frac{V}{th}$$

$$(167)$$

where v = average intensity of vertical shear stress.
  V = total shear on section.
  t = web thickness.
  h = depth of web proper = $d - 2k$.
  d = overall depth of beam.
  k = distance from outer face of flange, to toe of fillet.

For American Standard I-beams, the distance k is approximately equal to $0.56 + 0.0625$ $(d - 3)$. For wide flange beams the distance k is approximately equal to twice the flange thickness. Actual values of this dimension are given in the "Steel Manual" for all beam and channel sections.

In building construction, the A.I.S.C. Specifications (1946) require that the average shear on the gross section of the webs of rolled I-beams and plate girders, as given by Equation 167, be not greater than 13,000 pounds per square inch. For steel railway and highway bridges, the A.R.E.A. and the A.A.S.H.O. Specifications (1944) each limit this value to 11,000 pounds per square inch.

Except for unusual loading conditions, stiffeners are not required on rolled I-beams. When stiffeners are needed, the design is made in accordance with requirements specified for plate girders (see Article 108).

Crippling of the web due to stress concentration under concentrated loads and at the supports is avoided either by reinforcing the web with stiffeners or by distributing such loads or reactions over a sufficient length of beam to reduce the stress intensity to safe values. A concentrated load on the top flange, extending over a length of beam a (Fig. 172), is assumed to be uniformly distributed over an area $t(a_1 + 2k)$

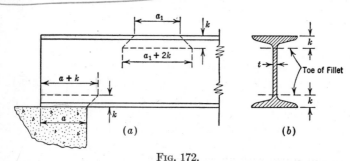

(a)   (b)

Fig. 172.

at the junction of the flange and web. Similarly, the reaction applied over a length a is assumed to be uniformly distributed over an area $t(a + k)$. It is recommended that the unit stress on these areas be limited to a value not in excess of 24,000 pounds per square inch, and,

based on such working stress, the required length of distribution may be computed as follows:

$$a \gtreqless \frac{R}{24{,}000t} - k \tag{168}$$

$$a_1 \gtreqless \frac{P}{24{,}000t} - 2k \tag{169}$$

where R = reaction in pounds.

P = concentrated load in pounds.

a = required length of bearing at support in inches.

a_1 = required length of distribution of concentrated load in inches.

t = thickness of web in inches.

k = distance from outer face of flange to toe of fillet in inches.

The deflection of a rolled beam is computed in the usual manner for beams of homogeneous material. The limit of permissible deflection depends upon the nature and use of the construction and is determined by judgment and experience. For beams carrying plastered ceilings, the customary deflection limit is $\frac{1}{360}$ of the span of the beam.

Typical computations for beams in an existing floor construction are shown in Fig. 173.

106   Design of Rolled-Beam Construction—Beam Selection

Since the shape and dimensions of the beam cross section is determined by the manufacturer, the design of a rolled-steel beam is a matter of selecting, from those available, the section which will most economically serve the purpose at hand. Steel is usually purchased by weight, and therefore the lightest-weight section that will safely carry the load will generally be selected. Consideration must be given to the availability of sections and lengths in dealers' yards or warehouses, as the selection of sections which are not carried in stock and which are infrequently rolled may lead to delay and thus offset any saving due to reduction in weight.

Regardless of theoretical strength for building construction it is customary to specify a minimum thickness of $\frac{1}{4}$ inch; for highway bridges $\frac{5}{16}$ inch; and for railway bridges $\frac{3}{8}$ inch.

The design starts with an assumed layout or arrangement of beams. This is subject to revision as the design proceeds, and frequently complete alternate arrangements are designed and compared on the basis of probable cost. Assuming a given arrangement, the weight of the construction is estimated, proper allowance being made for the probable weight of the beams that will be selected. Bending-moments and shears

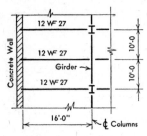

Floor Construction

> 3" Plank floor on 2"x10" joists which are 16" apart and rest on the top flange of the 12" beams. Beams have a 4" bearing on the concrete wall and are connected to the web of the girder by standard connection angles.

Live Load

> The floor carries a uniformly distributed load of 100 #/□'

Check beams for compliance with A.I.S.C. Specification (1946) and for deflection not greater than $L/360$

Floor Load

Plank flooring	7.5 #/□'
Joists	3.0
Live Load	100.0
Total	110.5 #/□'

Beam Load

From joists, 110.5 x 10 =	1105 #/lin. ft.
Weight of beam	27
Total	1132 #/lin. ft.

Dimensions and Properties of 12 W27

$S = 34.1$ $I = 204.1$ $d = 11.95$ in.
Flanges, $b = 6.5$ in.; $t = 0.4$ in.
Web, $t = 0.24$ in., $h = 10.375$ in., $k = 0.8125$ in.

Bending Stresses:

Allowable Unit Stress:
Tension, $f = 20,000$ #/□"
Compression, neglecting any lateral support by joists,
Unsupported length of flange = 192 in.

$$\frac{Ld}{bt} = \frac{192 \times 11.95}{6.5 \times 0.4} = 882 > 600$$

Hence, from Equation 165, $f = \dfrac{12,000,000}{882} = 13,600$ #/□"

Actual unit stress:

Span of beam = 16.12 ft.
Maximum B.M. = $1132 \times (16.12)^2 \times \frac{1}{8} \times 12 = 441,200$ in. lb.

$$f = \frac{441,200}{34.1} = 12,940 \text{ #/□"}$$

Shear Stress:

Allowable unit stress:
Slenderness ratio of web, $\dfrac{h}{t} = \dfrac{10.375}{0.24} = 43 < 70$

Allowable $v = 13,000$ #/□"

Actual average web shear,

$$v = \frac{9120}{0.24 \times 10.375} = 3,660 \text{ #/□"}$$

Bearing on Wall:

Required length $= \left[\dfrac{9,120}{24,000 \times 0.24}\right] - 0.81 = 2.39$ in.

Actual length = 4 in.

Deflection:

$$\frac{D}{L} = \frac{5 \times 1132 \times (192)^3}{12 \times 384 \times 29,500,000 \times 204.1} = \frac{1}{691}$$

FIG. 173.   Typical Computations for Steel Beams Supporting Floor.

are then computed for the total load, these being subject to revision as design computations produce more accurate data.

The tentative beam section is determined by computing the required section modulus, $S = M/f$. Some specifications and building codes limit the permissible depth of beam in terms of the span length. Thus the A.A.S.H.O. Specifications (1944) for highway bridges require that the depth of rolled beams be not less than one-twenty-fifth of the span. (For continuous beams, the span is considered as the distance between

Typical Steel Framing.

dead-load points of contraflexure.) The A.R.E.A. Specifications (1944) for steel railway bridges require that the depth of rolled-steel beams be not less than one-fifteenth of the span. Many building code ordinances of cities require that rolled beams have a depth of not less than one-twentieth of the span when used in floor construction and one-fortieth when used in roofs. Such limitations on the depth ratio are intended as a means of limiting the deflection and providing reasonable stiffness in the construction. The allowable unit stress in compression is determined from Equation 165 or 166 and will control the design for flexure. A tentative value of f is selected, the corresponding value of the section modulus is computed, and the beam or beams which will furnish this section modulus noted. The permissible compressive unit stress is then determined for the beam selected, with the lateral support of the compression flange, being taken into consideration, and a revised value of the section modulus is obtained. This process is repeated, if necessary, until a satisfactory section is obtained. The actual weight of the beam finally selected is then compared with the weight allowance previously

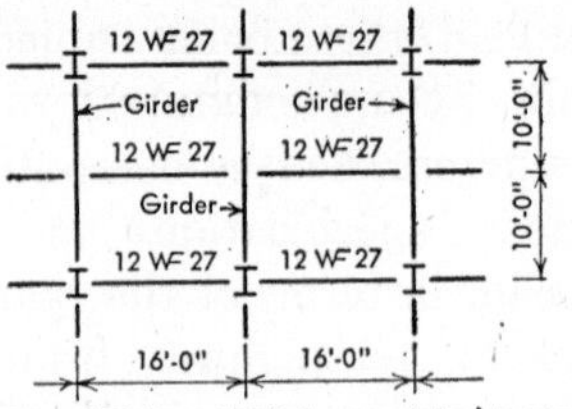

Floor Construction:
See (Fig. 173)
Live Load:
See (Fig. 173)
Specification:
Use A.I.S.C. (1946)

Span of Girder = 20.0 ft. (assume as simply supported)
Floor Load = 110.5 #/□"   (Fig. 173)
Beam Load = 1,132 #/□"   (Fig. 173)
Girder
Concentrated load at middle of span = 2 x 1132 x 16 x ½
= 18,112 lb.
Uniform load: weight of girder estimated as 40 # / lin. ft.
Maximum bending-moment:

Concentrated load, B.M. = 18,112 x 20 x ¼ x 12 = 1,086,720 " #
Uniform load,   B.M. = 40 x 20 x 20 x⅛ x 12 =   24,000 " #
                                    Total B.M. = $\overline{1,110,720}$ " #

Required Section:
Assume allowable unit stress at 20,000 #/□"
Required section modulus $= \dfrac{1,110,720}{20,000} = 55.6$

From Table, the following sections might be considered.

        16 W36 $S = 56.3$ $w = 36 \#/'$
        14 W43 $S = 62.7$ $w = 43 \#/'$
        12 W45 $S = 58.2$ $w = 45 \#/'$

Since there are no stated limitations on depth, the
lightest section, which is the 16 W 36, will be selected
for further trial. Hence, for this beam,

        Flange width, $b = 6.992$ in.,
        Flange thickness, $t = 0.428$ in.,
        Actual height, $d = 15.85$ in.
Unsupported length of compression flange = 120 in.

$$\frac{Ld}{bt} = \frac{120 \times 15.85}{6.99 \times 0.428} = 636$$

and, since this exceeds 600, the allowable unit stress
on the extreme fiber of the compression flange must
be obtained from Equation 165.

$$\text{Allowable } f = \frac{12,000,000}{636} = 18,870 \#/\square''$$

$$\text{Required } S = \frac{1,110,720}{18,870} = 58.9 > 56.3$$

and the 16 W36 beam is unsatisfactory.
The next lightest beam was the 14 W43 which
will now be selected for trial,

        Flange width, $b = 8.0$ in.,
        Flange thickness, $t = 0.528$ in.,
        Actual depth, $d = 13.68$ in.

$$\frac{Ld}{bt} = \frac{120 \times 13.68}{8.0 \times 0.528} = 389 < 600$$

and hence, allowable $f = 20,000 \# / \square''$ as originally assumed.
Since the actual weight per ft. is only 3 lb more than
that assumed for computing the bending-moment,
no change in the computed value need be made.
For the 14 W 43 beam,
t = web thickness = 0.308 in.
h = clear depth between flanges = 11.375 in.,
(from Steel Construction Manual)

$$\frac{h}{t} = \frac{11.375}{0.308} = 36 \text{ hence no web stiffeners are required.}$$

Maximum end shear = ½ [18,112 + (43 x 20)] = 18,972 lb.
Average shear stress on gross section of web.

$$v = \frac{18,972}{11.375 \times 0.308} = 5,405 \#/\square''$$

$$\text{Allowable } v = 13,000 \#/\square''$$

DEFLECTION: (neglect deflection due to weight of beam as negligible)
$$I = 429 \text{ in.}^4$$

$$D = \frac{18112 \times (240)^3}{48 \times 29.5 \times 429 \times (10)^6} = 0.412 \text{ in.}$$

$$\frac{L}{360} = \frac{240}{360} = 0.667 \text{ in.}$$

FIG. 174.   Typical Rolled-Steel-Beam Design.

made, and, if necessary, the entire computation is revised to accord with these later data. The result of these computations is the selection of a section which will have the requisite resisting-moment. This section is then checked for shear, crippling of the web, and deflection, and if inadequate in any of these particulars a different section is chosen and previous computations repeated.

A typical example of beam selection is given in Fig. 174. With reference to this design, it should be noted that the wide-flange section finally chosen is the lightest available section of adequate strength. Web crippling is not a critical matter here since the concentrated load is applied through standard connection angles (see "Steel Manual") to the web of the girder, and the girder reaction is delivered to the column through similar standard connection angles. These connection angles will act as stiffeners and reinforce the web of the girder against buckling. There will be no concentration of stress on a horizontal section at the toe of the fillet joint, the flange and web. Should the girder rest on a bearing wall, then the necessary minimum length of bearing would be computed from Equation 168.

107 Rolled-Steel Beams with Flange Plates

The resisting moment of a rolled-steel beam is sometimes supplemented by plates riveted or welded to the flanges of the beam as in Fig. 175. Thus, if the clearance limits the beam depth or if additional

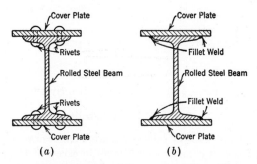

FIG. 175. Rolled-Steel Beam with Flange Plates.

flange width is needed to support other construction, this procedure affords a possible solution. The analysis of such a beam can best be discussed through the medium of numerical examples.

Example 1

Given an American Standard 12 I 31.8 which is reinforced by flange plates 8 × ½ riveted to the top and bottom flanges as shown in Fig. 175a. The beam

is simply supported on a span of 15 ft, and the compression flange is braced against lateral movement at the supports only.   The rivets fastening the plates to the beam are $\frac{3}{4}$-in. rivets in pairs spaced at 6-in. intervals.

Determine the safe total uniformly distributed load that this beam may carry, according to the A.I.S.C. Specifications (1946) based upon the resisting moment of the section.

Gross area of section:

$$
\begin{array}{ll}
\text{2 Plates, } 8 \times \tfrac{1}{2} = & 8.00 \text{ sq in.} \\
\text{I-beam} \quad\quad = & 9.26 \\
\hline
 & 17.26 \text{ sq in.}
\end{array}
$$

From tables given in the "Steel Construction Manual," the depth of web between fillets is 9.75 in., and its thickness is 0.35 in.   Hence the web area is approximately

$$0.35 \times 9.75 = 3.41 \text{ sq in.}$$

$$\text{Gross Area of each flange} = \frac{17.26 - 3.41}{2} = 6.98 \text{ sq in.}$$

The length of grip (see Fig. 176) for rivets connecting the plates to the flanges is $\frac{1}{2}$ in. plus the plate thickness.   For $\frac{3}{4}$-in. rivets the diameter of holes to be

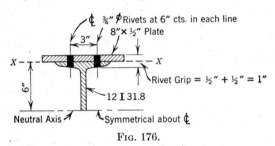

FIG. 176.

deducted is $\frac{3}{4}$ in. $+ \frac{1}{8}$ in. $= \frac{7}{8}$ in.   The area of two rivet holes in each flange is thus

$$2 \times \tfrac{7}{8} \times 1 = 1.75 \text{ sq in.}$$

This area is $1.75/6.98 = 25$ per cent of the gross flange area, and in accordance with the specifications the area of rivet holes in excess of 15 per cent must be deducted in determining the moment of inertia of the section.

Moment of inertia:

$$
\begin{array}{llr}
\text{Gross section, } I\text{-beam, } I = & & 215.8 \\
\text{Plates,} \quad I = 2 \times 4 \times (6.25)^2 & = & 312.5 \\
\text{(I_g of plates neglected)} & & \overline{528.3}
\end{array}
$$

$$
\begin{array}{llr}
\text{Rivet holes, } 2 \times 1.75 \times (6)^2 & = & 126.0 \\
\text{Excess to be deducted} = \tfrac{10}{25} \times 126.0 & = & 50.4 \\
I = & & \overline{477.9}
\end{array}
$$

Allowable unit stress:

For tension, allowable f = 20,000 psi
For compression

> Unsupported length of flange = 15 × 12 = 180 in.
> Width of flange = 8 in.
> Depth of beam = 12 + (2 × $\frac{1}{2}$) = 13 in.
> Thickness of flange = $\frac{1}{2}$ + $\frac{1}{2}$ = 1 in.
> $$\frac{Ld}{bt} = \frac{180 \times 8}{13 \times 1} = 110$$

and, since this is less than 600, the allowable unit stress is 20,000 psi.

Resisting moment:

$$M = \frac{20,000 \times 477.9}{6.5} = 1,470,500 \text{ in.-lb}$$

Safe load:

$$\text{Total load, } W = \frac{8 \times 1,470,500}{12 \times 15} = 65,350 \text{ lb}$$

$$M = \frac{1}{8} W L^2$$

Example 2

Determine the safe total uniformly distributed load for the beam given in Example 1, based upon the strength of rivets connecting the flange plates to the I-beam.

Rivet value (Table 16):

> Single shear valve of $\frac{3}{4}$-in. rivet = 6,630 lb
> Bearing on $\frac{1}{2}$-in. plate (or flange) = $\frac{3}{4}$ × $\frac{1}{2}$ × 32,000 = 12,000 lb

Therefore single shear controls, and R = 6630 lb

Horizontal shear:

Since there are 2 rivets in a 6-in. length of beam, the total horizontal shear in a 6-in. length may safely equal 2 × 6630 = 13,260 lb. From Equation 131, $VQ/I = 13,260/6$

where Q = moment of connected plate area about neutral axis
   = 8 × $\frac{1}{2}$ × 6.25 = 25.0
I = 477.9

$$\text{Safe } V = \frac{13,260 \times 477.9}{6 \times 25} = 42,250 \text{ lb}$$

Safe load:

$$\text{Total load, } W = 2 \times 42,250 = 84,500 \text{ lb}$$

Note that the safe load as determined by flexure in Example 1 will govern.

Crippling of the web is determined in the usual manner for the *I*-beam section. Deflection is computed in the usual manner, the net moment of inertia of the built-up section, as previously computed, being used.

108   Plate Girders

Plate girders are beams built up of plates and shapes.   While any desired arrangement may be provided, the one most commonly employed consists of a vertical web plate with flanges, made up of angles and cover plates, attached to its edges (Fig. 177).   The parts are fastened together by rivets or by welding in such a manner as to resist the internal shear stresses developed on the planes of contact.   The designer is not limited to a particular series of cross sections, as was true for rolled-steel beams and hence may compose the built-up section to meet his particular needs.   It is possible, moreover, to provide for some variation in the cross section and thus furnish resisting-moments more nearly equal to the bending-moments on the several sections of the beam. Because of the added labor needed to fasten the parts together, plate girders will cost more per pound than rolled-steel sections; hence for economy rolled sections will generally be chosen whenever adequate sections are available.

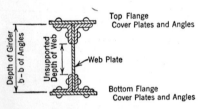

Top Flange
Cover Plates and Angles

Web Plate

Bottom Flange
Cover Plates and Angles

Fig. 177.   Plate Girder.

The stresses produced in a plate girder due to a given loading are determined in accordance with the same principles and procedures as previously outlined for rolled-steel sections (see typical computations, Fig. 178).   Critical sections for investigation will obviously include the one on which the bending-moment is greatest, also those which are reduced by cuts, holes, or absence of cover plates.   When the section is unsymmetrical, the neutral axis must be located and the moment of inertia computed for such axis.   Opinions differ as to whether the neutral axis should be located at the centroid of the net section or at the centroid of the gross section.   In view of the fact that its location is primarily a function of the deflection and that this is determined largely by the gross section, it is believed by the author that the centroid of the gross section more accurately locates the neutral axis.   In considering the behavior of a plate girder, it should be noted that the principal function of the flange areas is to resist the bending-moment; the principal function of the web plate is to resist the vertical shear.   Critical sections as regards bending-moment may therefore be determined by the character of the flange area and should be taken through such combinations of rivet holes as may most seriously reduce the strength of the section.   Allowable working unit stresses on the extreme fibers of the tension and

compression flanges of plate girders are the same as for rolled-steel sections (see Article 105).

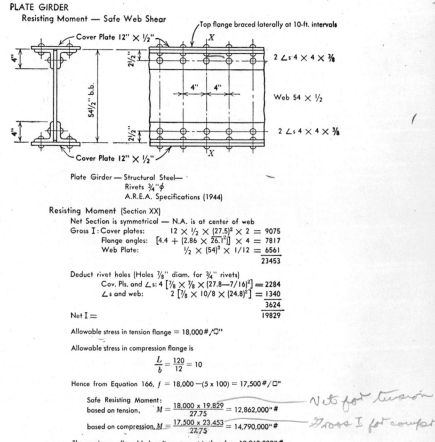

PLATE GIRDER
Resisting Moment — Safe Web Shear

Top flange braced laterally at 10-ft. intervals

Cover Plate 12" × ½"

2 ∠s 4 × 4 × ⅜

Web 54 × ½

2 ∠s 4 × 4 × ⅜

Cover Plate 12" × ½"

Plate Girder — Structural Steel —
Rivets ¾"φ
A.R.E.A. Specifications (1944)

Resisting Moment (Section XX)

Net Section is symmetrical — N.A. is at center of web
Gross I : Cover plates: $12 \times \frac{1}{2} \times (27.5)^2 \times 2 = 9075$
       Flange angles: $[4.4 + (2.86 \times \overline{26.1}^2)] \times 4 = 7817$
       Web Plate: $\frac{1}{2} \times (54)^3 \times 1/12 = \underline{6561}$
                                  23453

Deduct rivet holes (Holes ⅞" diam. for ¾" rivets)
     Cov. Pls. and ∠s: $4 \left[\frac{7}{8} \times \frac{7}{8} \times (27.8 - 7/16)^2 \right] = 2284$
     ∠s and web: $2 \left[\frac{7}{8} \times 10/8 \times (24.8)^2 \right] = \underline{1340}$
                                         3624
Net I =   19829

Allowable stress in tension flange = 18,000 #/□"

Allowable stress in compression flange is
$$\frac{L}{b} = \frac{120}{12} = 10$$

Hence from Equation 166, $f = 18,000 - (5 \times 100) = 17,500 \ \#/\square"$

Safe Resisting Moment:
based on tension, $M = \dfrac{18,000 \times 19,829}{27.75} = 12,862,000" \#$

based on compression, $M = \dfrac{17,500 \times 23,453}{27.75} = 14,790,000" \#$

The maximum allowable bending moment is therefore 12,860,000" #

Net for tension
Gross I for compr.

Shear —

Unsupported depth of web = 54½ — 8 = 46½ : $\frac{h}{t} = 93$

This is within max. limit of $\frac{h}{t} \gtreqless 170$ but since ratio exceeds 60, intermediate stiffeners are required.
Max. Shear based on Gross Web Area = $11000 \times 54 \times \frac{1}{2} = 297000 \#$

Fig. 178.   Analysis of Plate Girder.

The principal function of the web plate is to resist the vertical shear. Vertical shear stress in the web is seldom critical, but its effect in producing buckling of the web under the resultant diagonal compression is a matter requiring careful consideration. Permissible working stresses

for average intensity of vertical shear (total shear divided by the gross area of the web plate) on the gross section of the web plate are as follows:

Building construction	13,000 psi
Highway bridges	11,000 psi
Railway bridges	11,000 psi

Web stiffeners to prevent buckling of the web plate between the flanges are always required at the reactions and under concentrated loads. Web stiffeners are usually pairs of angles with the web plate between and are riveted or welded to the web plate (Fig. 179). Stiffener angles must be

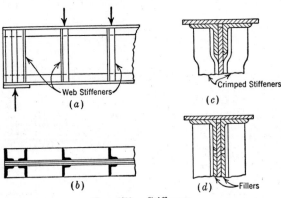

Fig. 179.   Stiffeners.

of such length as to fit tightly between the flange angles. In order that a tight connection can be made to the web, they must be crimped to fit over the flange angles as at *c* or else filler plates of the same thickness as the flange angles must be used as at *d* to fill the spaces which would otherwise exist. It is considered best practice not to crimp the end stiffeners nor those under concentrated loads. The A.I.S.C. Specifications (1944) for the design, fabrication, and erection of structural steel for buildings require that when h/t equals or exceeds 70, intermediate stiffeners shall be used at all points where

$$v \text{ exceeds,} \quad \frac{64,000,000}{\left(\frac{h}{t}\right)^2} \tag{170}$$

where h = unsupported depth of web (Fig. 177).

t = thickness of web plate.

v = greatest unit shear in panel in pounds per square inch under any condition of complete or partial loading.

These specifications further provide that the clear distance between intermediate stiffeners, when stiffeners are required, shall not exceed 84 inches or that given by the following formula:

$$d = \frac{11,000t}{\sqrt{v}} \qquad (171a)$$

The A.R.E.A. Specifications (1944) for railway bridges require stiffeners at end bearings of plate girders and beams and at points of bearing of

Deck Plate Girder Railroad Bridge over Woodward Ave., Detroit, Michigan.

concentrated loads. These specifications also require intermediate stiffeners whenever h/t exceeds 60 and limits the spacing to 72 inches or that given by the following formula:

$$d = \frac{10,500t}{\sqrt{v}} \qquad (171b)$$

The A.A.S.H.O. Specifications (1944) for highway bridges require that the webs of plate girders be stiffened at end bearings and at points of concentrated loading and whenever h/t exceeds 60. The spacing of intermediate stiffeners is limited to a maximum of 72 inches or that given by the following formula:

$$d = \frac{9,000t}{\sqrt{v}} \qquad (171c)$$

End stiffener angles and those under concentrated loads are designed for bearing of their outstanding legs against the flange angles, only that part of the leg outside the fillet of the flange angle being used. The connection to the web must have sufficient strength to transmit the total load or reaction to the web plate. The A.S.I.C. Specifications (1946) allow 30,000 pounds per square inch bearing stress for milled stiffeners and 27,000 for fitted stiffeners. The A.A.S.H.O. Specifications (1944) for highway bridges and the A.R.E.A. Specifications (1944) for steel railway bridges allow 27,000 pounds per square inch bearing on milled stiffeners and 18,000 pounds per square inch axial compression on the stiffener assembly.

The A.I.S.C. Specifications (1946) for buildings require that bearing stiffeners at the ends and at concentrated loads have a close bearing against the loaded flanges and that they shall extend as closely as possible to the edge of the flange plates or flange angles. Such stiffeners are designed as columns, assuming that the column section consists of the pair of stiffeners and a centrally located strip of the web equal to not more than 25 times the web thickness, for interior stiffeners, or a strip equal to not more than 12 times the web thickness for stiffeners located at the ends of the web. The column length is taken as $\frac{3}{4}$ the length of the stiffeners in computing the ratio L/r. Only that portion of the stiffeners outside of the angle fillet or the flange to web welds is considered effective in bearing. Intermediate stiffeners which are not at the ends of the girder or at points of concentrated load are required by these specifications to have a section not less than that required by the formula

$$I_s = 0.00000016 H^4 \tag{172}$$

where H = total depth of web.

I_s = moment of inertia of the stiffeners or stiffener (figured with a common axis at the centerline of web for stiffeners in pairs and with the axis at the interface between stiffener and web for single stiffeners).

The A.R.E.A. and A.A.S.H.O. Specifications (1944) for railway and highway bridges, respectively, require that stiffeners at the ends and at points of concentrated loading be proportioned for bearing on the outstanding legs of the flange angles with no allowance made for the portions of the legs fitted to the fillets of the flange angle. They must extend as nearly as practicable to the edges of the flange and be connected to the web with enough rivets to transmit the load. The width of the outstanding leg of intermediate stiffeners must be not more than

16 times its thickness and not less than 2 inches plus $\frac{1}{30}$ of the depth of the web.

Typical computations of stiffeners are shown in Fig. 180.

PLATE GIRDER
Web Stiffeners

Data—Same as in Fig. 178
    End Stiffeners   4∠s 3½ × 3½ × ½
    Intermediate Stiffeners 2∠s 3½ × 3½ × ⅜
                    Spaced @ 4'-6"
Applied Loading is uniformly distributed.
A.R.E.A. Specifications (1944)

End Stiffeners

Gross Area—4∠s = 4 × 3.25 = 9.75¹ "
Allowed Axial Compression on Gross Area = 18000 × 9.75
                                     = 175,500#
Allowed Bearing Value = 4 × 1.51 × 27000 = 163000#
    Bearing of Stiffeners governs Reaction.
Note:—Reaction must not exceed aggregate value of
    rivets of connecting stiffeners to web.

Intermediate Stiffeners

Width of outstanding leg:
    must not exceed 16 × thickness = 16 × ⅜ = 6 in.
    must not be less than $2 + \frac{54.5}{30}$ = 3.8 in.
    Note: Width of angles used is insufficient.

Required Spacing:
    Maximum permissible spacing = 72 in.
    $\frac{h}{t} = \frac{46.5}{0.5}$ = 93 > 60   use Eq. 154.
    End shear = 130,000 (computed from loading).
    $v = \frac{130000}{54 \times 0.5}$ = 4800 #/□"
    Required distance (min) to first intermediate
    stiffener = $d = \frac{255000 \times 0.5}{4800} \sqrt[3]{\frac{4800 \times 0.5}{46.5}}$ = 98
    Spacing given is satisfactory.

FIG. 180.   Plate Girder Analysis—Web Stiffeners.

The connection of flange to web and, when cover plates are used, of cover plates to flange angles must have sufficient strength to resist the horizontal shear on the planes of contact. Thus the horizontal shear on *aa*, Fig. 181, a section between the flange angles and the web plate, is determined from the equation

$$R_H = \left(\frac{VQ}{I}\right) p \qquad (173)$$

where V = maximum vertical shear in any portion p of span length.

Q = statical moment of the net area of cover plates and angles connected about the neutral axis of the girder.

I = moment of inertia as determined for bending.

p = spacing (pitch) of rivets A.

R_H = total force on one rivet.

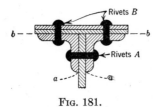

FIG. 181.

When a vertical load is also applied on the flange (Fig. 182), the total force on a rivet is the resultant of R_H, as computed from Equation 173 and the vertical load per rivet.

The rivets connecting the cover plates to the flange angles must resist the horizontal shear on the plane of contact (plane bb Fig. 181).

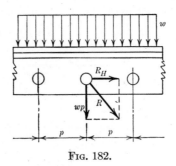

FIG. 182.

The force on each such rivet is determined from the following equation:

$$R = \frac{VQ}{I} \times \frac{p}{n} \tag{174}$$

where R = force on one rivet.

V = maximum vertical shear in space p.

Q = statical moment of the net area of cover plates outside shear plane, about the neutral axis.

I = moment of inertia as determined for bending.

p = spacing of rivets B in either line.

n = number of longitudinal rivet lines.

Typical plate girder rivet computations are shown in Fig. 183.

For more complete data and discussion of the behavior of plate girders and theory of action, the reader is referred to the several specifications quoted and to more complete textbooks on design.

PLATE GIRDER
Flange Riveting

Data—Same as in Fig..178
  Rivets ¾"   Spaced as shown throughout span.

Note: Since rivets are equally spaced over entire span maximum force on rivet will occur at end of span where V is max. Force will be determined for $V = 130000$

RIVETS — FLANGE TO WEB

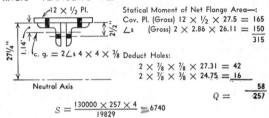

Statical Moment of Net Flange Area—:
Cov. Pl. (Gross) $12 \times \frac{1}{2} \times 27.5 = 165$
$\angle s$ (Gross) $2 \times 2.86 \times 26.11 = \underline{150}$
                                              315
c. g. $= 2\angle s\ 4 \times 4 \times \frac{3}{8}$ Deduct Holes:
            $2 \times \frac{7}{8} \times \frac{7}{8} \times 27.31 = 42$
            $2 \times \frac{7}{8} \times \frac{3}{8} \times 24.75 = \underline{16}$
                                                  58
                                   $Q = \quad \overline{257}$

$$S = \frac{130000 \times 257 \times 4}{19829} = 6740$$

Value of Rivet (Double Shear governs) $= 13250$ lbs.
Note: Above computation applies to bottom flange rivets. Force on top flange rivets is resultant of Horiz. and Vertical force on rivet.

RIVETS — COVER PLATE TO FLANGE ANGLES

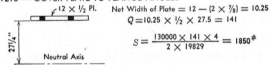

Net Width of Plate $= 12 - (2 \times \frac{7}{8}) = 10.25$
$Q = 10.25 \times \frac{1}{2} \times 27.5 = 141$

$$S = \frac{130000 \times 141 \times 4}{2 \times 19829} = 1850^{\#}$$

Value of one rivet (Single Shear governs) $= 6630^{\#}$

FIG. 183. Plate Girder Riveting.

109 Plate Girders—Design Procedure

The procedure followed in the design of a plate girder is usually that of successive approximation. By assumption, a trial section is set up which is then investigated and adjusted until the designer is satisfied no further changes are necessary or desirable. The investigation of such trial section is carried out in accordance with principles and methods previously outlined so that there remains for further discussion only the matter of determining rational trial sections.

The first step is the determination of a suitable layout and the establishment of the controlling dimensions such as the span length and the available clearance to provide for the girder depth. The probable weight of the supported construction is then estimated, and a reasonable allow-

ance is made for the weight of the girder. The maximum bending-moment and shear are then computed using these estimated weights and the live load which is expected to occupy the structure. When the make-up of the section has been more definitely determined, it will usually be necessary to determine the maximum bending-moment and the maximum shear on each of several sections in the span, but at the outset merely the greatest bending-moment in the span and maximum end shear will suffice.

The next step in the design is the determination of the tentative girder depth and width of the web plate. For maximum economy of material, the depth of a plate girder (back to back of angles) should be about one-twelfth to one-fifteenth of the span. Some building code ordinances and specifications [15] place definite limitations on the depth ratios. The distance back to back of angles establishes the width of the web plate and, when cover plates are used, this distance should be $\frac{1}{4}$ to $\frac{1}{2}$ inch more than the width of the web plate to provide allowance for possible overrun in web-plate width. It should also be noted that preferred variation in plate widths is by inches although $\frac{1}{2}$-inch variations may be obtained.

When the width of the web plate has been established, its required thickness may then be determined. In order to conform with acceptable standards as represented by current design specifications, the web thickness should satisfy the following conditions:

(1) It should be not less than the specified minimum allowable thickness of material, $\frac{1}{4}$ inch in buildings, $\frac{5}{16}$ inch in highway bridges, and $\frac{3}{8}$ inch in railway bridges.

(2) It should have a thickness not less than $\frac{1}{170}$ of the unsupported distance between flange angles. (An estimated size of flange angle may be used pending a later check.)

(3) The average unit-shear stress on the gross web area should not exceed 13,000 pounds per square inch in buildings and 11,000 pounds per square inch in bridges.

(4) If no stiffeners are to be used, the thickness should be at least one-seventieth of the unsupported distance between flange angles for building construction and one-sixtieth in bridges. If it is expected that stiffeners will be used, the first three requirements will establish the neces-

[15] A.A.S.H.O. Specifications (1944) for Highway Bridges state that plate girders shall have a depth preferably not less than one-twenty-fifth of span. The A.R.E.A. Specifications (1944) for Steel Railway Bridges state that the depth shall be preferably not less than one-twelfth of the span.

sary minimum thickness, and stiffeners should then be provided in accordance with given specifications.

The next step in the design is the determination of the required flange section which is generally a combination of flange angles and cover plates but may include other suitable structural shapes. Tables published in the "Steel Manual" and in other engineering handbooks which give properties of plate-girder sections are extremely useful for this purpose. Lacking such tabular data, the *approximate* or *chord-stress* method may be used to determine a trial section. This method is as follows:

First, the girder section is assumed to be divided into three parts (Fig. 184), the top flange (or top chord), the bottom flange (or bottom

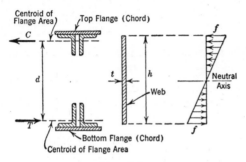

FIG. 184.

chord), and the web. The flanges are assumed to act jointly to furnish a resisting couple represented by the forces C and T, and the unit stress is assumed to be uniformly distributed over each flange area; the web is assumed to act as a rectangular beam. Proper allowance must be made for reductions in section due to rivet holes. The approximate resisting moment of the section is then determined as follows:

Where M = resisting moment of section = $M_F + M_W$.

    M_F = resisting moment of flanges (net section).

    M_W = resisting moment of web plate (net section).

     d = effective depth of girder. (Distance between centroids of flange areas.)

     t = thickness of web plate.

     h = width of web plate.

     f = allowable working stress.

    A_F = net area of one flange.

    A_W = gross area of web plate = th.

Since

$$C = T = fA_F$$

the resisting moment of the net flange area will be

$$M_F = fA_Fd$$

In determining the resisting moment of the net web plate, it is customary to assume that this will be three-fourths the value obtained for the gross section; also no material error is introduced by assuming $h^2 = hd$; hence

$$M_W = \frac{3}{4} \times \frac{fthd}{6} = \frac{1}{8}fA_Wd$$

therefore,

$$M = M_F + M_W = fd(A_F + \tfrac{1}{8}A_W) \tag{175}$$

To determine the approximate required net area of the flange, Equation 175 is arranged in the following form:

$$A_F = \frac{M}{fd} - \frac{1}{8}A_W \tag{176}$$

A tentative solution of Equation 176 is obtained by assuming M to be equal to the computed maximum bending-moment, f equal to the allowed unit stress on the extreme fiber, and d equal to the distance back to back of angles, less $1\frac{1}{2}$ inches for girders without cover plates and less 1 inch for cover-plated girders. A combination of shapes and plates is then chosen whose net area after allowing for probable rivet holes is equal to or greater than this computed value. When the flange is composed of angles and cover plates it is good practice to provide at least one-half of the combined area in the angles, and some specifications require that the centroid of the combined area must lie inside the backs of angles. With a tentative combination of shapes and plates selected, the centroid of their gross section is located, and a corrected value is obtained for d. The preceding computation is then repeated, and the section is revised until all factors are in substantial agreement.

At this point it is advisable to check the weight, allowing for stiffeners and other details, and make such revision in the original assumed value as may be necessary or desirable.

Details of the design, such as stiffener spacing, pitch of rivets, and length and location of cover plates, are then developed and the sections finally checked, using the moment of inertia of the section in accordance with the procedure outlined in Article 109.

Typical design computations for a plate girder are illustrated by the following example:

Example

Design of Plate Girder

 Data

  Span 45 ft center to center of supports.

  Top flange is imbedded in a concrete slab which gives it full lateral support at all points.

  Total load (except weight of girder) delivered on top of top flange = 3900 lb per linear ft.

  Use A.I.S.C. Specifications (1944) for steel buildings.

 Design Computations

  Estimated weight of girder = 200 lb per ft
  Load delivered to top of girder 3900
             ———
       Total 4100 lb per ft

  Maximum bending-moment = $4100 \times (45)^2 \times \frac{1}{8} \times 12 = 12{,}500$ in.-kips
  Maximum shear = $4100 \times \frac{1}{2} \times 45 = 92.2$ kips
  Assumed depth of girder about $\frac{1}{15} \times 45 = 3$ ft
  Make back to back of angles = $36\frac{1}{2}$ in.
  Width of web plate = 36 in.

Assuming flange angles with 4-in. vertical legs, unsupported width of web is $36\frac{1}{2} - 8 = 28\frac{1}{2}$ in.

Minimum thickness of web plate

 Minimum thickness of metal permitted by specifications for interior construction = $\frac{1}{4}$ in.

 Based on the unsupported depth of web plate,

$$t \gtreqless \tfrac{1}{170} \times 28\tfrac{1}{2} = 0.168 \text{ in.}$$

 Based on average unit shear stress,

$$t \gtreqless \frac{92.2}{13 \times 36} = 0.197 \text{ in.}$$

Use plate $36 \times \frac{1}{4}$ for web.

$$\frac{h}{t} = \frac{28.5}{0.25} = 114$$

 Therefore stiffeners are required.

Overall depth of girder (assuming $\frac{1}{2}$-in. cover plates) = $37\frac{1}{2}$ in.
Effective depth (approximate) = $36\frac{1}{2} - 2 = 34\frac{1}{2}$ in.
Approximate allowable average working stress on flange = $34.5/37.5 \times 20$
 = 18.3

Assuming $d = 34\frac{1}{2}$ in. and $f = 18.3$ kips per sq in.,

$$A_F + \frac{1}{8} A_W = \frac{12,500}{18.3 \times 34.5} = 19.8 \text{ sq in.}$$

$$\tfrac{1}{8} A_W = \tfrac{1}{8} \times 36 \times \tfrac{1}{4} = 1.1$$

Required $A_F = 18.7$ sq in.

One-half or more of this area should be in the flange angles so that each angle should have an effective area of not less than $\frac{1}{2} \times 18.7 \times \frac{1}{2} = 4.68$ sq in.

On this basis, the following trial section is determined.

Gross area:

2 angles $6 \times 4 \times \frac{5}{8}$; 11.72 sq in.
1 cover plate $14 \times \frac{1}{2}$; 7.00

Total gross area = 18.72 sq in.

Assuming $\frac{3}{4}$-in. diameter rivets, two rivet holes in each angle and two out of the cover plate, the area of rivet holes in the section would be

$\tfrac{7}{8} \times \tfrac{5}{8} \times 4 = 2.19$ sq in.
$\tfrac{7}{8} \times \tfrac{1}{2} \times 2 = 0.88$

3.07 sq in.

$$\frac{3.07}{18.72} = 16.4\%$$

The reduction in effective area, in accordance with the specifications (see Article 105), is

$$\frac{(16.4 - 15) \times 18.72}{100} = 0.26 \text{ sq in.}$$

Revised flange area required = $18.7 + 0.26 = 18.96$ sq in.

Gross area:

2 angles $6 \times 4 \times \frac{5}{8}$; 11.72 sq in.
1 cover plate $14 \times \frac{9}{16}$; 7.88

Total gross area   = 19.60 sq in.

Rivet holes $(2.19 + 0.98) = 3.17$ sq in.
15% of 19.6   = 2.94

Excess   =   0.23

Net area =   19.37 sq in.

The centroid of the gross flange area is computed as follows (Fig. 185), taking moments about the center of gravity of the angles:

$$\text{c.g. angles to c.g. flange area} = \frac{7.88 \times (1.03 + \frac{9}{32})}{19.6} = 0.53 \text{ in.}$$

back of angles to c.g. flange = $1.03 - 0.53 = 0.5$ in.
effective depth, $d = 36.5 - (2 \times 0.5) = 35.5$ in.

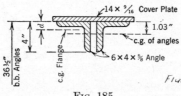

FIG. 185

With this computed value of d, the preceding computations are revised as follows:

$$\text{Approximate allowed } f = \frac{35.5}{37.625} \times 20 = 18.8 \text{ kips per sq in. (average on flange)}$$

$$\text{Required } (A_F + \tfrac{1}{8}A_W) = \frac{12,500}{18.8 \times 35.5} = 18.7 \text{ sq in.}$$

$$\tfrac{1}{8}A_W = 1.1$$

$$\text{Required } A_F = 17.6 \text{ sq in.}$$

Revised section

Gross area

2 angles $6 \times 4 \times \frac{5}{8}$; 11.72 sq in.
1 cover plate $14 \times \frac{7}{16}$;   6.13
_____
17.85 sq in.

$$\text{Rivet holes} = \frac{(2.19 + .67)}{17.85} = 16\%$$

$$\text{Required increase in required area} = \left(\frac{16 - 15}{100}\right) 17.85 = 0.18 \text{ sq in.}$$

Required flange area = $17.6 + 0.18 = 17.78$ sq in. < 17.85

It is not deemed necessary to make further revision, and the trial section will be made up as follows:

2 cover plates $14 \times \frac{7}{16}$

4 angles $6 \times 4 \times \frac{5}{8}$

1 web $36 \times \frac{1}{4}$

The girder section will now be checked using the moment of inertia. In computing the moment of inertia, the I_g of cover plates will be regarded as negligible. Tabular values as given in the "Steel Manual" are used where possible.

Moment of inertia (gross section)

Web, $36 \times \frac{1}{4}$ 970 in.⁴

4 angles, $6 \times 4 \times \frac{5}{8}$ at $36\frac{1}{2}$ in. back to back

$4[7.5 + (5.86 \times 17.22^2)]$ $=$ 7,010

2 plates, $14 \times \frac{7}{16}$

$2[14 \times \frac{7}{16} \times (18.47)^2]$ $=$ 4,180

Total   12,160 in.⁴

Deduction of 0.18 sq in. in each flange due to rivet holes,

$$2\left[0.18 \times \left(\frac{35.5}{2}\right)^2 \right] \qquad = \quad 115$$

Effective I $= 12,045$ in.⁴

Unit stress on extreme fiber,

$$f = \frac{12,500 \times 37.88}{2 \times 12,045} = 19,700 \text{ psi}$$

Since the allowable stress is 20,000 psi, the section will be deemed satisfactory, and no further revision is required.

The weight of the girder is now estimated as follows:

2 cover plates, $14 \times \frac{7}{16}$, weight per ft   41.6 lb

4 angles, $6 \times 4 \times \frac{5}{8}$ 80.0

1 web, $36 \times \frac{1}{4}$ 30.6

152.2

Allow 20% for rivet heads, stiffener angles, and other details   30.8

Total 183 lb per ft

Since 200 lb per ft was originally allowed, it is possible to make a reduction on the basis of this new estimation; however, the difference is only 10% of the original assumed weight and is less than one-half of 1% of the total load; hence no revision in load will be made.

The required length and position of cover plates may be either determined graphically from the diagram of maximum bending-moments (Fig. 186) or established by computation. When more than one cover plate is used, the thicknesses of plates used should either be equal or should diminish from the flange angles outward. No cover plate should be thicker than the thickness of the flange angles, and it is considered to be the best practice to extend at least one

plate over the entire length of the girder. Some specifications require the cover plate to extend past the theoretical allowed end to provide for specified rivet strength. In the given example, it is assumed that all cover plates will extend over the entire length of the girder.

Since the section in this example is constant over the span, the minimum rivet pitch will be obtained from the maximum value of V at the support. For rivets fastening the flange to the web plate, considering the top or loaded flange we see that the value of one rivet (bearing on web governs) is 7500 lb.

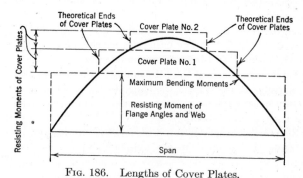

Fig. 186. Lengths of Cover Plates.

With vertical load per rivet being neglected, the required maximum spacing at the end of the girder is computed from Equation 173 as follows:

$$Q = \frac{(17.85 - 0.18) \times 35.5}{2} = 313$$

$$p = \frac{RI}{VQ} = \frac{7500 \times 12,045}{92,200 \times 313} = 3.1 \text{ in.}$$

Assuming $p = 3$ in., and taking into account the vertical load on each rivet, we have

$$\text{Vertical load per rivet} \quad = \frac{3900 \times 3}{12} = 980 \text{ lb}$$

$$\text{Horizontal force on rivet} = \frac{3}{3.1} \times 7500 = 7250$$

$$\text{Resultant force on rivet} \quad = \sqrt{(7250)^2 + (980)^2} = 7320 \text{ lb}$$

This rivet stress is satisfactory and 3-in. spacing will be adopted for both flanges at the end of the girder. The spacing may be made greater at other points in accordance with similar computations made for sections nearer the center of span but should never exceed 16 times the thickness of the angles.

The required spacing of rivets connecting the cover plate to the flange angle is determined from Equation 174, as follows. Here again the minimum spacing will be obtained at the end of the girder.

$$R = 6630 \text{ lb (single shear governs)}$$

$$Q = [6.13 - (\tfrac{6}{17} \times 0.18)] \times 18.47 = 112$$

$$p = \frac{RIn}{VQ} = \frac{6630 \times 12{,}045 \times 2}{92{,}200 \times 112} = 15.5 \text{ in.}$$

This computation indicates that the spacing of these rivets is not critical since, in conformance with the specifications for compression members (applicable to top flange), the maximum spacing in each line with staggered rivets must not exceed 24 times the thickness of the plate connected, with a maximum limit of 18 in. Hence the pitch in each line, assuming rivets staggered, should be not more than $24 \times \tfrac{7}{16} = 10\tfrac{1}{2}$ in. The actual spacing should provide for convenient fabrication and conform with this requirement.

The specifications require that the outstanding legs of bearing stiffeners extend as nearly as possible to the edge of the flange plates or angles. Allowing $\tfrac{1}{2}$ in. for the radius of fillet at the toe of the angle and $\tfrac{5}{8}$ in. for the flange angle thickness, the width of stiffener should be $6 - \tfrac{5}{8} - \tfrac{1}{2} = 4\tfrac{7}{8}$ in. to meet this requirement, and therefore an angle with a 4-in. outstanding leg will be used. The rivets connecting the stiffeners to the web transmit the end reaction, hence $92{,}200/7500 = 13$ rivets will be required. To provide space for these rivets, the four-angle arrangement shown in Fig. 179b will be adopted, each pair of angles transmitting one-half the reaction and requiring 7 rivets in the depth of the girder.

Assuming fitted stiffeners, each of the four outstanding legs must have a bearing area of $92{,}200/(4 \times 27{,}000) = 0.85$ sq in. on the flange angles. Deducting width occupied by the $\tfrac{1}{2}$-in. fillet of the flange angle, the bearing width is $3\tfrac{1}{2}$ in., hence the required thickness is $0.85/3.5 = 0.24$ in.

The specifications also require that projecting elements under compression, such as outstanding legs of stiffener angles, have a ratio of width to thickness not more than 16. To meet this requirement for a 4-in. angle, the thickness must be not less than $\tfrac{1}{4}$ in. Assuming $4 \times 3 \times \tfrac{1}{4}$ stiffener angles, the assembly will next be checked for column action. Each pair of angles, together with a strip of web $12 \times \tfrac{1}{4} = 3$ in. wide are considered to act as a column with a length of $\tfrac{3}{4} \times 35.25 = 27$ in. and a general area of cross section of 4.13 sq in. The angles are spaced $(2 \times \tfrac{5}{8}) + \tfrac{1}{4} = 1\tfrac{1}{2}$ in. back to back, and the radius of gyration of the assembly about the axis along the center of the web is 2.14. According to the provision for columns outlined in Article 101,

$$L/r = \frac{27}{2.14} = \quad 13$$

$$\text{Allowable } f = 17{,}000 - [0.485 \times (13)^2] = 16{,}920$$

$$\text{Safe load} = 16{,}920 \times 4.13 = 70{,}000 \text{ lb}$$

$$\text{Actual load} = \frac{92{,}200}{2} = 46{,}100 \text{ lb}$$

Therefore the assembly of 4 angles $4 \times 3 \times \tfrac{1}{4}$ appears to be satisfactory.

Since the value of h/t for the web of the girder is 114 thus exceeding 70, intermediate stiffeners are required at all points where v exceeds the value given by Equation 170, or

$$\frac{64,000,000}{(114)^2} = 4900 \text{ psi}$$

The total vertical shear on this section will equal $4,900 \times 36 \times \frac{1}{4} = 44,100$ lb, and its distance from the center of the span is $44,100/3,900 = 11.3$ ft. The specifications therefore require stiffeners for a distance of $(22.5 - 11.3) = 11.2$ ft from each end reaction. The spacing in these zones must not exceed 84 in. or that given by Equation 171a.

End panel

$$v = \frac{92,200}{36 \times \frac{1}{4}} = 10,250 \text{ psi}$$

$$\text{Required } d = \frac{11,000 \times \frac{1}{4}}{\sqrt{10,250}} = 27 \text{ in. to first stiffener}$$

Second panel (section 2 ft 3 in. from end of girder)

$$v = \frac{92,200 - (2.3 \times 3900)}{36 \times \frac{1}{4}} = 9250 \text{ psi}$$

$$\text{Required } d = \frac{11,000 \times \frac{1}{4}}{\sqrt{9250}} = 29 \text{ in.}$$

Use spacing of 27 in. between first and second stiffeners.
Third panel (section 4 ft 6 in. from end of girder)

$$v = \frac{92,200 - (4.5 \times 3900)}{36 \times \frac{1}{4}} = 8300 \text{ psi}$$

$$\text{Required } d = \frac{11,000 \times \frac{1}{4}}{\sqrt{8300}} = 30 \text{ in.}$$

Use 2 ft 6 in. between second and third stiffeners.
Fourth panel (section 7 ft from end of girder)

$$v = \frac{92,200 - (7 \times 3900)}{36 \times \frac{1}{4}} = 7200 \text{ psi}$$

$$\text{Required } d = \frac{11,000 \times \frac{1}{4}}{\sqrt{7200}} = 33 \text{ in.}$$

Use 2 ft 6 in. between third and fourth stiffeners.
Fifth panel (section 9 ft 6 in. from end of girder)

$$v = \frac{92,200 - (9.5 \times 3900)}{36 \times \frac{1}{4}} = 6127 \text{ psi}$$

$$\text{Required } d = \frac{11,000 \times \frac{1}{4}}{\sqrt{6127}} = 35 \text{ in.}$$

Use 2 ft 6 in. between fourth and fifth stiffeners.

The foregoing stiffener spacings provide a total of 12 ft, which covers the distance over which stiffeners are required.

The required size of the intermediate stiffeners is determined in accordance with Equation 172, as follows:

$$H = 36 \text{ in.}$$

$$\text{Required } I_s = 0.00000016 \times (36)^4 = 0.2687$$

For a $4 \times 3 \times \frac{1}{4}$ single angle, crimped over the flange angles with the 3-in. leg against the web,

$$\text{Actual } I_s = 1.0(1.69 \times 1.24 \times 1.24) = 3.6$$

These stiffeners therefore satisfy the requirements of the specifications.

PROBLEMS

10·1   A rolled-steel beam is to be designed to carry a load of 2000 lb per ft (not including its own weight) uniformly distributed over a simple span of 20 ft. Assuming the beam to have full lateral support and using the allowable stresses for buildings as specified by the A.I.S.C. (1946), select the minimum weight beam required (wide flange or American Standard).

10·2   A floor slab is supported on 12*I*31.8 I-beams spaced at 3-ft centers and having a span of 12 ft. The dead weight of the floor is 100 lb per sq ft. (*a*) What is the safe live load per square foot of floor for a maximum fiber stress in the I-beams of 15,000 psi? (*b*) What live load will cause the I-beams to deflect a total amount of $\frac{1}{360}$ of the span?

10·3   The continuous steel beam shown is to carry the front wall of a building over two store fronts. Assume that the load shown includes the dead weight of the beam. Select the most economical beam (American Standard) that can be used.

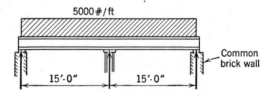

Assume that the floor at this beam level furnishes full lateral support. What length of bearing plate would be required at the support to prevent crippling of the web? What area of bearing plate is required at the brick walls to prevent crushing of the brick, if the allowable bearing stress is 200 psi (A.I.S.C. Specifications, 1946)?

10·4   An 18 WF 50 steel beam carries a total uniform load of 300 lb per linear ft over a simple span of 20 ft. The beam is supported laterally only at the center and ends. Is the beam satisfactory in the light of the A.I.S.C. Specifications (1946) for buildings, for tension and compression on extreme fiber, for shear, and for web crippling with ends bearing on 8-in. walls? Show computations.

10·5 The beam ABC is simply supported at A and rests on a bearing plate at B. A concentrated load of 100,000 lb is applied at C. If the allowable unit stresses are

18,000 psi for normal fiber stress
12,000 psi for average shearing stress
15,000 psi for vertical buckling of web

select an I-beam section (either wide flange or standard) based on (*a*) the required section modulus, and (*b*) the required web thickness for shear and vertical buckling, (*c*) check compressive stress in web over support.

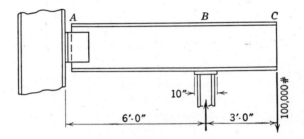

10·6 A 16 WF 36 beam is simply supported at A, overhangs the support at B, and is laterally supported throughout. Neglecting the weight of the beam, if the allowable unit stresses are

Tension and compression—20,000 psi
Average shear on web—13,000 psi
Direct compression causing web crippling—24,000 psi

can the beam safely carry a concentrated load P of 40,000 lb?

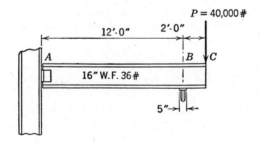

10·7 Is the beam shown satisfactory as judged by the following allowable unit stresses:

Tension and compression on extreme fibers, 18,000 psi

Average unit shearing stress in web, $\dfrac{18,000}{1 + \dfrac{h^2}{7200t^2}}$, but not to exceed 12,000 psi.

Vertical compression on web, $16,000-170 \frac{d}{t}$, but not to exceed 14,000 psi.

Direct compression between flange and web over support is 24,000 psi.

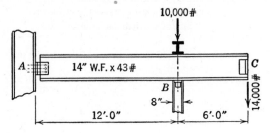

10·8 A beam of the section shown is assembled from four standard channels. If the span length is 40 ft, determine the maximum allowable moment and the corresponding uniformly distributed live load. Consider the compression flange as being effectively supported against lateral deflection only at its ends and midpoint.

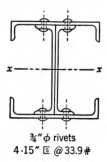

¾″ φ rivets
4·15″ ⌷ @ 33.9#

What is the maximum allowable spacing of ¾-in. rivets in pairs at a point where the transverse shear force is 73,000 lb? Use the American Institute of Steel Construction "Specification for the Design Fabrication and Erection of Structural Steel for Buildings," 1946.

10·9 A 12 in. × 25 lb channel is riveted with ¾-in. rivets in pairs to a 21 WF 63 beam as shown. (*a*) Using the A.I.S.C. Specifications (1946), determine the safe resisting moment of this beam which is carrying a uniform load over a span of 20 ft

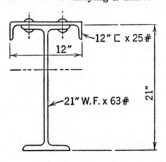

laterally supported only at the ends. (*b*) If the allowable stresses on rivets are 15,000

psi in shear and 32,000 psi in bearing, what should be the theoretical spacing of the rivets at a point where the vertical or transverse shear is 40,000 lb?

10·10 A plate-girder section is composed of the following:

$$1 \text{ web plate, } 58 \times \tfrac{3}{8}$$
$$4 \text{ flange angles, } 6 \times 6 \times \tfrac{1}{2}$$
$$2 \text{ cover plates, } 14 \times \tfrac{1}{2}$$
$$\text{Rivets, } \tfrac{7}{8} \text{ in. as shown}$$

The distance back to back of angles is $58\tfrac{1}{2}$ in. If the allowable stress is 18,000 psi, what is the safe resisting moment of the girder section according to the A.R.E.A.

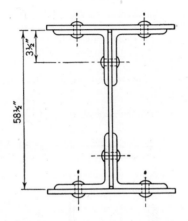

Specifications (1944)? If the allowable intensity of stress on rivets is 13,500 psi in shear and 32,000 psi in bearing, what spacing of rivets connecting the flange to the web will be required at a point where the vertical shear, V, is 140,000 lb?

10·11 Two 10 in. × 15 lb channels are fastened to a 14 WF 34 beam by $\tfrac{3}{4}$ in. diameter rivets, as shown. The beam thus formed carries a uniform load over a simple span of 16 ft with lateral support at the ends only. (*a*) Using the A.R.E.A.

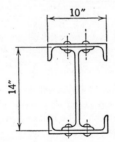

Specifications (1944) for the design and construction of steel railway bridges, find the maximum permissible total uniform load for this beam. (*b*) If the allowable rivet stresses are 15,000 psi in shear and 32,000 psi in bearing, determine the theoretical spacing of flange rivets at a section where the shear is 25,000 lb.

10·12 For the girder section shown, using the approximate method, and assuming one-eighth the web effective as flange area, determine the safe resisting moment based on a tensile flange stress of 16,000 psi.

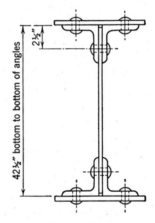

10·13 A plate girder is composed of the following section:

$$2 \text{ cover plates, } 10 \times \tfrac{1}{2}$$
$$4 \text{ flange angles, } 4 \times 4 \times \tfrac{1}{2}$$
$$1 \text{ web plate, } 42 \times \tfrac{3}{8}$$
$$\text{Rivets—}\tfrac{7}{8} \text{ in. as shown.}$$

Using net section in both flanges and the moment of inertia method, what is the safe resisting moment of this girder if the allowable fiber stress is 18,000 psi?

10·14 A 10 WF 49 section is to be used as an axially loaded, pin-end column with a length of 20 ft. Find the allowable load for such a column (*a*) according to the A.I.S.C. Specifications (1946), and (*b*) according to the A.R.E.A. Specifications (1944).

10·15 If a 10 WF 49 section is subjected to an axial load of 100,000 lb, what concentrated transverse load can be carried at the center of the effective span of 20 ft if the ends are free to rotate? The bending occurs about the major axis, and the allowable combined stresses are

$$\text{Tension} \qquad 18,000 \text{ psi}$$

$$\text{Compression} \qquad \dfrac{20,000}{1 + \dfrac{L^2}{2000b^2}}$$

10·16 This column is a 14 WF 202 section. It carries a load of 400,000 lb acting through pins 4 in. from the midaxis of the column as shown. Check the design

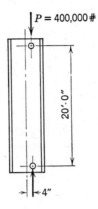

against the A.I.S.C. Specifications (1946) for buildings, using the following formula as the criterion for safe stress conditions:

$$\frac{f_a}{F_a} + \frac{f_b}{F_b} = 1$$

10·17 A load of 3 tons moves along the 12-ft arm of the post crane. Assume no impact. Design column AB in accordance with A.I.S.C. Specifications (1946).

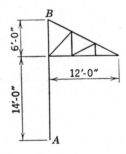

Chapter 11

LIGHT-GAGE STEEL CONSTRUCTION

110 Description

Structural members formed from light-gage sheet and strip steel are now frequently used for light building construction. Since sheet and strip steel can be readily cold formed into a wide variety of shapes, its usefulness is limited only by the ingenuity of the designer and the

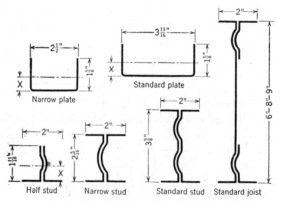

Fig. 187. Stran-Steel Sections.

economy of the resulting construction. Typical of the structural members which can be made in this manner are those produced by the Stran-Steel Division of Great Lakes Steel Corporation and whose dimensions and general properties are shown in Fig. 187 and Table 35. A distinctive feature of Stran-Steel members is the patented nailing groove (Fig. 188), which permits the fastening of collateral material to wall studs or joists by ordinary nailing methods. Typical Stran-Steel roof framing is shown in Fig. 189.

111 Properties of Sheet and Strip Steel

The base material, from which light-gage members are formed, is usually steel strip produced on a continuous strip-steel mill which is mechanically equipped to govern both the width and gage of the material and thus insure uniformity of the resulting product. The steel may

have such physical and chemical properties as are desired, and, as a safeguard against corrosion, copper-bearing steel is commonly used. The steel is produced by the strip mill in the form of continuous coils several thousand feet in length. These coils are then passed through a

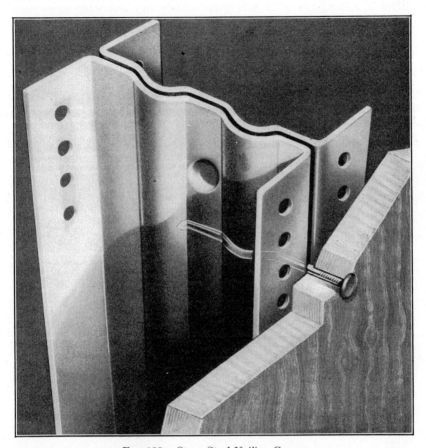

FIG. 188. Stran-Steel Nailing Groove.

straightening roll and slitter, which cuts the material to the required width for forming, after which shears cut it to the specified lengths. The pieces are then passed through forming rolls or other cold-forming devices which produce the desired shape of section and are spot-welded together to make the desired assembly.

The A.S.T.M. Specifications [1] for light-gage structural quality flat-rolled carbon steel specifies chemical composition and tensile properties

[1] American Society for Testing Materials, Serial Designation A 246-41T.

for four grades of steel of thicknesses varying from 0.0477 to 0.0225 inch corresponding to the United States Standard Gage 18 to 24. Grade C steel by this specification has a minimum tensile strength of 52,000 pounds per square inch and a yield point of 33,000. Strip steel furnished in accordance with this specification may not vary more than 0.003 inch from the specified gage thickness.

Courtesy Stran Steel Division Great Lakes Steel Corp.

FIG. 189.   Typical Roof Framing with Stran-Steel Sections.

Another A.S.T.M. Specification [2] for light-gage structural quality flat-rolled carbon steel specifies chemical composition and tensile properties for four grades of steel of thicknesses varying from 0.2499 to 0.0478 inch corresponding to the United States Standard Gage 3 to 18. Grade C steel by this specification has a minimum tensile strength of 55,000 pounds per square inch and a yield point of 33,000. Strip steel over $3\frac{1}{2}$ inches wide, furnished in accordance with this specification, may not vary more than 0.003 to 0.006 inch from the specified gage thickness.

112   Elastic Stability

The distinguishing characteristic of light-gage steel members as compared with hot-rolled structural sections is the large ratio of width to

[2] American Society for Testing Materials, Serial Designation A 245-41T.

thickness of webs and outstanding elements of the sections. A cold-formed C-shaped section, 8 in. × 4 in. × $\frac{3}{4}$ in., made of 15-gage material will have b/t ratios of 11 for the lips, 59 for the flanges, and 119 for the web, whereas the A.I.S.C. Specifications for the design, fabrication, and erection of structural steel for buildings,[3] covering the use of hot-rolled sections, specifies that projecting elements of members shall not have a greater ratio of width to thickness than 12 for single angle struts and 16 for other members including compression flanges of beams and girders.

A member is elastically stable when it is able to retain its alignment under compressive buckling load without aid from outside stabilizing influence. Consideration of elastic stability is of particular importance for such material as steel which at the yield stress may suffer relatively large deformation without corresponding increase in load. It is, however, of importance only for material in compression since tensile force tends to pull the material into the line of action of the applied force.

The elastic stability of material acted upon by a compressive force was first discussed by L. Euler in 1744 with respect to the overall buckling of columns. Thus, when an axial compressive force is applied to a pin-ended bar, some bending-moment will be induced by unintentional eccentricity of loading or crookedness of the bar with the result that it will bend out of its original alignment. If a small lateral force is now applied to the bar its deflection will increase, but the bar will return to its original deflected form when the lateral force is removed, provided the axial load is less than that defined as the *critical load*. At the *critical* value of the axial load P_{cr}, however, any small lateral force will cause deflection from which the bar will not recover, and it is said to become *elastically unstable* at this point. For a bar with pin ends, Euler [4] determined the critical axial load to be

$$P_{cr} = \frac{\pi^2 EI}{L^2} \tag{177}$$

The average unit stress over the cross section, under this condition of loading, is obtained from Equation 177 as

$$f_1 = \frac{P_{cr}}{A} = \frac{\pi^2 E}{(L/r)^2} \tag{178}$$

It should be observed that the assumptions used in the derivation of Equations 177 and 178 are valid only within the proportional limit for the material and that the bar always becomes unstable when f_{cr} equals the yield stress of the material.

[3] Revised Edition, February, 1946.
[4] S. Timoshenko, *Theory of Elastic Stability*, McGraw-Hill Book Company, 1936.

113   Elastic Stability of Thin Plates in Compression

The Euler theory, discussed in Article 112, is based upon the assumptions ordinarily made for pure bending; that cross sections of the bar remain plane and rotate only so as to remain normal to the deflection curve; that the deflection is quite small compared with the dimension of the section in the direction of the deflection; and that the differential equation of the elastic curve is

$$M = EI \frac{d_2 y}{dx^2} \qquad (179)$$

Equation 179 takes into account only the resistance of the material to bending in one direction, and the term E is the measure of the resistance of the material to deformation from stress in one direction only. For thin wide plates with restrained or supported edges, the material between the edge supports will be bent simultaneously in two directions by buckling action, and the term E must therefore be modified in such a manner as to take into account the resistance to change in form produced by this condition.   Thus, for such a condition, the term E should be replaced [5] by

$$E' = \frac{E}{(1 - u^2)} \qquad (180)$$

where E = Young's modulus = $29.5 \times (10)^6$ for steel.
u = Poisson's ratio = 0.3 for steel.

With this interpretation of the value of E', Equation 178 would be written in the form

$$f_1 = \frac{\pi^2 E t^2}{12(1 - u^2)L^2} \qquad (181)$$

The Bryan-Timoshenko formula is the most generally accepted expression for the critical compressive stress on thin plates with restrained or supported edges.   The theoretical analysis from which this formula was derived is accredited to G. H. Bryan,[6] and the discussion has been extended principally by Timoshenko but also by others.   Expressed in general form, for steel plates, this formula gives the following valve for the critical stress.

$$f_{cr} = K f_1 = \frac{\pi^2 K E t^2}{12(1 - u^2)b^2} = 0.9038 K E \left(\frac{t}{b}\right)^2 \qquad (182)$$

[5] Timoshenko and Lessels, *Applied Elasticity*, p. 52, Westinghouse Technical Night School Press, 1925.

[6] "London Mathematical Society," *Proc.*, Vol. XXII, 1891, p. 54.

where f_{cr} = critical buckling unit stress.

f_1 = critical compressive stress as regards buckling in the direction of the width of the plate as given by the Euler formula (Equation 181) when $L = b$.

t = thickness of plate.

b = width of plate.

K = a coefficient depending upon the ratio of the length to the width of the plate and upon an integer m which represents the number of half waves into which the plate buckles.

$= (L/mb + mb/L)^2$ (183)

It has been established by several investigators [7] that for plates whose length in the direction of the applied compression force exceeds two to three times the width, the value of K may be taken as follows:

One edge supported, other edge free	$K = 0.5$
One edge clamped, other edge free	$K = 1.33$
Both edges supported	$K = 4.0$
Both edges clamped	$K = 7.0$

A *supported* edge is one which is prevented by some suitable means from deflecting in a direction perpendicular to the width of the plate; a *clamped* edge represents one which is, in addition, restrained against rotation. According to the A.I.S.I. Specifications,[8] an element which is stiffened at only one edge parallel to the direction of stress is defined as an *unstiffened element*; elements which are stiffened along both edges by connections to a stiffening means, such as a web, flange, or stiffening lip, are regarded as *stiffened* elements. These specifications require that the stiffener running along the edge of the element have the following minimum moment of inertia:

$$I_{\min} = 1.83t^4 \sqrt{\left(\frac{b}{t}\right)^2 - 144}$$ (184)

where b = width of the element.

t = thickness of the element.

When the stiffener consists of a simple lip, bent at right angles to the stiffened element, the required depth d of such lip may be approximated by the formula [8]

$$d = 2.8t \left[\left(\frac{b}{t}\right)^2 - 144\right]^{1/6}$$ (185)

---

[7] Timoshenko and Lessels, *Applied Elasticity*, p. 292: "The Problem of Elastic Stability," by L. Donnell, *Aeronautical Engg.*, Vol. 5, No. 4, October–December,1933, p. 141.

[8] American Iron and Steel Institute Specifications for the Design of Light-Gage Structural Members, 1946.

It is of course often impossible to establish precisely the condition or degree of support or restraint furnished the edges of the plate by adjacent elements of construction; therefore the value of K to be used for a particular condition must depend largely upon judgment and should be chosen to provide reasonable and safe limitations on design.

Since the basic conditions assumed in the derivation of the Bryan-Timoshenko formula are the same as were noted for the Euler formula, Equation 182 is invalid beyond the proportional limit, and the critical stress will never be greater than the yield stress of the material. The proportional limit is that point at which the stress-strain curve deviates from a straight line, and the determination of its value requires precise instrumentation and testing procedure. Tests reported by various investigators have shown values of the proportional limit for steel ranging from 30 to 100 per cent of the tensile yield stress. The lower values were obtained with exceptionally precise instruments and with the loading applied slowly; whereas the large values were determined with rapidly applied loading and by measuring instruments incapable of detecting minute deformations. The higher values are also generally applied to high-carbon steels. For steels with a yield point of 25 to 40,000 pounds per square inch, the proportional limit will generally be definite at a stress of about five-eighths of the yield stress.

Various procedures [9] have been proposed for estimating values of the critical stress when its value is between the proportional limit and the yield stress. The method adopted for the following derivations is based on the assumption that the proportional limit is five-eighths of the yield stress, Young's modulus of elasticity equals $29.5 \times (10)^6$ and that between the proportional limit and the yield point the value of E in Equation 182 varies in accordance with the relationship shown by the following equation:

$$E = \left[\frac{f_y - f_{cr}}{f_y - f_{pl}}\right] 29.5 \times (10)^6 \qquad (186)$$

where f_y = yield stress.

f_{pl} = proportional limit.

f_{cr} = critical stress (between f_{pl} and f_y).

Based upon this interpretation of E, Equation 182 would be replaced by two equations, one covering the range where f_{cr} is greater than f_{pl} and the other the range where f_{cr} is less than f_{pl}.

[9] S. Timoshenko, *Theory of Elastic Stability*, p. 157, McGraw-Hill Book Company, 1936.

When f_{cr} is greater than f_{pl},

$$f_{cr} = \frac{71,100,000\ K}{\left(\dfrac{b}{t}\right)^2 + \dfrac{71,100,000\ K}{f_y}} \tag{187}$$

When f_{cr} is less than f_{pl},

$$f_{cr} = \frac{26,662,000\ K}{\left(\dfrac{b}{t}\right)^2} \tag{188}$$

Values of f_{cr} as given by Equations 187 and 188 are represented graphically by the solid line curves in Fig. 190 for steel having a yield stress of 33,000 pounds per square inch. For plates supported along one edge $K = 0.5$ and supported along both edges $K = 4.0$.

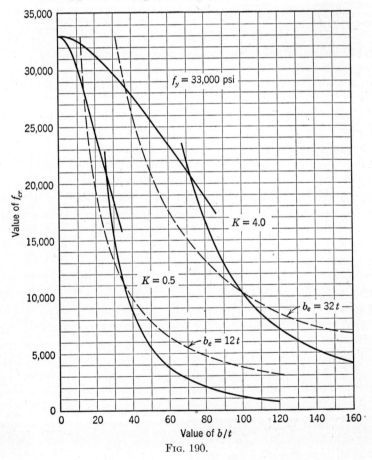

Fig. 190.

114   Ultimate Compressive Load

As a result of research on Dural sheets to which stiffening elements are attached, as commonly used in the aeronautical industry, it has been established that the contribution of the sheet to the combination is somewhat greater than that obtained by computing the ultimate resistance of the sheet as that produced by the critical stress. This condition is more pronounced for sheets whose b/t ratio is large (in excess of 100) than for sheets with smaller values of b/t. Equations 187 and 188 are based upon a uniform distribution of the load over the area of the section and up to the value of f_{cr} given by these equations, the usual assumptions made in flexural analysis hold with satisfactory accuracy. If, however, the load is increased, some portions of the section will develop no further resistance, and the local buckles will become more pronounced as the load is increased further. Portions of the section adjacent to supported edges will be prevented from developing local buckles by the support, and these areas will thus continue to develop increased resistance to the load. The ultimate value of P will be reached when these areas develop a unit stress approaching, f_y and the value of P_{ult} will generally be greater than P_{cr}. At the ultimate stage of loading, however, the unit stress on the section will not be uniform; near supported edges it may approach closely the value f_y; at the outer edge of a plate supported along one edge only or at the center of a plate supported along two edges, it may likely be less than the value of f_{cr} given by Equation 182. For a plate supported along two edges it is sometimes assumed that at the ultimate load the stress in the section is distributed in the form of a sine curve [10] with the unit stress equal to f_{cr} at the center of the width and represented by f_e (not greater than f_y) at the supported edges. The resulting ultimate load is then expressed as

$$P_{ult} = \tfrac{1}{2}bt(f_e + f_{cr}) \tag{189}$$

The foregoing analysis of the value of the ultimate load gives rise to the employment of a so-called *effective width* with P_{ult} expressed in the form

$$P_{ult} = f_e b_e t \tag{190}$$

where $\tfrac{1}{2}b_e$ = width of effective strip along supported edge.

Equating the values of P_{ult} as given by Equations 189 and 190 we have

$$\tfrac{1}{2}b_e = 0.25b(1 + f_{cr}/f_e) \tag{191}$$

The value of f_{cr}/f_e will vary from a maximum of unity when $f_e = f_{cr}$ to a minimum of f_{cr}/f_y when $f_e = f_y$.

---

[10] Sechler and Dunn, *Airplane Structural Analysis and Design,* John Wiley and Sons, 1942.

When f_e has the limiting value of f_y from Equation 190

$$f_{ult} = \frac{P_{ult}}{bt} = \frac{f_y b_e t}{bt} = f_y \left(\frac{b_e}{b}\right) \tag{192}$$

Based upon laboratory tests of stiffened Dural sheets, E. E. Sechler [11] proposed the use of the following empirical equation for the effective width:

$$\frac{1}{2} b_e = 0.447b \sqrt{\frac{f_{cr}}{f_e}} \tag{193}$$

Substituting the appropriate values for Dural in Equation 182 gives

$$E = 10.3 \times (10)^6$$

$$u = 0.3$$

$$K = 4.0 \text{ for plate supported along two edges}$$

$$f_{cr} = \frac{37.2366 \times (10)^6}{\left(\dfrac{b}{t}\right)^2}$$

Based on the limiting value of $f_e = f_y = 40,000$ pounds per square inch, the effective width from Equation 193 is $b_e = 27.3t$.

The American Institute of Steel Construction Specification (1946) for the design, fabrication, and erection of structural steel for buildings permits b/t ratios of 12 to 16 for projecting elements of members under compression and states that, when a projecting element exceeds the width-to-thickness ratio prescribed and would satisfy the stress requirements with a portion of its width removed, the member will be considered acceptable without the actual removal of the excess width. According to this specification, therefore, the limiting value of P_{cr} would be determined from Equation 190 when $f_e = f_y$ and $b_e = 12$ to $16t$.

The A.I.S.C. Specification further states that for compression members the unsupported width of web, cover, or diaphragm plates shall not exceed 40 times the thickness but that when the width exceeds the limit and a portion of its width no greater than 40 times the thickness would satisfy the stress requirements, the member will be considered as acceptable. According to this specification the limiting value of P_{cr} would be determined from Equation 190 when $f_e = f_y$ and $b_e = 40t$.

[11] "The Strength of Thin Plates in Compression," by T. von Kármán, E. E. Sechler, and L. H. Donnell, *Trans. A.S.M.E.* Vol. 54, No. 2, January 30, 1932.

While the foregoing limits of effective width may be satisfactory for structural steel members composed of material more than $\frac{3}{16}$ inch thick, the author recommends more conservative limits for light-gage material less than $\frac{3}{16}$ inch thick and suggests a limiting value of $12t$ for plates supported along one edge and $32t$ for plates supported along both edges.

Values of f_{cr}, as given by Equation 192, corresponding to b_e equal to $12t$ and $32t$, respectively, are shown graphically by the dotted line curves in Fig. 190 for steel with a yield stress of 33,000 pounds per square inch.

115   Critical Stress

In structural design, working stresses and loads are based upon the yield stress of the material despite the fact that members may withstand ultimate loads considerably beyond this limit. For tension members this practice is perhaps conservative, since stress beyond the yield point may possibly do no harm other than producing some permanent elongation or perhaps excessive deflection of the structure. In tests of rolled-structural-steel I-beams, conducted at the University of Illinois,[12] it was found that, for nearly all the beams tested, "excessive deformation, large permanent set, or other signs of structural damage was observed at computed fiber stresses not much higher, if any, than the yield strength of the material." For this reason, the report of these tests states, "It is unsafe practice to regard as the ultimate stress in flexure any value higher than the yield point strength of the material of the beam." For material in compression elastic instability will always be encountered when the unit stress equals the yield stress; local wrinkles will develop when the average unit stress reaches the values determined by Equations 187 and 188, and the limit of resistance will be reached when the unit stress reaches the value determined by Equation 190. For thin plates subject to the condition of elastic instability, the critical stress should be used in place of the yield stress of the material, to determine working stresses.

For practical design purposes, the author recommends that the critical stress be determined by the use of a straight-line equation coupled with the provision that f_{cr} be considered not less than the value given by Equation 192 when b_e equals $12t$ for elements supported along one edge and $32t$ for elements supported along both edges. Thus, when $f_{cr} = kf_y$, *for elements supported along one edge,*

$$k = \frac{f_{cr}}{f_y} = \left[1.05 + \frac{f_y}{103,000} \right] - \left[0.0048 + \frac{f_y}{1,270,000} \right] \frac{b}{i}   (194)$$

[12] "The Strength of Steel I-Beams in Flexure," by Herbert F. Moore, University of Illinois, Engineering Experiment Station, Bulletin No. 68.

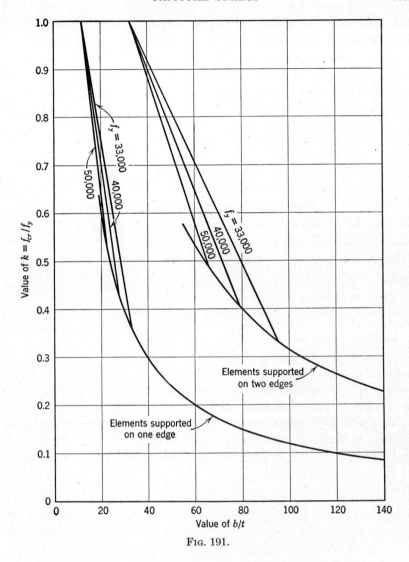

Fig. 191.

but not less than $12/(b/t)$ and not greater than unity. *For elements supported along both edges,*

$$k = \frac{f_{cr}}{f_y} = \left[1.062 + \frac{f_y}{121,000} \right] - \left[0.0019 + \frac{f_y}{3,846,000} \right] \frac{b}{t} \quad (195)$$

but not less than $32/(b/t)$ and not greater than unity. When $f_y = 33,000$, Equation 194 reduces to the form

For elements supported along one edge

$$k = 1.371 - 0.0308 \left(\frac{b}{t}\right) \tag{196}$$

but not less than $12/(b/t)$ and not greater than unity. When $f_y = 33{,}000$, Equation 195 reduces to the form

For elements supported along both edges

$$k = 1.335 - 0.0105 \left(\frac{b}{t}\right) \tag{197}$$

but not less than $32/(b/t)$ and not greater than unity. Values of k as given by Equations 194 and 195 are shown graphically in Fig. 191 for various values of f_y.

In determining the b/t ratios of elements composing the section, the author recommends that b equal the width of the flat portion of the element exclusive of curved edge fillets, and t is the thickness of the element.

116　Form Factor for Sections in Compression

The ultimate compressive load resisted by a section made up of rectangular elements will be a composite of the strength of the elements comprising the section. Let such a section be divided into rectangular elements which have the respective areas a_1, a_2, etc. Let the values of $k = f_{cr}/f_y$ for each of these elements be indicated as k_1, k_2, etc. Then, if k_1 is the least of these values of k, element a_1 will reach its limit of resistance when the total load on the section has the value

$$P_1 = k_1 f_y (a_1 + a_2 + a_3 \cdots + a_n)$$

This element will be prevented from actually failing at this point by virtue of the greater resistance of the other elements of the section, and, if the total load on the section is increased, its resistance will remain nearly constant until substantial deformation of other elements has occurred. Now if the load is increased to a value P_2, assuming element a_1 to offer no additional resistance, element a_2 will reach its limit of its resistance when

$$P_2 = k_1 f_y a_1 + k_2 f_y (a_2 + a_3 \cdots + a_n)$$

As the load on the section is increased further, each additional element will, in a similar manner, successively reach the limit of its resistance,

and the limit of load will be reached when

$$P_{ult} = k_1 f_y a_1 + k_2 f_y a_2 + k_3 f_y a_3 \cdots + k_n f_y a_n$$
$$= f_y \Sigma k a = F f_y A, \text{ where}$$

$$F = form\ factor\ \text{of section} = \frac{\Sigma k a}{A} = \frac{\Sigma k b t}{\Sigma b t} \qquad (198)$$

A = gross area of section.

$k = f_{cr}/f_y$ determined from Equations 194 and 195.

b = flat width of any element (exclusive of fillets).

t = thickness of any element.

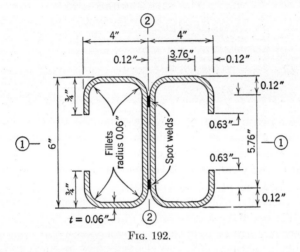

FIG. 192.

The determination of the form factor of the section shown in Fig. 192 is as follows:

Example

The section will be considered as made up of rectangular elements having the following flat width to thickness ratios.

$$\text{2 webs} \qquad \frac{b}{t} = \frac{5.76}{0.06} = 96$$

$$\text{4 flanges} \qquad \frac{b}{t} = \frac{3.76}{0.06} = 62.5$$

$$\text{4 flange stiffeners} \qquad \frac{b}{t} = \frac{0.63}{0.06} = 10.5$$

The webs are supported along both edges by the outstanding flanges; the flange stiffening lips are supported along one edge; the flanges are supported along one

edge by the web and may also be considered as supported along the other edge
since (Equation 185)

$$\tfrac{3}{4} \text{ in.} > 2.8 \times 0.06[(62.5)^2 - 144]^{\frac{1}{6}} = 0.662 \text{ in.}$$

Assuming the section to be made of structural grade steel ($f_y = 33,000$) values
of the k factors for the several elements are obtained from Equations 196 and
197 as follows:

Webs $\qquad\qquad k = 1.335 - (0.0105 \times 96) = 0.33$

$$\text{use } k = \tfrac{32}{96} = 0.33$$

Flanges $\qquad\quad\, k = 1.335 - (0.0105 \times 62.5) = 0.68$

Stiffening lips $\quad k = 1.371 - (0.0308 \times 10.5) = 1.047$

$$\text{use } k = 1.0$$

$$F = \frac{(2 \times 0.33 \times 5.76) + (4 \times 0.68 \times 3.76) + (4 \times 1 \times 0.63)}{(2 \times 5.76) + (4 \times 3.76) + (4 \times 0.63)}$$

$$= \frac{16.55}{29.08} = 0.57$$

It will be noted that F measures the ultimate unit stress on the composite section in terms of the yield stress of the material and that for
the section used in the above example, the *effective* yield stress is
57 per cent of the yield stress of the material. It will also be observed
that, since the value of F never exceeds unity, only sections composed
entirely of elements, which are elastically stable at unit stresses equal
to the yield stress, have a form factor of unity.

This procedure can be applied only to sections which may be divided
into rectangular elements; curved elements have a much greater buckling resistance, but no data is yet available for theoretical analysis of
their behavior.

When sections are comprised of elements which have a wide diver-
gence in their values of k, considerable distortion of the more elastically
unstable elements may occur before actual failure of the composite
section. For such members the factor of safety should be chosen with
due regard to these more unstable elements.

117 Allowable Unit Stress on Light-Gage Steel

For hot-rolled structural shapes made of steel with a yield stress of
33,000 pounds per square inch, the basic unit stress allowed by the
A.I.S.C. Specification is 20,000 pounds per square inch, which corresponds to $f_y/1.65$. Since the permissible underrun in thickness is 0.01
inch, a $\tfrac{3}{16}$-inch plate designed for 20,000 pounds per square inch might
actually be stressed to 21,200 pounds per square inch.

Tolerance in thickness of strip steel is a greater percentage of the thickness than for hot rolled plates; hence, for the same limiting stress on material with maximum underrun in thickness, the basic unit stress should be decreased accordingly. On this account, a safety factor of 1.85 based on the yield stress is recommended for light-gage steel, and the basic unit stress would therefore be expressed as follows:

For material in tension,

$$f = \frac{f_y}{1.85} \tag{199}$$

For material in compression,

$$f = \frac{F f_y}{1.85} \tag{200}$$

where F = form factor.

The American Iron and Steel Institute Specifications (1946) for the design of light-gage structural members specifies a basic tensile stress of $f_y/1.85$ and the same value in compression for elements supported on one edge when b/t is not greater than 12. When b/t is greater than 12 but less than 30, these specifications allow a value of unit stress given by the following formula:

$$f_c = \left(\frac{5}{3} f_b - 5430\right) - \frac{1}{18} (f_b - 8150) \frac{b}{t} \tag{201}$$

where b = flat width of projecting element, exclusive of fillets.
  t = thickness.
  $f_b = f_y/1.85$.

When b/t is greater than 30 but not more than 60,

$$f_c = 12{,}600 - 148.5 \left(\frac{b}{t}\right) \tag{202}$$

For elements supported along both edges, the A.I.S.I. Specifications allow the basic stress of $f_y/1.85$ on an *effective design width*, computed as follows: For stress determinations for b/t equal or less than

$$M = \frac{[17.5 \times (10)^6 + \sqrt{[17.5 \times (10)^6]^2 - [436 \times (10)^6][7600\sqrt{f} - 25f]}}{7600\sqrt{f} - 25f} \tag{203}$$

$$b_e = \left\{ \frac{[17.5 \times (10)^6]\left(\frac{b}{t} - 25\right)}{fM^2} + 25 \right\} t \tag{204}$$

When b/t is greater than M,

$$b_e = \frac{7600t}{\sqrt{f}}\left[1 - \frac{2300}{\left(\frac{b}{t}\right)\sqrt{f}}\right] \tag{205}$$

For deflection determinations, when b/t is equal or less than

$$N = \frac{[32.2 \times (10)^6] + \sqrt{[32.2 \times (10)^6]^2 - [805 \times (10)^6][10{,}320\sqrt{f} - 25f]}}{10{,}320\sqrt{f} - 25f} \tag{206}$$

$$b_e = \left\{\frac{[32.2 \times (10)^6]\left[\dfrac{b}{t} - 25\right]}{fN^2} + 25\right\}t \tag{207}$$

For b/t greater than N,

$$b_e = \frac{10{,}320t}{\sqrt{f}}\left[1 - \frac{3120}{\left(\frac{b}{t}\right)\sqrt{f}}\right] \tag{208}$$

where b = flat width of compression element (exclusive of curved fillets).

b_e = effective design width used in determining the area, moment of inertia, etc., of the effective section.

f = unit stress on the compression element computed on the basis of the effective design width.

The portion of the width considered as removed to arrive at the effective design width is located symmetrically about the centerline of the element.

118 Light-Gage Steel Beams

The load capacity of light-gage steel beams will usually be controlled by the allowable unit stress on the compression flange. Shear stress in the web at the supports and at concentrated loads must also be given careful consideration.

When the elements of the compression flange have such proportions that the flange is elastically unstable at stresses corresponding to the yield stress of the material, consideration must be given to the form factor of the flange. The effective-yield stress may be considered as equal to Ff_y, where F is the form factor of the elements comprising the flange area, if the flange is secured against lateral deflection.

When the compression flange is not fully secured against lateral bending, the allowable stress for vertical bending must be further reduced to allow for the additional stress induced by such lateral bending action.

The A.I.S.I. Specifications (1946) require that the maximum compression in pounds per square inch on the extreme fiber of laterally unsupported compression flanges of straight I-shaped members shall not exceed

$$f = \frac{250{,}000{,}000}{\left(\dfrac{L}{r}\right)^2} \tag{209}$$

where r is the radius of gyration of the entire section about the gravity axis parallel to the web.

Web stresses in light-gage beams are frequently critical under concentrated loads and at bearing on supports. The A.I.S.I. Specifications (1946) require that the maximum average shear stress on the gross area of a flat web shall not exceed

$$v = \frac{64{,}000{,}000}{\left(\dfrac{h}{t}\right)^2} \tag{210}$$

with a maximum of $\frac{2}{3} \times f_y/1.85$

where h = clear distance between flanges.

t = web thickness.

In webs consisting of two or more sheets, each sheet is to be considered as a separate member carrying its share of the stress.

To avoid crippling of flat webs, the A.I.S.I. Specifications (1946) require lengths of bearing as follows:

(a) For concentrated load at any point in the span or for the reaction of continuous supports

$$B = t\left[\frac{1.85P}{2.41t^2f_y} - 4.62\right]^2 \tag{211}$$

= minimum length of bearing (inches)

(b) For concentrated loads on the outer end of cantilevers or simple end reaction of beams

$$B = t\left[\frac{1.85P}{0.93t^2f_y} - 8\right]^2 \tag{212}$$

= minimum length of bearing (inches)

The following examples illustrate the procedures discussed in this article.

Example 1

Using the form factor procedure discussed in Article 116, determine the safe total uniformly distributed load for a simply supported beam of 12-ft span. The beam is made of structural-grade steel and has the cross section shown in Fig. 193. The top flange is continuously supported against lateral deflection at all points in the span.

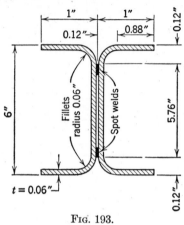

Fig. 193.

The properties of the gross section are computed by the usual methods, with the following results: Neutral axis at mid-point of depth

$$I = 4.15 \text{ in.}^4 \qquad S = 1.38$$

Allowable unit stress:
  Tension flange

$$f = \frac{f_y}{1.85} = \frac{33,000}{1.85} = 18,000 \text{ psi}$$

  Compression flange. Flange is assumed to consist of the outstanding flat elements supported along one edge only by the web.

$$\frac{b}{t} = \frac{0.88}{0.06} = 14.7$$

From Equation 196,

$$k = 1.371 - (0.0308 \times 14.7)$$

$$= 0.92$$

Allowable $f = 0.92 \times 18,000 = 16,600$ psi

$$\text{Safe } W = \frac{1.38 \times 16,600}{1.5 \times 12} = 12,700 \text{ lb}$$

Example 2

Given the same beam and span as in Example 1, determine the safe load in accordance with the A.I.S.I. Specifications (1946): (*a*) when the top flange is continuously supported against lateral deflection, and (*b*) when the top flange is braced laterally only at the supports and at mid-span. Properties of the section are the same as determined for Example 1.

Allowable unit stresses:

Tension flange

$$f = \frac{f_y}{1.85} = \frac{33,000}{1.85} = 18,000 \text{ psi}$$

Compression flange. For case (*a*), flange is assumed to consist of the outstanding flat elements, supported along one edge only by the web.

$$\frac{b}{t} = \frac{0.88}{0.06} = 14.7$$

and from Equation 201

$$f_c = \left(\frac{5 \times 18,000}{3} - 5430\right) - \frac{1}{18}(18,000 - 8150)14.7$$

$$= 16,530 \text{ psi}$$

For case (*b*); unsupported length of flange = 72 in. Radius of gyration of entire section about axis parallel to web, computed by usual methods, is

$$r = 0.292 \text{ in.} \quad \text{and} \quad \frac{L}{r} = 246.6$$

From Equation 209,

$$f_c = \frac{250,000,000}{(246.6)^2} = 4110 \text{ psi}$$

(*a*) $$\text{Safe } W = \frac{1.38 \times 16,530}{1.5 \times 12} = 12,600 \text{ lb}$$

(*b*) $$\text{Safe } W = \frac{1.38 \times 4110}{1.5 \times 12} = 3150 \text{ lb}$$

Example 3

Given the beam section shown in Fig. 192 to determine the safe resisting moment based upon the form factor of the compression flange. The material is structural-grade steel ($f_y = 33,000$ psi). The compression flange is continuously supported against lateral deflection.

Properties of gross section (computed in accordance with usual methods):

$$\text{Area} = 1.83 \text{ sq in.}$$

$$I = 11.93$$

$$S = 3.97$$

Compression flange will be assumed to consist of the outstanding elements, 4 in. wide with $\frac{3}{4}$-in. stiffening lips. Check adequacy of stiffening lips.

$$\frac{b}{t} \text{ of outstanding flange element} = \frac{[3.76}{0.06} = 62.5$$

From Equation 185,

$$\min d = 2.8 \times 0.06[(62.5)^2 - 144]^{\frac{1}{6}}$$

$$= 0.662 \text{ in.} < \tfrac{3}{4} \text{ in.}$$

Stiffening lips are therefore adequate, and outstanding flange elements may be considered as supported along both edges.

Allowable unit stresses:

Tension flange

$$f = \frac{f_y}{1.85} = \frac{33,000}{1.85} = 18,000 \text{ psi}$$

Compression flange. Horizontal elements $b/t = 62.5$; hence, from Equation 197,

$$k = 1.335 - (0.0105 \times 62.5) = 0.68 > \frac{32}{62.5}$$

Stiffening lips $b/t = 0.69/0.06 = 11.5$, hence, from Equation 196,

$$k = 1.371 - (0.0308 \times 11.5) = 1.01 \text{ (use 1.00)}$$

Form factor (Equation 198) is

$$F = \frac{(0.68 \times 3.76 \times 0.06 \times 2) + (1.00 \times 0.69 \times 0.06 \times 2)}{(3.76 \times 0.06 \times 2) + (0.69 \times 0.06 \times 2)}$$

$$= \frac{0.3068 + 0.0828}{0.4512 + 0.0828} = \frac{0.3896}{0.5340}$$

$$= 0.73$$

Hence, from Equation 209, the allowable unit stress is,

$$f = 0.545 \times 0.73 \times 33,000 = 13,130 \text{ psi}$$

Safe resisting moment.

$$M = 13,130 \times 3.97$$

$$= 52,130 \text{ in.-lb}$$

Example 4

For the same data given for Example 3, compute the safe resisting moment according to the requirements of the A.I.S.I. Specifications (1946). (See Example 3 for properties of gross section, and for check of adequacy of stiffening lips.)

Effective design width, compression flange. From Equation 203, $f = 18,000$,

$$M = \frac{\left\{ \begin{matrix} [17.5 \times (10)^6] \\ + \sqrt{[17.5 \times (10)^6]^2 - [436 \times (10)^6][7600\sqrt{18,000} - (25 \times 18,000)]} \end{matrix} \right\}}{7600\sqrt{18,000} - (25 \times 18,000)}$$

$$= 44.1$$

Since $b/t = 62.5 > 44.1$, use Equation 205.

$$b_e = \frac{7600 \times 0.06}{\sqrt{18,000}}\left[1 - \frac{2300}{62.5\sqrt{18,000}}\right]$$

$$= 2.47$$

The width to be deducted from gross flange width $= 4 - 2.47 = 1.53$ in. The effective section will be as shown in Fig. 194a.

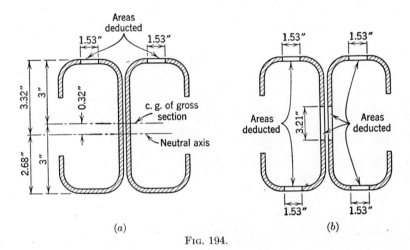

(a)   (b)

Fig. 194.

Properties of effective section. Deduction of the areas indicated in Fig. 194a will reduce the area by $2 \times 1.53 \times 0.06 = 0.18$ sq in. The neutral axis of the effective section will be located

$$\frac{0.18 \times 2.97}{(1.83 - 0.18)} = \frac{0.5346}{1.65} = 0.32 \text{ in.}$$

below the axis of the gross section. The moment of inertia of the effective section is computed as follows:

I_g of gross section	$= 11.93$
$1.83 \times (0.32)^2$	$= 0.19$
I of gross section about neutral axis of effective section	$= 12.12$
Deduct $0.18 \times (2.97)^2$	$= 1.59$
I of effective section	$= 10.53$
Safe resisting moment	$= \dfrac{18,000 \times 10.53}{3.32} = 57,060$ in.-lb

119   Light-Gage Steel Columns

Considering the elastic stability of the elements comprising a section in compression, it was shown in Article 116 that $P_{ult} = Ff_yA$. This would therefore represent the limit of compressive load which could be placed on a very short compression member (L/r approaching zero) with no eccentricity of loading. The quantity Ff_y represents the modified or *effective yield stress* which should therefore be substituted for f_y in column load determinations. For a member with $L/r = 0$, no eccentricity of loading and based on a safety factor of 1.85, the value of the average compressive stress should never exceed

$$f = \frac{P}{A} = 0.54Ff_y \qquad (213)$$

Since some eccentricity of loading and crookedness of member is unavoidable, the column formula must allow for such conditions and provide a rational reduction in the allowable load. The author therefore recommends the following working formulae for light-gage steel members:

When L/r is less than $24,000/\sqrt{Ff_y}$,

$$f = \frac{P}{A} = 0.464Ff_y - \frac{(Ff_y)^2}{2494 \times (10)^6}\left(\frac{L}{r}\right)^2 \qquad (214)$$

When L/r is greater than $24,000/\sqrt{Ff_y}$,

$$f = \frac{P}{A} = \frac{134 \times (10)^6}{\left(\dfrac{L}{r}\right)^2} \qquad (215)$$

For structural-grade steel members ($f_y = 33,000$), Equation 214 may be expressed in the following form:

When L/r is less than $132/\sqrt{F}$,

$$f = \frac{P}{A} = 15,300F - 0.437F^2\left(\frac{L}{r}\right)^2 \qquad (216)$$

When L/r is greater than $132/\sqrt{F}$, use Equation 215.

The foregoing column formulae are determined from a consideration of the secant formula (see Equation 150, Chapter 10) when the unintentional eccentricity of loading is $e_1 = 0.25r^2/c$, the eccentricity due to crookedness of member is $e_2 = L/480$, and the total eccentricity is $e = e_1 + e_2$. The results given by the formula will approximate those given by the secant formula for a member with $r/c = 0.8$. It will also

be observed that Equation 214 is the Johnson-type parabolic formula where Ff_y, representing the *effective yield stress* of the section based on its elastic stability, has been substituted for f_y.

The determination of the safe axial load on a typical section is as follows:

Example 1

Consider the section shown in Fig. 192 to be used as a column having an unsupported length of 8 ft. Properties of gross section (computed in the usual manner) are

$$\text{Area} = 1.83 \text{ sq in.}$$

For axis (1)–(1), $I = 11.93, r = 2.55$
For axis (2)–(2), $I = 2.08, r = 1.06$
Form factor (see Article 116) $F = 0.57$

$$\frac{L}{r} = \frac{96}{1.06} = 91 < \frac{132}{\sqrt{0.57}} = 175 \quad \text{(Use Equation 216)}$$

$$\frac{P}{A} = (15,300 \times 0.57) - 0.437(0.57 \times 91)^2$$

$$= 8721 - 1176 = 7545 \text{ psi}$$

Safe axial load $= 7545 \times 1.83 = 13,810 \text{ lb}$

The A.I.S.I. Specifications (1946) specify column formulae similar to Equations 214, 215, and 216 except that a term Q is substituted for the form factor F. The factor Q is defined by these specifications as follows:

(*a*) For members composed entirely of stiffened elements, Q is the ratio between the effective design area as determined from the effective design widths of such elements (Equation 204 or 205) and the full or gross area of the cross section. The effective design area used in determining Q is to be based upon the basic design stress $f_y/1.85$.

(*b*) For members composed entirely of unstiffened elements, Q is the ratio between the allowable stress f_c (Equation 201 or 202), for the weakest element of the cross section (the element having the largest flat-width ratio), and the basic design stress $f_y/1.85$.

(*c*) For members composed of both stiffened and unstiffened elements, the factor Q is to be the product of a stress factor Q_s computed as outlined in (*b*) and an area factor Q_a computed as outlined in (*a*), except that the stress upon which Q_a is to be based shall be that value of the unit stress f_c which is used in computing Q_s, noting that the effective area to be used in computing Q_a is to include the full area of all unstiffened elements. The following example illustrates the application of the A.I.S.I. Specifications to a typical problem.

Example 2

Same problem as Example 1, computed in accordance with the A.I.S.I. Specification. The *effective section*, according to this specification, is represented in Fig. 194b.

Since the section is composed of both stiffened and unstiffened elements, the procedure outlined in (c) will apply. The stiffening lips are the only unstiffened elements of the section and, since $b/t = 10.5 < 12$, $f_c = 18,000$, and $Q_s = 1.0$.

The value of Q_a is determined in accordance with the provisions stated in (a) as follows: From Equation 203, when $f = 18,000$, $M = 44.1$ and since b/t for both the web and the flanges exceeds this value, the values of b_e are given by Equation 205.

For the flanges,

$$b_e = \frac{7600 \times 0.06}{\sqrt{18,000}} \left[1 - \frac{2300}{62.5\sqrt{18,000}} \right]$$

$$= 2.47 \text{ in.}$$

For the webs,

$$b_e = \frac{7600 \times 0.06}{\sqrt{18,000}} \left[1 - \frac{2300}{96\sqrt{18,000}} \right]$$

$$= 2.79 \text{ in.}$$

To determine the effective section (Fig. 194b), the following widths must therefore be deducted.

$$
\begin{array}{ll}
\text{Flanges} & 4 - 2.47 = 1.53 \text{ in.} \\
\text{Webs} & 6 - 2.79 = 3.21 \text{ in.} \\
\text{Gross area} & \quad\quad\quad = 1.83 \\
\quad\text{Deduct } 4 \times 1.53 \times 0.06 = 0.37 \\
\quad\quad\quad\quad\quad 2 \times 3.21 \times 0.06 = \underline{0.38} \\
& \quad\quad\quad\quad\quad\quad 0.75 \\
\end{array}
$$

$$\text{Effective area} = 1.08 \text{ sq in.}$$

$$Q_a = \frac{1.08}{1.83} = 0.59$$

The Q factor used to replace F in the column formula (Equation 216) is therefore

$$Q = Q_s Q_a = 1 \times 0.59 = 0.59$$

$$\frac{P}{A} = (15,300 \times 0.59) - 0.437(0.59 \times 91)^2$$

$$= 9027 - 1260 = 7767 \text{ psi}$$

$$\text{Safe axial load} = 7767 \times 1.83 = 14,210 \text{ lb}$$

PROBLEMS

11·1 The section shown is to be used as a beam, bending about axis 1-1. What is the minimum value of t for which the compression flange can be considered elastically stable?

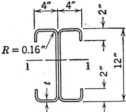

11·2 Using a value of $t = 0.08$ in. for the beam section in Problem 11·1, calculate the form factor of the compression flange and the allowable stress in compression. Assume grade C steel ($f_y = 33,000$ psi).

11·3 The section shown is to be used as a simple beam 12 in. wide, on a span of 7 ft. Determine the safe uniformly distributed load (a) using the form factor to find allowable stress, and (b) according to the A.I.S.I. Specifications (1946).

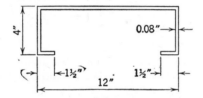

11·4 For the beam section shown calculate the allowable stress in compression and the resisting moment of the section (a) using the form factor, and (b) using the A.I.S.I. Specifications (1946). Neglect fillets in finding properties of section, and assume full lateral support for compression flange.

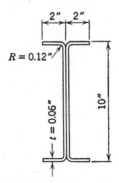

11·5 A rectangular steel plate 10 in. wide, 0.10 in. thick, and 3 ft long is uniformly loaded in compression in the direction of its length. The longitudinal edges are clamped (fixed). $f_y = 33,000$ psi. (a) According to the Bryan-Timoshenko

formula for the buckling of thin plates, calculate the critical buckling unit stress and also the total load on the plate at that stress. (b) Is the total load calculated in (a) the maximum load the plate will resist? Explain.

11·6 The section shown in Problem 11·1, with $t = 0.08$ in., is used as a beam on an 18-ft span. The compression flange is braced laterally at the ends and at mid-span. Calculate the allowable stress in compression ($f_y = 33,000$ psi) (a) using the form factor of the compression flange, and (b) according to the A.I.S.I. Specifications (1946).

11·7 According to the A.I.S.I. Specifications (1946) calculate for the section in Problem 11·4 (a) the maximum allowable reaction for a simply supported beam, bearing length 3 in. (b) the allowable concentrated load on a bearing plate 2 in. long.

11·8 A column of length 8 ft has the section shown. $f_y = 33,000$ psi. (a) Find the allowable load using the form factor of the section. (b) Find the allowable load

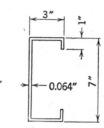

according to the A.I.S.I. Specifications (1946). (c) At what load would failure by local buckling be expected in a very short column having this section?

11·9 An axially loaded strut is made up of two angles arranged as shown. $F_y = 33,000$ psi. Calculate the allowable load if the length is 10 ft.

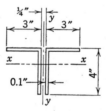

11·10 A column is made up of two C-sections placed as shown with the lips welded together at 2-ft intervals. If $L/r = 45$ and $f_y = 33,000$ psi, calculate the safe axial load.

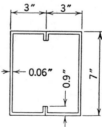

Chapter 12

REINFORCED CONCRETE BEAMS, SLABS, AND COLUMNS

120   Physical Properties of Concrete

Concrete is an artificial stone consisting of a mixture of particles of stone, Portland cement, and water. This mixture in plastic or liquid condition is poured into molds or *forms* which give it the desired shape, and it is then allowed to set for such time as is necessary for it to harden and attain necessary strength. The forms and their supports are then removed and the exposed surface of the concrete left rough or finished as may be desired.

The active ingredients in the concrete mixture are the Portland cement and the water. These combine chemically,[1] forming a stone-like matrix in which the particles of stone in the concrete mixture are imbedded. The *richness* of the mixture is determined by the percentage of cement in the resulting concrete, and the *mix* is expressed by the ratio of the parts of cement to parts of stone particles (aggregate). Thus a mix 1:3 means one part cement to three parts of aggregate, and a 1:4 mix is a leaner mix because of the reduced percentage of cement. Mixes are sometimes expressed in the form 1:2:4, meaning 1 part cement to 2 parts fine aggregate to 4 parts coarse aggregate.

The mixture of cement and water forms a paste which fills the spaces or voids between the particles of stone, and the volume of these voids determines the quantity of cement paste required for a unit volume of finished concrete. The strength of the concrete is proportional to the quality of this cement paste as measured by the water-cement ratio or ratio between the quantity of cement and quantity of water per unit volume of concrete. (See Fig. 195.) The cement paste also acts as a lubricant applied to the stone particles and gives the resultant concrete mixture plasticity which permits it to flow into place. Increasing the quantity of water will also increase the fluidity of the concrete, but if

[1] See "Digest of the Literature on the Nature of the Setting and Hardening Process in Portland Cement," by R. H. Bogue, Paper 1617 of the Portland Cement Fellowship at the Bureau of Standards, Washington, D. C.

water alone is added without corresponding increase in the cement, the resultant concrete will have impaired strength.

The stone particles contained in the mixture are called *aggregate* and classified as *fine aggregate* and *coarse aggregate*. The fine aggregate includes particles less than about $\frac{1}{4}$ inch in diameter; the coarse aggregate includes the remainder of the stone particles. The maximum size of stone in the coarse aggregate is determined by the massiveness of the

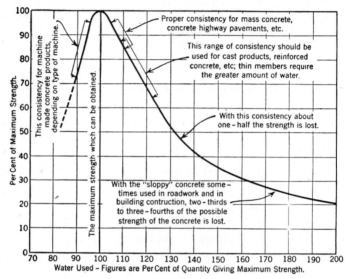

Fig. 195.   Effect of Quantity of Mixing Water on Strength of Concrete.

finished construction and the necessity for complete imbedment of all stone particles. Aggregate should be reasonably well graded from fine to coarse in order to provide the most dense mixture and therefore reduce the required quantity of cement paste to a minimum. It should be comprised of sound, strong, and durable pieces of stone or stones and should be free from organic matter, loam, and material which would reduce the strength or durability of the concrete.

The combining of cement and water constitutes the hardening process and requires an appreciable interval of time, during which setting or curing period the fresh concrete must be supported. The temperature maintained during this period is also important, as reduced temperatures will retard, and increased temperatures accelerate, the setting process. The period of time which must be allowed for curing must therefore be adjusted accordingly. (See Fig. 196.) On the basis of strength, the quality of concrete is defined by the crushing strength of concrete cylin-

ders made and tested under laboratory conditions at the age of 28 days.[2] The test cylinders are stored and cured under ideal conditions and maintained at a temperature of 70° F during this period. This strength forms the basis for establishing working stresses used in reinforced concrete structures, and, in all cases where loads may be applied to the structure before the expiration of this 28-day period, either the green construction must be adequately supported or else the design adjusted to

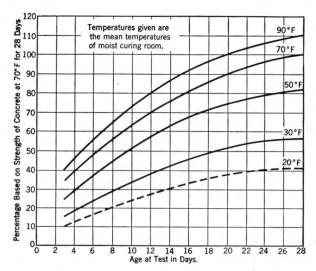

FIG. 196. Percentages of Strength for Different Temperatures.

(From *Bulletin 81*, University of Illinois Engineering Experiment Station.)

provide for the reduced strength of the concrete. The same conclusions apply for concrete cured under temperature conditions lower than the normal of 70 degrees. Freezing temperatures are likely to produce permanent mechanical damage to the concrete and are never permitted. Most specifications require that concrete be maintained at temperatures in excess of 50 degrees during the curing period.

Long-time tests (Fig. 197) indicate that concrete continues to gain in strength with age. The rate of increase depends upon the quality of the concrete and the moisture conditions surrounding it. This fact is of importance in considering the strength of existing concrete structures.

Concrete is used primarily for resisting compressive stress, and its behavior in compression is reasonably reliable and predictable. Quite

[2] "Standard Method of Making and Storing Compression Test Specimens of Concrete in the Field," A.S.T.M., Serial Designation C 31-39; "Standard Method of Test for Compressive Strength of Concrete," A.S.T.M., Serial Designation C 39-39.

the reverse is true of its resistance to tension; hence its tensile strength is rarely utilized in design. Concrete is not perfectly elastic even under low unit stresses and continues to deform slowly over a long period of time under sustained stress.[3] Stresses caused by fixed loading should therefore be kept relatively small. For the purpose of computing probable values of internal stress and required dimensions of concrete members it is necessary to establish the ratio between unit stress and corresponding deformations of the material. For so-called elastic materials,

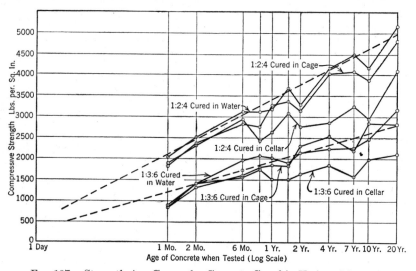

FIG. 197.   Strength-Age Curves for Concrete Cured in Various Manners.

(From paper, "Some Long Time Tests of Concrete," by M. O. Withey, *J. Am. Concrete Inst.,* February, 1931.)

such as steel, this ratio (modulus of elasticity) is constant up to the proportional limit and the stress-strain diagram is practically a straight line for unit stresses from zero to the proportional limit. For concrete, the stress-strain ratio varies (Fig. 198) and diminishes in value as the unit stress increases. The ratio of unit axial stress to corresponding unit axial deformation in concrete is called the *secant modulus* and is what is meant when the term modulus of elasticity is used.

The selection of a proper modulus [4] for use in computations of internal stress is a matter which involves careful consideration of all the factors

[3] See "Flow of Concrete under the Action of Sustained Loads," by Davis and Davis, *J. Am. Concrete Institute*, March, 1931.

[4] See "Modulus of Elasticity and Poisson's Ratio for Concrete and the Influence of Age and Other Factors upon These Values," by Davis and Troxell, *Proceedings A.S.T.M.*, 1929, Part II, p. 678.

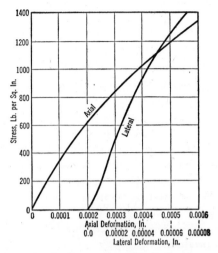

FIG. 198. Typical Stress-Strain Curves for a Single Specimen at the Age of Three Months.

(From "Modulus of Elasticity and Poisson's Ratio for Concrete," by Davis and Troxell, *Proc. A.S.T.M.*, 1929, Part II, p. 684.)

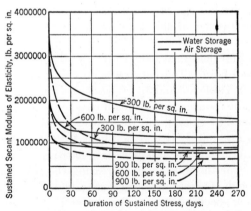

FIG. 199. The Effect of Sustained Stress upon the Sustained Secant Modulus of Elasticity; Stress Applied at twenty-eight Days.

(From "Modulus of Elasticity and Poisson's Ratio for Concrete," Davis and Troxell, *Proc. A.S.T.M.*, 1929, Part II, p. 696.)

relating to the behavior of concrete. Particular consideration must be given to such factors as the quality of the concrete, its age, moisture conditions, and magnitude of sustained stress (Fig. 199).

121   Reinforcing Steel

Steel is imbedded in concrete for the purpose of carrying tensile stresses and the two materials, steel and concrete, must effectively cooperate to resist such internal compressive and tensile stresses as may be developed in the structure. Steel used for reinforcement may be of any convenient form, but, since the surface of the steel is a natural cleavage plane, the necessary cooperation between steel and concrete will not exist unless there is adequate resistance to the shearing forces which may be developed on the steel surfaces; moreover it is necessary that the steel areas be well distributed over the tensile stress zones. To meet these conditions steel in the form of round or square bars is usually preferable. Wire mesh, welded-wire fabric, and expanded metal are also all useful products.

Steel used in the manufacture of round and square reinforcement bars is designated as *billet steel* (A.S.T.M. Serial Designation A 15-39), *rail steel* (A.S.T.M. Serial Designation A 16-35), or *axle steel* (A.S.T.M. Serial Designation A 160-39).

Billet steel used in the manufacture of plain, deformed, or cold-twisted concrete reinforcement bars may be made by either the open-hearth, electric-furnace, or acid-Bessemer process. Bars must be rolled from new billets, and rerolled material is not acceptable under this designation. Plain and deformed bars are made in three grades, *structural, intermediate,* and *hard.* Tension and bend test requirements for billet steel are given in Tables 36 and 37. *Cold-twisted* bars are made from steel conforming to the requirements of plain bars of structural grade. *Plain bars,* either round or square, are those with relatively smooth surface. *Deformed bars* are rolled with rolls which have corrugations of some particular pattern. These produce irregularities or deformations on the bar surface for the purpose of increasing the resistance to slipping of the bar through concrete in which it may be imbedded. While there are no prevailing specifications for the character of these deformations, it should be noted that usual design allowances assume 25 per cent higher resistance to bond (shear on the surface of the bar) for deformed bars than for plain bars; the character of the deformation should therefore be such as to justify such increased allowance (see Fig. 200). Billet steel is regarded as more reliable than other steels used in the manufacture of reinforcement bars and is therefore generally preferred. Intermediate-grade billet steel is more commonly used than the other grades.

Where the reinforcement must be severely bent to meet design requirements, structural grade may be preferred, owing to its greater ductility (see Table 37).

Rail-steel concrete reinforcement bars are rolled from standard section T-rails, and material known by the terms *rerolled, rail-steel equivalent,* or *rail-steel quality* is not acceptable. Three classes of bars are made from this material, *plain, deformed,* and *hot-twisted.* The tensile and bend test requirements for plain bars correspond with those for billet-steel plain bars of hard grade; the requirements for deformed and hot-twisted bars are the same as hard-grade deformed bars of billet steel.

Axle-steel reinforcement bars are rolled from carbon-steel axles for cars and locomotive tenders of specified journal sizes. They are either plain or deformed and in three grades, structural, intermediate, and hard. Tensile and bend-test requirements are the same as for billet steel.

The Building Regulations for Reinforced Concrete (A.C.I. 318-41T) of the American Concrete Institute permit the following allowable unit stresses in reinforcement.

(*a*) Tension. (f_s = tensile unit stress in longitudinal reinforcement) and (f_v = tensile unit stress in web reinforcement) 20,000 pounds per square inch for rail-steel concrete reinforcement bars, billet-steel concrete reinforcement bars (of intermediate and hard grades), axle-steel concrete reinforcement bars (of intermediate and hard grades), and cold-drawn steel wire for concrete reinforcement. 18,000 pounds per square inch for billet-steel concrete reinforcement bars (of structural grade) and axle-steel concrete reinforcement bars (of structural grade).

(*b*) Tension in one-way slabs of not more than 12-foot span. (f_s = tensile unit stress in main reinforcement.) For the main reinforcement, $\frac{3}{8}$ inch or less in diameter in one-way slabs, 50 per cent of the minimum yield point specified in the Standard Specifications of the American Society for Testing Materials for the particular kind and grade of reinforcement used, but never to exceed 30,000 pounds per square inch.

(*c*) Compression, vertical column reinforcement. (f_s = nominal working stress in vertical reinforcement.) Forty per cent of the minimum yield point specified in the Standard Specifications of the American Society for Testing Materials for the particular kind and grade used but never to exceed 30,000 pounds per square inch.

The A.A.S.H.O. Specifications (1944) for highway bridges require all reinforcement to be deformed bars made of billet steel of structural or intermediate grade made by the open-hearth process. The use of cold twisted bars is prohibited. Tensile unit stress of 18,000 pounds per square inch is permitted for structural grade steel and 20,000 pounds per square inch on intermediate grade steel in flexural members. For web reinforcement the allowed tensile stress is 16,000 for structural-grade steel and 18,000 pounds per square inch for intermediate grade steel.

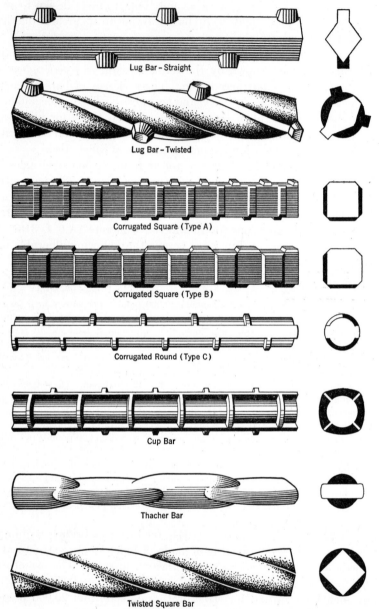

Lug Bar – Straight

Lug Bar – Twisted

Corrugated Square (Type A)

Corrugated Square (Type B)

Corrugated Round (Type C)

Cup Bar

Thacher Bar

Twisted Square Bar

Fig. 200.   Deformed Bars—Load-Slip

(From *Bulletin 71*, Engineering Experiment

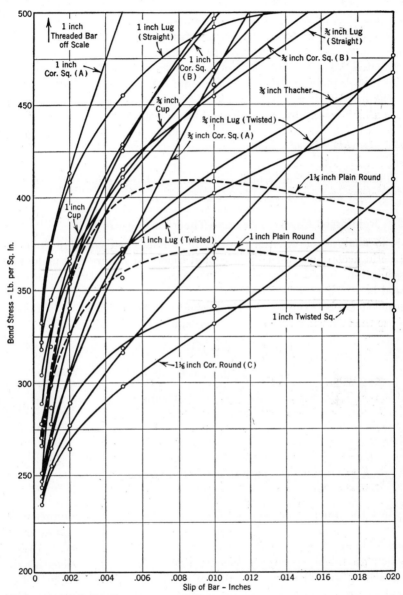

Curves from Pull-Out Tests.

Station, University of Illinois.)

The American Railway Engineering Association Specifications (1944) for concrete and reinforced concrete railroad bridges and trestles require that all steel bars used for reinforcement, and which carry calculated stress, shall be of structural or intermediate grade billet steel. Steel bars which are used for temperature reinforcement, and do not carry calculated stress, may be made of rail or axle steel. These specifications permit both plain and deformed bars and define an approved deformed bar as one which will develop at least 25 per cent greater bond stress than a plain round bar of equivalent cross section. The permitted unit tensile stresses are 18,000 pounds per square inch on structural grade steel bars and 20,000 pounds per square inch on intermediate- and hard-grade steel bars.

Standard sizes of deformed reinforcement bars ordinarily carried in stock order are given in Table 38.

122   Reinforced Concrete Beams—Theory of Flexure

The analysis of internal stresses in a reinforced concrete beam is made in accordance with the accepted theory of flexure and under the assumption that the stresses do not materially exceed the values indicated hereafter as safe working stresses. It is further assumed that all tensile stress is taken by the steel reinforcement. It is also customary to use the following values for the modulii of elasticity:

$$E_c = 1000\, f_c'\ \text{psi}$$

$$E_s = 30{,}000{,}000\ \text{psi}$$

$$n = E_s/E_c = \frac{30{,}000}{f_c'} \qquad (217)$$

where E_c = modulus of elasticity of concrete.
E_s = modulus of elasticity of steel.
f_c' = crushing strength of concrete at 28 days.
n = ratio of modulii.

Since the concrete is assumed to carry no tension, steel reinforcement must be imbedded in the lower part of the beam to resist the tensile stresses induced by flexure. Figure 201 represents a beam with a right section xx taken at any intermediate point in the span length. In accordance with the accepted theory of flexure, plane sections before bending are assumed to remain plane sections after bending. This means that unit deformations must be proportional to distances from the neutral axis as indicated at b. The unit stresses resulting from these deformations are shown at c where it will be noted that the compressive unit stresses on the concrete vary from zero at the neutral axis to a

maximum at the extreme fiber, in accordance with the assumption of constant proportionality of unit stress to unit strain for concrete. At the extreme fiber in compression

$$f_c = e_c E_c$$

where e_c = unit deformation of extreme fiber.

Below the neutral axis the unit stresses produced in the concrete are omitted, in accordance with the assumption of zero tensile stress on concrete, and the actual section which resists bending-moment in accordance

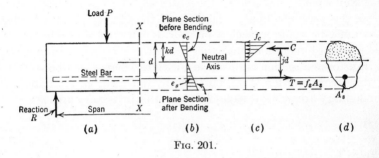

FIG. 201.

with these assumptions is indicated at d. The steel will have a unit stress,

$$f_s = e_s E_s$$

where e_s = unit deformation of steel.

From similar triangles (Fig. 201b),

$$\frac{e_c}{e_s} = \frac{f_c E_s}{f_s E_c} = \frac{n f_c}{f_s} = \frac{kd}{d - kd} \qquad (218)$$

The loads, reaction and unit stresses acting on the part of the beam on one side of the given section, constitute a force system in equilibrium and must fulfill the general conditions for static equilibrium, $\Sigma H = 0$ and $\Sigma M = 0$. The shear on the section is for the present omitted as it will be made the basis of a special stress determination; therefore (Fig. 201c)

$$C = T = \frac{M}{jd} \qquad (219)$$

where

$$M = Cjd = Tjd$$

where C = total resultant compressive force on concrete.
  T = total resultant tensile force on concrete.
  M = bending-moment.
  jd = lever arm of couple CT.

It will be observed that the effective section shown at d is the same as one which might have been taken through a crack in the lower part of the beam.

123   Reinforced Concrete Beams—Transformed Section

The actual determination of the location of the neutral axis and calculation of the values of unit stresses, or the safe resisting moment, can most readily be accomplished through the medium of the *transformed section*. This is an imaginary cross section obtained by substituting an imaginary material for the steel area. This material is assumed to have the same modulus of elasticity as the concrete, and the substitution must be made in such a manner as not to disturb the internal stress relationship outlined in Article 122. The comparison of the actual and transformed section is shown in Fig. 202 where it will be seen that the transformed section at b is obtained by replacing the steel area with the imaginary area nA_s; the unit stress on this imaginary area is

$$f' = e_s E_c = \frac{f_s E_c}{E_s} = \frac{f_s}{n} \tag{220}$$

and from Equation 218,

$$\frac{kd}{d - kd} = \frac{f_c}{f'} \tag{221}$$

This shows that line ab (Fig. 202b), indicating the stress distribution across the section, is a straight line such as would be found for a homogeneous beam. In accordance therefore with the laws of internal unit-stress distribution developed for homogeneous beams, the neutral axis must coincide with the centroid of the transformed area, and the statical moment of the compressive area with respect to the neutral axis equals the statical moment of the transformed tensile area with respect to the same axis. Moreover, the resisting moment of the section may be expressed as follows:

$$M_s = Tjd = \frac{f'I}{d - kd} = \frac{f_s I}{n(d - kd)} \tag{222}$$

$$M_c = Cjd = \frac{f_c I}{kd} \tag{223}$$

where M_s = resisting moment based on unit stress in steel.
M_c = resisting moment based on unit stress in concrete.
I = moment of inertia of transformed section.

For sections of irregular outline, the determination of the location of the neutral axis and value of the moment of inertia of the transformed

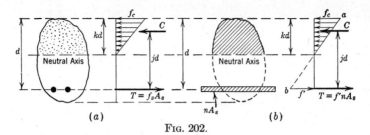

FIG. 202.

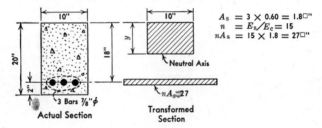

FIG. 203.

Rectangular Beam — B. M. = 480000"#

$A_s = 3 \times 0.60 = 1.8 \square"$
$n = E_s/E_c = 15$
$nA_s = 15 \times 1.8 = 27 \square"$

Actual Section

3 Bars ⅞" φ

Transformed Section

$nA_s = 27$

Neutral Axis

Equating statical moment of Compression Area to statical moment of "transformed" Steel Area:

$$\frac{10y^2}{2} = 27\,(18 - y\;) = 486 - 27y$$

$$5y^2 + 27y = 486$$
$$y^2 + 5.4\,y + (2.7)^2 = 97.2 + (2.7)^2 = 104.49$$
$$y + 2.7 = 10.25$$
$$y = 7.55"$$

Moment of Inertia (transformed section)

Concrete	$10 \times (7.55)^3 \times \frac{1}{3} =$	1435
Transf. Steel	$27 \times (10.45)^2 =$	2960
$I =$		4395 in.⁴

$$f_c = \frac{480{,}000 \times 7.55}{4395} = 825\#/\square"$$

$$f_s = \frac{480000 \times 10.45 \times 15}{4395} = 17150\#/\square"$$

FIG. 204. Analysis of Rectangular Beam.

section is a somewhat complicated matter. For such sections a semi-graphical solution may be made as follows: The transformed section is determined as outlined above and as indicated in Fig. 203. Line AB is laid off to scale representing the distance d. Curve AC is plotted with

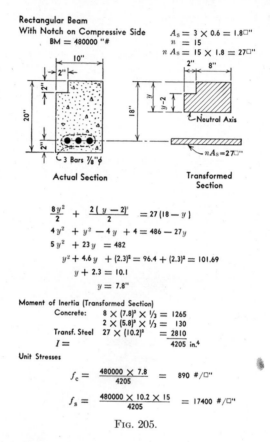

Rectangular Beam
With Notch on Compressive Side
BM = 480000 "#

$A_s = 3 \times 0.6 = 1.8\square"$
$n = 15$
$n A_s = 15 \times 1.8 = 270\square"$

Actual Section

Transformed Section

$$\frac{8y^2}{2} + \frac{2(y-2)^2}{2} = 27(18 - y)$$

$$4y^2 + y^2 - 4y + 4 = 486 - 27y$$

$$5y^2 + 23y = 482$$

$$y^2 + 4.6y + (2.3)^2 = 96.4 + (2.3)^2 = 101.69$$

$$y + 2.3 = 10.1$$

$$y = 7.8"$$

Moment of Inertia (Transformed Section)

Concrete:	$8 \times (7.8)^3 \times \frac{1}{3} =$	1265
	$2 \times (5.8)^3 \times \frac{1}{3} =$	130
Transf. Steel	$27 \times (10.2)^2 =$	2810
$I =$		4205 in.⁴

Unit Stresses

$$f_c = \frac{480000 \times 7.8}{4205} = 890 \; \#/\square"$$

$$f_s = \frac{480000 \times 10.2 \times 15}{4205} = 17400 \; \#/\square"$$

FIG. 205.

intercepts representing the statical moment of areas X with respect to their bases mn. This is done by assuming successive locations for mn, dividing the corresponding area X into areas of convenient geometric form and computing the sum of the moments of these areas about mn. Line BC is drawn to represent the equation $y_2 = nA_s x$. The neutral axis will then be located at C, the intersection of curve AC with line BC, and the distance kd may be scaled. It should be noted that for steel in more than a single layer the line BC will be a broken line with y_2 representing the sum of the moments of transformed steel areas about a given point in the depth. The moment of inertia of the transformed

section will be the area ABC with intercepts y scaled as statical moments and distances along AB scaled in inches.

For rectangular shaped beam sections it is easier to locate the neutral axis, by equating the statical moment of the area in compression to the

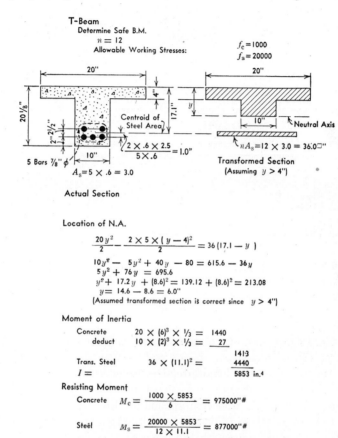

T-Beam
Determine Safe B.M.
$n = 12$
Allowable Working Stresses:

$f_c = 1000$
$f_s = 20000$

Location of N.A.

$$\frac{20\,y^2}{2} - \frac{2 \times 5 \times (y-4)^2}{2} = 36\,(17.1 - y\ )$$

$$10y^2 - 5y^2 + 40y - 80 = 615.6 - 36y$$
$$5y^2 + 76y = 695.6$$
$$y^2 + 17.2\,y + (8.6)^2 = 139.12 + (8.6)^2 = 213.08$$
$$y = 14.6 - 8.6 = 6.0''$$

(Assumed transformed section is correct since $y > 4''$)

Moment of Inertia

Concrete	$20 \times (6)^3 \times \frac{1}{3} =$	1440
deduct	$10 \times (2)^3 \times \frac{1}{3} =$	27
		1413
Trans. Steel	$36 \times (11.1)^2 =$	4440
$I =$		5853 in.⁴

Resisting Moment

Concrete $\quad M_c = \dfrac{1000 \times 5853}{6} = 975000''\#$

Steel $\quad M_s = \dfrac{20000 \times 5853}{12 \times 11.1} = 877000''\#$

Safe B.M. (is determined by Steel) $= 877000''\#$

FIG. 206. Safe Load for Reinforced Concrete T-Beams.

statical moment of the transformed steel area. Typical solutions of such beams are shown in Figs. 204, 205, and 206.

124 Bond Stress

The *bond stress* on the reinforcing steel is the shear developed on the surface of the bars due to changes in tensile force in the length of the bar. Thus for two successive sections (Fig. 207) a differential distance

apart, assumed as unity, the bending-moments will in general differ in magnitude and from Equation 219

$$T_1 = \frac{M_1}{jd}$$

$$T_2 = \frac{M_2}{jd}$$

$$T_1 - T_2 = \frac{M_1 - M_2}{jd} = \frac{V}{jd} \tag{224}$$

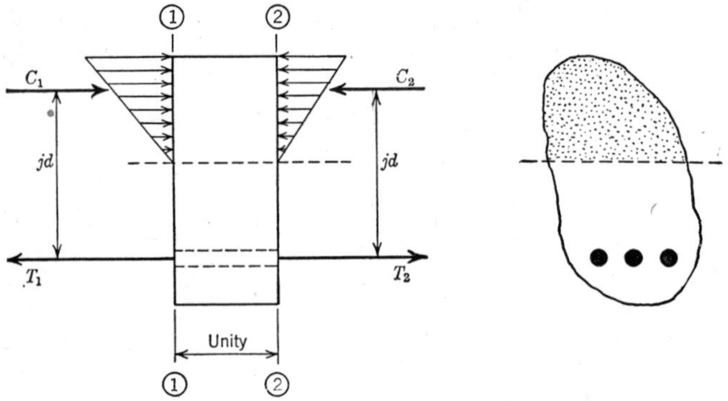

Fig. 207.

The building regulations of the American Concrete Institute (ACI 318-41) permit an increase in the allowable shear and bond stress when special anchorage of the longitudinal steel is provided. To meet the requirement for special anchorage, every bar must be terminated in a standard hook in a region of compression or else bent across the web at an angle of not less than 15 degrees with the longitudinal portion of the bar and made continuous with the negative or positive reinforcement. A standard hook means either (a) a complete semicircular turn with a radius of bend on the axis of the bar of not less than 3 and not more than 6 bar diameters at the free end of the bar, or (b) a 90-degree bend having a radius of not less than 4 bar diameters plus an extension of 12 bar diameters.

This difference in force must be resisted by the unit shear stresses or *bond* on the surface of the reinforcement; hence

$$u = \frac{V}{\Sigma_0 jd} \tag{225}$$

where u = unit bond stress in pounds per square inch.

V = total vertical shear on the given section.

Σ_0 = sum of perimeters of the bars.

jd = lever arm of the internal couple, CT.

From Equation 222, substituting $T = f_s A_s$, gives

$$jd = \frac{I}{nA_s(d - kd)} \tag{226}$$

Thus for the beam in Fig. 204, the bond stress on the reinforcement at a section where the vertical shear is 12,800 pounds would be computed as in the following example.

Example

$$V = 12{,}800 \text{ lb}$$

$$d - kd = 10.45 \text{ in.}$$

$$nA_s = 27 \text{ sq in.}$$

$$I = 4395 \text{ sq in.}$$

$$jd = \frac{4395}{27 \times 10.45} = 15.5 \text{ in.}$$

$$\Sigma_0 = 3 \times 2.749 = 8.247 \text{ in.}$$

$$u = \frac{12{,}800}{8.247 \times 15.5} = 100 \text{ psi}$$

When the compressive area is rectangular as in Fig. 204, C is located at the center of gravity of the triangular stress distribution in compression, and

$$jd = d - \tfrac{1}{3}kd \tag{227}$$

For irregular-shaped compressive areas, such as are represented in Figs. 205 and 206, the value of jd is obtained from Equation 226.

125 Shear and Diagonal Tension

The intensity of the horizontal shearing stress at any point in the depth of a beam may be computed from the general formula developed for homogeneous beams, using the transformed section. The intensity will be maximum at the neutral axis, and, noting that the statical moment of the area on the compression side about the neutral axis equals the statical moment of the transformed steel, with respect to the neutral axis:

$$v = \frac{VnA_s(d - kd)}{Ib} = \frac{V}{bjd} \tag{228}$$

where b = breadth of beam at the neutral axis.

As established in the accepted theory of flexure, the intensity of vertical shear on any element of a beam equals the intensity of the horizontal shear determined by Equation 228. At the neutral axis these shearing stresses will induce diagonal tension stress in the material (Fig. 208) which will be inclined at 45 degrees to the horizontal and equal in intensity to the horizontal shear stress. In accordance with the assumption of no flexural stress on concrete below the neutral axes, this diagonal tension stress will remain constant over the lower part of the beam. Above the neutral axis, particles of concrete are acted upon by a compressive unit flexural stress in addition to the horizontal and vertical shear stresses, and the direction and magnitude of diagonal tension stress will vary accordingly. This variation in stress is, however, not computed, and it is assumed that the diagonal tension stress computed at the neutral axis exists over the entire section. To take care of diagonal tension stresses, steel reinforcing must be arranged either in a vertical or inclined position so that it will traverse all diagonal planes on which such diagonal tension stress may exist. Contrary to the assumption made in connection with flexural stresses, the concrete is

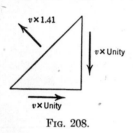

Fig. 208.

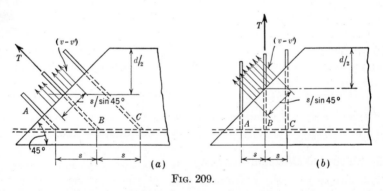

Fig. 209.

allowed to carry part of the diagonal tension stress, the remainder being cared for by the steel reinforcement.

For the arrangement shown at *a* in Fig. 209 the total tension on inclined bars *B* would be determined as follows:

$$T = \frac{(v - v')bs}{\sin 45°} = f_v A_v \qquad (229)$$

where v' = diagonal tension unit stress allowed on the concrete.

$\quad\quad b$ = breadth of beam at the section corresponding to the location of bars B.

$\quad\quad s$ = spacing of bars in the span.

$\quad\quad f_v$ = unit tensile stress on steel bars.

$\quad\quad A_v$ = total steel area in width b.

When the inclined bars are at an angle α to the axis of the beam, the total tension is computed by the following formula

$$T = \frac{(v - v')bs}{\sin\alpha + \cos\alpha} = f_v A_v \tag{230}$$

For the arrangement shown at b in Fig. 209, the total tension in the vertical bars is the component of the diagonal tension on the area $sb/\sin 45°$; hence

$$T = \frac{(v - v')bs}{\sin 45°} \cdot \sin 45°$$

$$= (v - v')bs = f_v A_v \tag{231}$$

For more complete details and discussion of web reinforcement the reader is referred to standard textbooks and reference books on reinforced concrete; also to standard specifications such as the "Building Regulations for Reinforced Concrete" adopted by the American Concrete Institute. Typical web reinforcement computations are shown in Figs. 217 and 218.

126 Design of Rectangular Beams

Working stresses in reinforced concrete building construction as recommended in the Building Regulations for Reinforced Concrete of the American Concrete Institute (ACI 318-41) are given in Table 39.

While it would be possible to determine the required section and arrangement of reinforcement in a concrete beam from the general relationships stated in Articles 122 and 123, these can, for a rectangular section, be expressed in more convenient form for practical use. In the expressions which follow, it should be clearly understood that they are applicable only to beams having a rectangular cross section in compression, and in general they cannot be used for any other type of section.

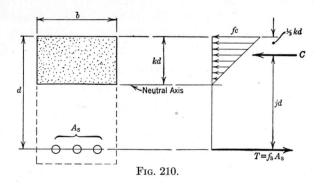

FIG. 210.

Standard design formulae for rectangular beam may be derived as follows (Fig. 210):

$$n = \frac{E_s}{E_c} \tag{232}$$

$$p = \frac{A_s}{bd} \tag{233}$$

$Q_c = Q_T \longrightarrow$
$$k = \sqrt{2pn + (pn)^2} - pn \tag{234}$$

$$j = 1 - \tfrac{1}{3}k \tag{235}$$

$$\begin{cases} C = \tfrac{1}{2}f_c kbd \\ T = f_s A_s = f_s pbd \end{cases}$$

$Cjd = jd \tfrac{1}{2} f_c kbd$ $= M$ (236)

$Tjd = jd f_s pbd$ (237)

$$d = \sqrt{\frac{2M}{kjbf_c}} \quad \text{or} \quad \sqrt{\frac{M}{pjbf_s}} \tag{238}$$

For simultaneous stresses f_c and f_s,

$$\text{normal } p = \frac{\tfrac{1}{2}}{\dfrac{f_s}{f_c}\left(\dfrac{f_s}{nf_c} + 1\right)} \tag{239}$$

Equation 238 may also be arranged in the form

$$\frac{M}{bd^2} = \tfrac{1}{2}f_c kj \quad \text{or} \quad f_s pj = K \tag{240}$$

$$d = \sqrt{\frac{M}{Kb}} \tag{241}$$

In designing a concrete beam, the bending-moments and shears are computed in the usual way with proper allowance, assumed in the loading, for the weight of the beam. The computations are therefore subject to adjustment when a more accurate estimate of the weight of the beam is available and the design is on this account one of successive approximations. Materials of suitable quality are then decided upon and the allowable working stresses established. If it is assumed that the concrete and steel will be simultaneously stressed to these working stresses, the *normal* steel ratio p is obtained from Equation 239. Corresponding values of k and j are computed from Equations 234 and 235. The values of p (normal), k, j, and corresponding value of K are all con-

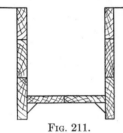

FIG. 211.

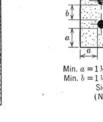

Min. $a = 1\frac{1}{2}''$
Min. $b = 1\frac{1}{2}$ Diam. of Round Bar or
Side of Square Bar
(Not Less Than 1")

FIG. 212.

stant for the given materials. The value of d is obtained from Equation 238 or 241 by assuming practical values for b and computing the corresponding values of d. Values of b should be chosen with proper consideration for the economy of form construction and in conformance with limitations imposed by the supporting construction at the ends of the beam; sufficient width must be provided to enable the bars to be arranged without crowding and to furnish sufficient section for shear or diagonal tension resistance. Beam forms are usually made with longitudinal planks which form the bottom and sides (Fig. 211) and in general, maximum overall economy of forms and of concrete will be obtained when the width is approximately six-tenths of the overall depth of the beam.

Tables and diagrams can be prepared from the foregoing design formulae and are useful aids in the computing work. Table 40 gives values of p, k, j, and K for various commonly used combinations of unit stresses.

The value of d finally selected should be based on making the overall depth a practical dimension (preferably in $\frac{1}{2}$-inch variations) sufficient

to allow for proper imbedment of the steel. The area of steel required is computed from Equation 233, using the *normal* value of p and the theoretical depth; it may also be computed from the formula

$$A_s = \frac{M}{f_s jd}$$

where d = theoretical depth.

Bars are then selected to furnish this area in conformance with the required spacing of reinforcing bars (see Fig. 212). Finally the shear, diagonal tension, and bond stresses are checked and such adjustments made as may be indicated by these computations.

A typical design of a rectangular beam is given in Fig. 213.

DESIGN OF RECTANGULAR REINFORCED CONCRETE BEAM

Data: Span 20'-0", simply supported.
  Total Live Load = 600#/ lin. ft.
  Allowable unit stress
    f_c = 1,000#/□"
    f_s = 20,000#/□"   18,000
    n = 12

Maximum Bending Moment:
  Live Load   600#/ft.
  Dead Load (Assume beam 10¼ × 16)   170
                                           770#/ft.

  B.M. = 770 × 20² × ⅛ × 12 = 462000 in. lb.
Required Section for B.M.
  From table   normal p = 0.0111 ⎫
                                k = 0.400   ⎬ For f_s = 18,000 psi
                                j = 0.867   ⎪
                                K = 173   ⎭

  For b = 10¼ in.

  Reqd. $d = \sqrt{\dfrac{462000}{10.25 \times 173}}$ = 16.2

  Allow for protection   2.3
  Overall   18.5

Revised total load = 600 + 198 = 798# ft.

Revised B.M. = $\dfrac{798}{770}$ × 462000 = 480,000 in. lb.

  Reqd. $d = \sqrt{\dfrac{480000}{10.25 \times 173}}$ = 16.5

  Reqd. A_s = 0.111 × 10.25 × 16.5 = 1.88□"
  Use 2 bars ⅞" φ and 1 bar 1" φ (A_s = 1.99□")

  bar spacing:

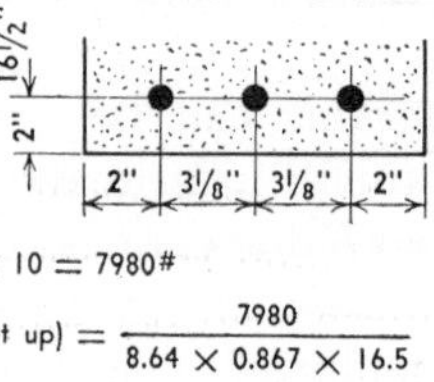

Max. end shear = 798 × 10 = 7980#

Bond. stress. (no bars bent up) = $\dfrac{7980}{8.64 \times 0.867 \times 16.5}$ = 65#/□

FIG. 213.   Typical Design Computation—Rectangular Beam.

The formulae derived for the design of rectangular beams may also be used for analysis of stresses in an existing beam. Here, however, Equation 239 cannot be used since the simultaneous stresses in steel and concrete are unknown, and therefore Equation 233, which expresses the *actual* value of p, must be employed. Values of k and j are then obtained from Equations 234 and 235, and the unit stresses in concrete and steel obtained from Equation 240. The safe resisting moment determined separately for the concrete or for the steel may be determined from Equation 240 as follows:

$$M_c = \tfrac{1}{2} f_c k j b d^2$$

$$M_s = f_s A_s j d$$

where M_c = safe bending-moment based on strength of concrete.

M_s = safe bending-moment based on strength of steel.

f_c = safe working stress in concrete.

f_s = safe working stress on steel.

A_s, k, j, b, and d are actual values for the given beam. The smaller of these two resisting moment values will control the value of the safe load.

Design Charts VI and VII are useful in determining unit stresses in rectangular beams. These are used by locating a point on the chart from the computed values of M/bd^2 and p, and the corresponding simultaneous stresses in concrete and steel determined by interpolation between the curves which are shown for the various values of f_s and f_c.

127 Solid Slabs—One-Way Reinforcement

A solid reinforced concrete slab with one-way reinforcement is essentially a wide shallow beam. Such slabs are frequently used for floors and to support distributed loads over area openings. The analysis or design of such slabs is based upon the same principles and relationships as have been previously outlined for rectangular beams. It will usually be found convenient to assume the slab divided into parallel strips and to consider each strip as constituting a rectangular beam carrying its prorated share of the loading. When the slab carries a uniformly distributed loading it is convenient to assume these strips as 1 foot (12 inches) in width, and then the load per lineal foot on a beam strip will equal the uniform load per square foot on the slab. The reinforcement may not be evenly spaced in these 1-foot strips, since there is no actual physical division, and the amount in any one strip is assumed

to equal the total area of steel in the entire slab width, multiplied by the ratio of the strip width to the slab width.   The modifications which

Safe Load on Solid Slab
Span 14'—0 in.   Simply Supported
Slab thickness 8¼"
Reinforcement ¾" φ @ 9" cts. — Deformed Bars
Bottom of Slab to center of bars = 1¼"
Allowable unit stresses:

$$n = 15; \quad f_s = 16000; \quad f_c = 800; \quad v = 40; \quad u = 100$$

For each 12" of slab width:

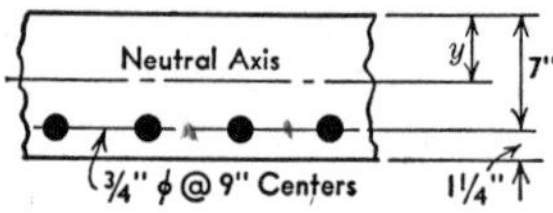

$$A_s = \frac{0.44 \times 12}{9} = 0.585\square"$$

$$\frac{A_s}{12} = \frac{\pi d^2}{4}$$

$$n A_s = 15 \times .585 = 8.8\square"$$

$$\frac{12 y^2}{2} = 8.8 (7 - y) ;$$

$$y = kd = 2.56"$$
$$jd = 7 - 1/3(2.56) = 6.15"$$

Max. Safe B.M.

I of Concrete above N. A. $= 12 \times (2.56)^3 \times 1/3 = \quad 67$
I of Transf. Steel Area $= 8.8 \times (4.44)^2 \qquad\qquad = \underline{174}$
I of 12" strip—Transf. Section $\qquad\qquad\qquad = 241$

$$M_c = \frac{800 \times 241}{2.56} = 75300"\# \text{ for 12" width of slab.}$$

$$M_s = \frac{16000 \times 241}{4.44 \times 15} = 58000"\# \text{ for 12" width of slab.}$$

∴Max. Safe B. M. = 58000"#

Max. Safe Shear — (for 9" width of slab)
Based on Diagonal Tension $= 40 \times 9 \times 6.15 = 2210\#$
Based on Bond $\qquad = 100 \times 2.356 \times 6.15 = 1450\#$
∴ Max. Safe $v = 1450\#$

Safe Total Distributed Load

$$\text{Based on B. M.} = \frac{8 \times 58000}{14 \times 14 \times 12} = 197\#/\square'$$

$$\text{Based on Shear} = \frac{2 \times 12 \times 1450}{9 \times 14} = 277\#/\square'$$

∴ Max. Safe Total Load $= 197\#/\square'$

Safe Live Load
Safe Total Load $= \qquad\qquad\qquad 197\#/\square'$

$$\text{Wt. of Slab} = \frac{8.25 \times 12 \times 150}{144} = 103$$

Safe Live Load $= \qquad\qquad\qquad\qquad 94\#/\square'$

Fig. 214.   Safe Load on Solid Slab.

for convenience may be made in the formulae previously given for rectangular beams are as follows:

$$d = \sqrt{\frac{2M}{12kjf_c}} = \sqrt{\frac{M}{12pjf_s}} \tag{242}$$

$$A_s = 12pd \tag{243}$$

$$s = \frac{12a_s}{A_s} = \frac{a_s}{pd} \tag{244}$$

where d = distance from top of slab to center of steel.

A_s = area of steel per foot of slab width.

s = spacing of parallel reinforcement bars in inches.

a_s = area of one bar.

DESIGN OF SOLID SLAB

Data: Span 16'—0" , Simply supported
Live Load 150#/□'

Allowable unit stress

$$f_c = 1,000 \text{ #/□''}$$
$$f_s = 20,000 \text{ #/□''}$$
$$n = 12$$
$$v = 50$$
$$u = 125$$

Design for Flexure:

Assume t = 6"

D. L.	=	75#/□'
L. L.	=	150
Total	=	225#/□'

Max. B. M. (12" strip) = 225 × 16 × 16 × ⅛ × 12 = 86400''#

From Tables:

Required p = 0.0094
k = 164

Reqd. $d = \sqrt{\dfrac{86400}{12 \times 164}}$ = 6.7

Concrete protection = 1 (to center of bar)

t = 7.7

Revised D. L. (t = 8) = 100
L. L. = 150
Total = 250

B. M. $= \dfrac{250}{225} \times 86400 = 96000''\#$

Reqd. $d = \sqrt{\dfrac{96000}{12 \times 164}}$ = 6.98 — Use 7"

Concrete Protection = 1"

$t =$ 8"

Reqd. A_s = .0094 × 6.98 × 12 = 0.79

Use ⅝"φ bars @ 4½" cts.

Check for Shear

Max. End Shear (4½" strip) $= \dfrac{250}{12} \times 4\frac{1}{2} \times 16 \times \frac{1}{2} = 750\#$

j = 0.875 (Table 35) jd = 6.13"

$v = \dfrac{750}{4.5 \times 6.13} = 27\text{#/□''}$ (Allowed v = 50# □'')

Check for Bond

Assume no bars bent up

$u = \dfrac{750}{1.963 \times 6.13} = 62\text{#/□''}$ (Allowed 125#/□'')

Adopted Design

8" Slab (d = 7")
⅝"φ bars @ 4½" cts.

FIG. 215.   Typical Design Computations—Solid Slab.

Design Chart VIII may be used to determine the required spacing of bars to produce a given value of A_s.

The bond stress may be computed from Equation 225, using the shear on a strip of width equivalent to the spacing of bars. In making this computation, the following values are substituted for V and Σ_0 in Equation 235.

$$V = \frac{s}{12} \times \text{(vertical shear computed for 12-in. strip)}.$$

Σ_0 = perimeter of one bar.

It is preferable to use relatively small bars in order to provide well-distributed reinforcement. Bars should be protected by at least $\frac{3}{4}$ inch of concrete and should be spaced not further apart than 3 times the thickness of the slab nor closer together than $2\frac{1}{2}$ times the diameter or side of the bar. A typical computation of the safe live load on a solid slab is given in Fig. 214. The design of a solid slab is illustrated in Fig. 215.

128   Reinforced Concrete T-Beams

In ordinary building construction, the concrete in floor slabs, beams, girders, and columns is usually placed in such a manner as to make the entire construction as nearly monolithic as possible. The slab reinforcement extends across the tops of the beams and is arranged to provide

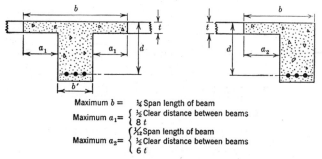

Maximum b = ¼ Span length of beam

Maximum a_1 = $\begin{cases} \text{½ Clear distance between beams} \\ 8\,t \end{cases}$

Maximum a_2 = $\begin{cases} \text{¼ Span length of beam} \\ \text{½ Clear distance between beams} \\ 6\,t \end{cases}$

FIG. 216.   Reinforced Concrete T-Beams.

for resisting the negative moment at the points of support. The concrete at the junction of slab and beam serves in a dual capacity, carrying stresses at right angles to the beam as a part of the slab and also forming the upper or compressive portion of the beam. The effective cross section of the beam will therefore include parts of the adjoining slab, and the dimensions of the beam for purposes of analysis are determined in accordance with the accepted standards indicated in Fig. 216. Building ordinances of cities may require the use of dimensions at variance with those indicated.

Formwork for Reinforced Concrete Beam, Girder, and Slab Construction.

Reinforced Concrete Beam and Girder Construction.

For solid-slab construction, the flange width is assumed as wide as the foregoing limitations will permit, since there is no physical division between the beam flange and the slab.   In ribbed-slab construction,

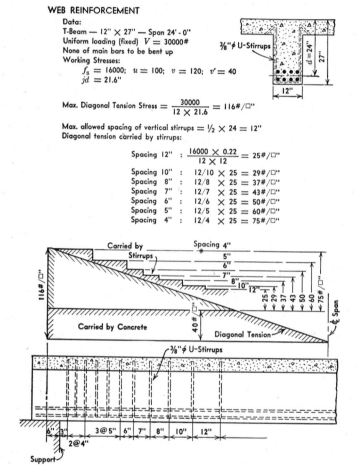

WEB REINFORCEMENT

Data:
T-Beam — 12" × 27" — Span 24' - 0"
Uniform loading (fixed) $V = 30000\#$
None of main bars to be bent up
Working Stresses:

$f_s = 16000; \quad u = 100; \quad v = 120; \quad v' = 40$
$jd = 21.6"$

Max. Diagonal Tension Stress $= \dfrac{30000}{12 \times 21.6} = 116\#/\square"$

Max. allowed spacing of vertical stirrups $= \frac{1}{2} \times 24 = 12"$
Diagonal tension carried by stirrups:

Spacing 12" : $\dfrac{16000 \times 0.22}{12 \times 12} = 25\#/\square"$

Spacing 10" : $12/10 \times 25 = 29\#/\square"$
Spacing 8" : $12/8 \times 25 = 37\#/\square"$
Spacing 7" : $12/7 \times 25 = 43\#/\square"$
Spacing 6" : $12/6 \times 25 = 50\#/\square"$
Spacing 5" : $12/5 \times 25 = 60\#/\square"$
Spacing 4" : $12/4 \times 25 = 75\#/\square"$

Fig. 217. Web Reinforcement, Reinforced Concrete T-Beam, Vertical Stirrups.

the width of solid slab necessary to form the T must be determined, and this will establish the location of the ends of the tile or steel-pan forms which shape the ribs of the slab.

When the dimensions and reinforcement area of a T-beam have been established, the flexural stresses or resisting moment may be computed by using the transformed section as discussed in Article 124.

It should be noted that, when the neutral axis of the section is in the

flange ($kd \gtreqless t$), the analysis is the same as for a rectangular section, and the same design procedure may be followed. When the neutral axis is below the flange ($kd > t$), the design formulae used for rectangular

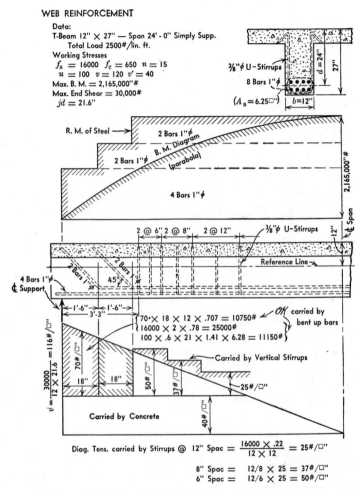

WEB REINFORCEMENT

Data:
T-Beam 12" × 27" — Span 24' - 0" Simply Supp.
    Total Load 2500#/lin. ft.
Working Stresses
    $f_s = 16000$ $f_c = 650$ $n = 15$
    $u = 100$ $v = 120$ $v' = 40$
Max. B. M. = 2,165,000"#
Max. End Shear = 30,000#
    $jd = 21.6"$

$\frac{3}{8}"\phi$ U-Stirrups
8 Bars 1"ϕ
($A_s = 6.25\square"$) $b=12"$
$d = 24"$ 27"

R. M. of Steel
2 Bars 1"ϕ
B. M. Diagram
2 Bars 1"ϕ
(parabola)
4 Bars 1"ϕ
2,165,000"#
$\mathbb{C}$ Span

2 @ 6" 2 @ 8" 2 @ 12" $\frac{3}{8}"\phi$ U-Stirrups 12"
Reference Line

4 Bars 1"ϕ
$\mathbb{C}$ Support
2 Bars 1"ϕ
45°

1'-6" 1'-6"
3'-3"
70·× 18 × 12 × .707 = 10750# ← OK carried by
16000 × 2 × .78 = 25000#   bent up bars
100 × .6 × 21 × 1.41 × 6.28 = 11150#
Carried by Vertical Stirrups
25#/$\square$"

$v = \frac{30000}{12 \times 21.6} = 116\#/\square"$
70#/$\square$"
18" 18"
50#/$\square$"
37#/$\square$"
Carried by Concrete
40#/$\square$"

Diag. Tens. carried by Stirrups @ 12" Spac = $\frac{16000 \times .22}{12 \times 12}$ = 25#/$\square$"

8" Spac = 12/8 × 25 = 37#/$\square$"
6" Spac = 12/6 × 25 = 50#/$\square$"

FIG. 218. Web Reinforcement, Reinforced Concrete T-Beam, Inclined Bars and Vertical Stirrups.

beams will not be applicable and special formulae based on this condition must be employed. For such formulae, the reader is referred to standard textbooks on reinforced concrete.

The width of stem b' must be sufficient to provide adequately for spacing the reinforcing steel, and the stem section $b'h$ must be sufficient

to resist the shear and diagonal tension. The approximate steel area required for bending-moment may be obtained closely by assuming $j = \frac{7}{8}$, from which

$$A_s = \frac{8M}{7f_s} \text{ (approx.)} \tag{245}$$

The diagonal tension stress (over the section $b'h$) is

$$v = \frac{V}{b'jd} = \frac{8V}{7b'd} \text{ (approx.)} \tag{246}$$

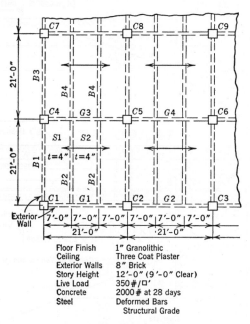

Floor Finish	1″ Granolithic
Ceiling	Three Coat Plaster
Exterior Walls	8″ Brick
Story Height	12′-0″ (9′-0″ Clear)
Live Load	350 #/□′
Concrete	2000 # at 28 days
Steel	Deformed Bars
	Structural Grade

Fig. 219.   Framing Plan.

Typical computations of web reinforcement in T-beams are shown in Figs. 217 and 218. The design of a solid slab, beam, and girder floor panel is shown in Figs. 219, 220, and 221.

129 Reinforced Concrete Columns

Reinforced concrete column construction is generally confined to short columns where the compressive resistance of the concrete controls the strength of the column. "The Building Regulations for Reinforced Concrete" of the American Concrete Institute (ACI 318-41) specify that "principal columns in buildings shall have a minimum diameter

Beam B2 at G1

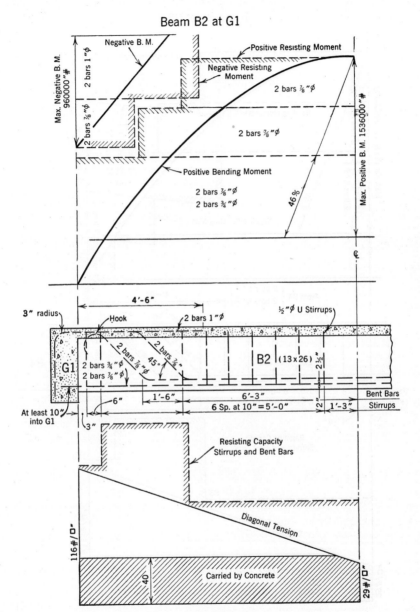

Fig. 220.

Beam B2 at G3

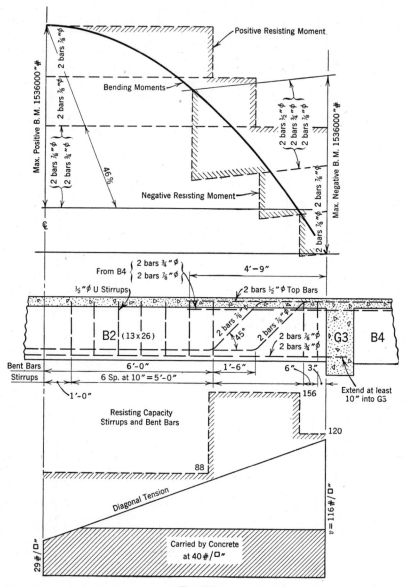

FIG. 221.

of 12 inches or rectangular columns, a minimum thickness of 10 inches and a minimum gross area of 120 square inches; posts that are not continuous from story to story shall have a minimum diameter or thickness of 6 inches." Short columns are defined as those whose unsupported length does not exceed 10 times the diameter or least lateral dimension of the column. The two principal types of reinforced concrete columns are referred to as *tied* columns and *spirally reinforced* columns.

Tied columns may be round, square, rectangular, or of any desired cross section and are reinforced with not less than four bars at the corners and evenly spaced around the periphery of the column; in addition lateral ties are placed at specified intervals in the length of the column to tie in and brace the longitudinal steel (see Fig. 222).

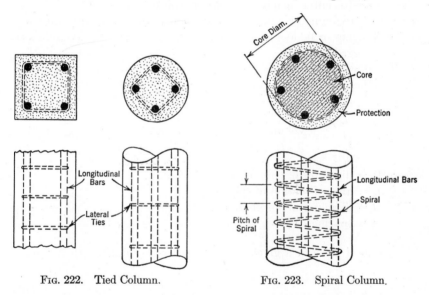

FIG. 222.　Tied Column.　　　　　FIG. 223.　Spiral Column.

Spirally reinforced columns, are those in which closely spaced spirals enclose a circular core (Fig. 223), which is reinforced with longitudinal bars. To qualify as a spirally reinforced column in accordance with the above noted building regulations, there must be provided not less than six vertical bars with a minimum diameter of $\frac{5}{8}$ inch to provide an area of not less than 1 per cent or more than 8 per cent of the gross area of the column section. The spiral reinforcement must consist of evenly spaced continuous spirals held firmly in place and true to line by at least three vertical spacer bars. The required ratio of the volume of

spiral reinforcement to the volume of the concrete core (out to out of spirals) is as follows:

$$p' = 0.45 \left(\frac{A_g}{A_c} - 1 \right) \frac{f_c'}{f_s'} \tag{247}$$

where A_g = gross area of column section
$\quad\ A_c$ = area of core of spirally reinforced column, measured to the outside diameter of spiral.
$\quad\ f_s'$ = useful limit stress of spiral reinforcement to be taken as 40,000 psi for hot-rolled rods of intermediate grade, 50,000 psi for rods of hard grade, and 60,000 psi for cold drawn wire.

The center-to-center spacing (pitch) of spirals must not exceed one-sixth the core diameter, and the clear spacing between spirals must not exceed 3 inches or be less than $1\frac{3}{8}$ inches or $1\frac{1}{2}$ times the maximum size of coarse aggregate used.

The value of the spiral steel ratio, in terms of the size of spiral bar, the pitch of the spiral, and the diameter of the core is expressed as follows:

$$p' = \frac{\text{volume of spiral bar for one turn}}{\text{volume of enclosed core for length } s}$$
$$= a_s \pi D / \tfrac{1}{4} \pi D^2 s = 4a_s / D_s \tag{248}$$

where D = diameter of core, out to out of spiral.
$\quad\ a_s$ = area of section of spiral bar.
$\quad\ d$ = diameter of spiral bar.
$\quad\ s$ = spacing or pitch of spiral.

The required pitch of a given-sized diameter of spiral bar then equals,

$$s = \frac{\pi d^2}{p'D} \tag{249}$$

Since there is no bending in a short column, the stresses produced by axial loading are uniformly distributed over the section, and

$$P = f_c A_g + f_s A_s \tag{250}$$

where P = total axial load on column.
$\quad\ A_g$ = gross area of concrete in cross section.
$\quad\ A_s$ = area of longitudinal bars in cross section.
$\quad\ f_c$ = unit stress on concrete.
$\quad\ f_s$ = unit stress on longitudinal steel.

Reinforcement in a Spirally Reinforced Concrete Column.

Assuming that the steel bars are properly bonded to the concrete so that their deformation is the same as that of the concrete, the unit deformation of concrete, f_c/E_c, equals the unit deformation of steel, f_s/E_s, and,

$$f_s = f_c \frac{E_s}{E_c} = nf_c$$

Substitute this value of f_s in Equation 250 and note that

$$A_c = A_g - A_s$$

$$P = f_c(A_g - A_s) + nf_cA_s$$

$$= f_c[A_g + (n-1)A_s]$$

$$f_c = \frac{P}{A_g + (n-1)A_s} \qquad (251)$$

In accordance with the previously quoted building regulations, the safe load on axially loaded short spirally reinforced columns is given by the following formula:

$$P = A_g \left(0.225f_c' + f_sp\right) \qquad (252)$$

where P = safe axial load.

- A_g = gross area of column section.
- f_c' = compressive strength of concrete (crushing strength at 28 days).
- f_s = 13,200 psi for structural-grade steel, 16,000 psi for intermediate-grade steel, and 20,000 psi for hard-grade steel.
- p = ratio of the effective cross-sectional area of the vertical reinforcement to the gross area A.

The safe load on *tied* columns is 80 per cent of that given by Equation 248. The steel ratio p to be considered in tied columns shall not be less than 0.01 or more than 0.04. (In other words, the steel is neglected if p is less than 0.01 and is never to be taken greater than $p = 0.04$.) In a spirally reinforced column this ratio must be at least 0.01 and never taken greater than 0.08.

130   Design of Tied Columns

For the purpose of designing short *tied* columns to carry axial loading, a factor of 80 per cent is applied to Equation 252, and

$$f = \frac{P}{A_g} = 0.8(0.225f_c' + f_sp) \qquad (253)$$

where f = allowable working stress on gross area of column.

(f_c' and f_s are given values in accordance with provisions of Article 129.)

For such columns the allowable working stress and also the corresponding required value of A_g depend on the percentage of vertical steel, and in accordance with the ACI regulations the value of p must lie between 0.01 and 0.04. The main purpose in using longitudinal steel is to give additional toughness and resilience to the column; the steel will, in general, work inefficiently as regards compression since its stress cannot exceed nf_c. Usually, therefore, a minimum of longitudinal steel will be used except where the column size is limited or when it is desired to produce a size to meet framing requirements. The design procedure is as follows: Calculate the value of the axial load including an allowance for the weight of the column. Assume a value for p (usually 0.01), and determine the allowable f from Equation 253. *When intermediate grade* steel is used, Equation 253 reduces to the following form:

$$f = 0.180f_c' + 16,000p \qquad (254)$$

The required area and reinforcement of column section are then determined from the relationships $A_g = P/f$ and $A_s = pA$, and practical dimensions and bar sizes are selected in accordance with these requirements. If it is necessary or desirable to make the column conform to given outside dimensions, the required value of p may be obtained from the following equation, which is derived from Equation 254.

$$p = \frac{P/A_g - 0.18f_c'}{16,000} \qquad (255)$$

Tied columns must have *lateral ties* which are at least $\frac{1}{4}$ inch in diameter and which are spaced at not over 16 vertical-bar diameters or 48 tie diameters or the least dimension of the column.

131 Design of Spirally Reinforced Columns

This type of column is more reliable than the type with lateral ties and hence is preferred for important loads. In the design of a spirally reinforced column, the steel ratio p for vertical steel is assumed at a value between 0.01 and 0.08, and the value of A_g is determined from Equation 252. The outside dimensions or diameter of the column is then established in order to produce this gross area, and the core diameter is fixed in order to provide suitable protection for the steel. To conform to the requirements of the ACI Building Regulations (ACI 318-41), the column reinforcement must be protected everywhere by a covering

of concrete cast monolithically with the core and with a thickness of not less than $1\frac{1}{2}$ in. or $1\frac{1}{2}$ times the maximum size of the coarse aggregate. This protective covering determines the diameter of the core, and the required ratio of spiral reinforcement is then found from Equation 247. The required size of the spiral bar and its pitch are then computed from Equations 248 and 249. It will be found convenient to assume the pitch at a suitable value and then to compute the required value of A_s from Equation 248. The nearest size diameter of spiral bar is then substituted in Equation 249 to determine its required pitch.

PROBLEMS

12·1   Determine the safe resisting moment of this reinforced concrete beam if the allowable stresses are

$$f_c = 1000 \text{ psi}$$

$$f_s = 20,000 \text{ psi}$$

$$n = 12$$

Note. The moment of inertia of a triangle about its gravity axis is $\frac{1}{36}bh^3$.

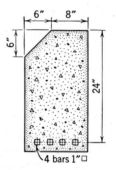

4 bars 1″□

12·2   If $A_s = 3$ sq in. and the allowable unit stresses are

$$f_s = 18,000 \text{ psi}$$

$$f_c = 1000 \text{ psi}$$

$$n = 12$$

What is the maximum safe resisting moment for the reinforced concrete section shown?

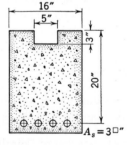

$A_s = 3\square''$

12·3   Given: the reinforced concrete beam section shown.

$$f_c = 1200 \text{ psi}$$

$$f_s = 18,000 \text{ psi}$$

$$n = 10$$

Find distance of neutral axis from top surface and the resisting moments as controlled by the steel and concrete.

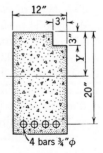

4 bars ¾″φ

12·4 A reinforced concrete beam of the section shown contains four bars, each 1 in. square. This beam is required to carry a total maximum bending-moment of 125,000 ft-lb. (*a*) If $n = 15$, what are the maximum fiber stresses in the steel and

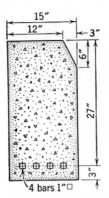

concrete? (*b*) What is the maximum total tension on the steel bars? (*c*) What is the maximum total compression on the concrete? (*d*) What is the intensity of bond on the steel at a point where the shear is 25,000 lb?

12·5 Determine the maximum safe resisting moment of reinforced concrete beam, the cross section of which is shown in the sketch.

$$n = 12$$

$$f_s = 20,000 \text{ psi}$$

$$f_c = 1,000 \text{ psi}$$

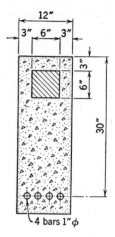

12·6 A duct 6 in. square runs lengthwise in a concrete beam as shown. Allowable stresses same as Problem 12·5 (*a*) What is the safe resisting moment of the beam? (*b*) What is the maximum intensity of shear at a point in the span where $V = 10,000$ lb?

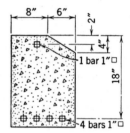

12·7 Given a beam with cross section as shown. Using specifications ACI 318-41, $f_c' = 3000$ psi, and intermediate grade steel, find the maximum permissible positive bending-moment.

12·8 Find the maximum permissible negative bending-moment for the beam given in Problem 12·7.

12·9 Determine the safe resisting moment of this section using transformed section method if the allowable fiber stresses are

$$n = 12$$

$$f_c = 1000 \text{ psi}$$

$$f_s = 20,000 \text{ psi}$$

12·10 (a) What area of tension steel is required for the reinforced concrete beam shown in order to have the theoretical position of the neutral axis 12 in. from the top? Use $n = 15$ and the transformed area method. (b) If the allowable unit stress in the steel is 18,000 psi and in the concrete 800 psi, what is the maximum safe resisting moment?

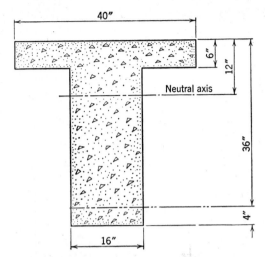

12·11 Allowable stresses:

$$f_c = 1000 \text{ psi}$$

$$f_s = 20,000 \text{ psi}$$

$$n = 12$$

(a) What is the safe resisting moment of this section? (b) What is the maximum intensity of shear at a point in the span where $V = 100,000$ lb?

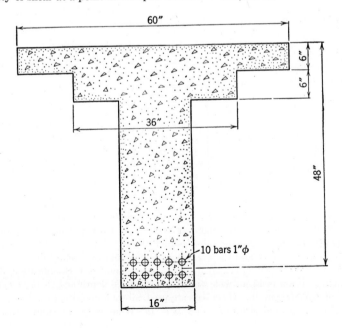

12·12   Determine the maximum safe resisting moment and the maximum safe vertical shear for the rectangular reinforced concrete beam section shown.   Allowable stresses:

$$f_c = 1200 \text{ psi}$$

$$f_s = 20,000 \text{ psi}$$

$$v = 60 \text{ psi}$$

$$n = 10$$

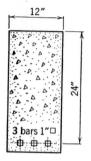

12·13   The reinforced concrete beam shown is simply supported on a span of 20 ft.   It is reinforced with four 1-in. diameter round bars.   Determine the safe live load per lineal foot of span based on flexural stresses not to exceed

$$f_s = 18,000 \text{ psi}$$

$$f_c = 700 \text{ psi}$$

$$n = 15$$

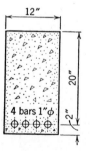

12·14   A rectangular reinforced concrete beam is to be designed to carry a total uniform load (includes its own weight) of 1800 lb per ft over a simple span of 18 ft. If the allowable stresses are the same as in Problem 12·12, calculate the depth required for a 12-in. width and the number of 1-in. round bars required.

12·15 $f_c' = 3000$ psi; intermediate-grade steel; and ACI Specification 318-41. A rectangular beam is 15 in. wide and 24 in. effective depth and carries a bending-moment of 2,200,000 in.-lb.   If six bars are used, all the same size, for reinforcing the tension side only, what size must they be?   (*b*) What is the maximum transverse

shearing force which this beam will carry as limited by bond and by diagonal tension if no stirrups are used? The bars are not hooked at the ends.

12·16 A rectangular reinforced concrete beam must resist a bending-moment of 2,000,000 in.-lb. The overall depth of the beam is fixed at 30 in. Determine the width, b, and the area of steel, A_s, which would be required to produce a balanced beam design.

$$n = 12$$

$$f_s = 20,000 \text{ psi}$$

$$f_c = 1000 \text{ psi}$$

12·17 A reinforced concrete floor slab is simply supported over an opening of 12 ft. The slab is 8 in. thick and is reinforced with $\frac{1}{2}$-in. round bars at 5-in. spacing, located $1\frac{1}{4}$ in. above the bottom of the slab. Based on $n = 15$ and allowable unit stresses of 16,000 psi in steel, and 650 psi in concrete, what safe live load (lb per sq ft) may be placed on this slab?

12·18 Design a simply supported slab to carry a live load of 150 lb per sq ft over a span of 10 ft if the allowable fiber stresses are the same as in Problem 12·17.

12·19 Design a square tied column 20 ft long, to carry an axial load of 215,000 lb. Make a free-hand sketch showing arrangement of steel. Use specifications ACI 318-41.

12·20 Use ACI Specifications 318-41; $f_c' = 3000$ psi; and intermediate-grade steel. Design a square tied column to carry an axial load of 290,000 lb, and to occupy minimum amount of space. The column is 12 ft long. (*a*) What is the minimum outside dimension, avoiding fractions of inches? (*b*) What is the minimum required number of $1\frac{1}{4}$-in. square bars which may be used? (*c*) Make a free-hand sketch showing the size, spacing, and arrangement of ties to meet the minimum requirement of the specifications.

12·21 A spirally reinforced square concrete column is required to carry an axial load of 650,000 lb. The column is 28 ft long. Use cold-drawn steel wire for the spiral reinforcement. Design the column in accordance with the ACI Specifications (318-41). $f_c' = 2500$ psi. (*a*) What is the outside dimension, avoiding fractional inches? (*b*) What is the required pitch of the spiral wire, using No. 7/0 wire and the minimum permissible thickness of concrete outside the spiral wire? (*c*) What is the required number, size, and spacing of longitudinal bars? Compare with minimum specification requirements, using intermediate-grade steel.

12·22 A spirally reinforced concrete column is 36 in. in diameter and is reinforced with 12 bars each 1 in. square. The spirals are protected by a covering of concrete 2 in. thick. Length equals 12 ft. (*a*) What is the maximum allowable axial load? (*b*) Determine the required size and pitch of spiral reinforcement, making the spirals of cold-drawn intermediate-grade steel wire, according to the ACI Specifications (318-41), when $f_c' = 3000$ psi.

12·23 A spirally reinforced column is 30 in. in outside diameter and is reinforced with 20 vertical bars each 1 in. in diameter. The spiral reinforcement is a $\frac{1}{2}$-in. round intermediate-grade steel bar, with a pitch of $2\frac{1}{2}$ in. The concrete protection is 2 in. thick. According to the ACI Regulations (ACI 318-41) and with $f_c' = 3000$ psi, determine the maximum permissible axial load. Is the spiral reinforcement adequate?

12·24 (*a*) Design a round spirally reinforced column to have a minimum diameter and to carry an axial load of 485,000 lb. Length = 12 ft. $f_c' = 2500$ psi. Use $1\frac{1}{4}$-in. square bars of hard-grade steel. Use maximum permissible spacing of spirals.

Show all computations and specification references.   (b) What is the safe load on this column if the length is increased to 22 ft?

12·25   A spirally reinforced concrete column is 30 in. in diameter and 20 ft long. It is reinforced with intermediate-grade longitudinal steel and cold-drawn spiral wire.   The maximum size of coarse aggregate is 2 in. $f_c' = 3500$ psi.   Find (a) The permissible axial load if the column is designed for the least amount of steel reinforcement.   (b) What is the required size of spiral wire if the maximum permissible pitch of the spirals is used?

APPENDIX

TABLE 1

Weights of Construction Materials

Roofs	Wgt. in lb per sq ft
Shingles	2.5
Yellow pine sheathing (1″ thick)	2.5
Corrugated iron or steel	1 to 4
Felt and gravel (5 ply)	6
Slate (¼″ thick)	9
Book tile (2″ thick)	12
Cement tile (1½″ thick)	16

Floors and Ceilings	Wgt. in lb per sq ft
⅞″ maple, finish flooring	4
Screeds or nailing strips	2
Cinder concrete fill (1″ thick)	7
Cement finish (1″ thick)	12
Reinforced concrete slabs (per inch thick)	12
Plaster ceiling on wood lath	8
Suspended metal lath and plaster	10
Plaster on brick, tile, or concrete	5

Walls and partitions	Wgt. in lb per sq ft of surface
4″ pressed brick	47
9″ common brick	85
13″ common brick	120
4″ tile	17
4″ gypsum block	12

Miscellaneous Materials	Wgt. in lb per cu ft
Concrete	150
Cinder concrete	110
Brick masonry (common brick)	120
Steel	490
Cast iron	450
Ashlar masonry—limestone	160
granite	165
Earth (moist-packed)	100
Timber—L. L. yellow pine (dry)	41–55
Douglas fir (dry)	34–38

TABLE 2

Moment Table—Cooper's E-60

Note: Loads and moments are given in thousands of pounds and foot-pounds for one rail.

	①	②	③	④	⑤	⑥	⑦	⑧	⑨	⑩	⑪	⑫	⑬	⑭	⑮	⑯	⑰	⑱	3.0 PER FT.	
Spacing		8'·0"	5'·0"	5'·0"	5'·0"	9'·0"	5'·0"	6'·0"	5'·0"	8'·0"	8'·0"	5'·0"	5'·0"	5'·0"	9'·0"	5'·0"	6'·0"	5'·0"	5'·0"	
Wheel load	15	30	30	30	30	19.5	19.5	19.5	19.5	15	30	30	30	30	19.5	19.5	19.5	19.5		
DIST. MOM. LOAD	0 0 15	8 120 45	13 345 75	18 720 105	23 1245 135	32 2460 154.5	37 3230 174	43 4280 193.5	48 5240 213	56 6950 228	64 8770 258	69 10060 288	74 11500 318	79 13090 348	88 16220 367.5	93 18060 387	99 20380 406.5	104 22420 426	109 24546 426	1
		0 0 30	5 150 60	10 450 90	15 900 120	24 1980 139.5	29 2680 159	35 3630 178.5	40 4520 198	48 6110 213	56 7810 243	61 9030 273	66 10390 303	71 11910 333	80 14900 352.5	85 16670 372	91 18900 391.5	96 20860 411	101 22910 411	2
			0 0 30	5 150 60	10 450 90	19 1260 109.5	24 1808 129	30 2580 148.5	35 3325 168	43 4670 183	51 6130 213	56 7200 243	61 8410 273	66 9780 303	75 12500 322.5	80 14120 342	86 16170 361.5	91 17980 381	96 19900 381	3
				0 0 30	5 150 60	14 690 79.5	19 1088 99	25 1680 118.5	30 2275 138	38 3380 159	46 4600 183	51 5320 213	56 6580 243	61 7800 273	70 10250 292.5	75 11720 312	81 13600 331.5	86 15250 351	91 17000 351	4
					0 0 30	9 270 49.5	14 518 69	20 932 88.5	25 1375 108	33 2240 123	41 3220 153	46 3990 183	51 4900 213	56 5970 243	65 8150 262.5	70 9470 282	76 11150 301.5	81 12670 321	86 14270 321	5
						0 0 19.5	5 97.5 39	11 331.5 58.5	16 624 78	24 1248 93	32 1992 123	37 2605 153	42 3370 183	47 4290 213	56 6200 232.5	61 7370 252	67 8880 271.5	72 10240 291	77 11700 291	6
							0 0 19.5	6 117 39	11 312 58.5	19 780 73.5	27 1368 103.5	32 1885 133.5	37 2555 163.5	42 3370 193.5	51 5110 213	56 6180 232.5	62 7570 252	67 8830 271.5	72 10190 271.5	7
								0 0 19.5	5 97.5 39	13 409.5 54	21 842 84	26 1262 114	31 1830 144	36 2550 174	45 4120 193.5	50 5090 213	56 6360 232.5	61 7530 252	66 8790 252	8
									0 0 19.5	8 156 34.5	16 432 64.5	21 755 94.5	26 1227 124.5	31 1850 154.5	40 3240 174	45 4110 193.5	51 5270 213	56 6340 232.5	61 7500 232.5	9
										0 0 15	8 120 45	13 345 75	18 720 105	23 1245 135	32 2460 154.5	37 3230 174	43 4280 193.5	48 5240 213	53 6310 213	10
											0 0 30	5 150 60	10 450 90	15 900 120	24 1980 139.5	29 2680 159	35 3630 178.5	40 4520 198	45 5510 198	11
												0 0 30	5 150 60	10 450 90	19 1260 109.5	24 1808 129	30 2580 148.5	35 3325 168	40 4160 168	12
													0 0 30	5 150 60	14 690 79.5	19 1088 99	25 1680 118.5	30 2275 138	35 2965 138	13
														0 0 30	9 270 49.5	14 518 69	20 932 88.5	25 1375 108	30 1915 108	14
															0 0 19.5	5 97.5 39	11 331.5 58.5	16 624 78	21 1015 78	15
																0 0 19.5	6 117 39	11 312 58.5	16 605 58.5	16
																	0 0 19.5	5 97.5 39	10 292.5 39	17
																		0 0 19.5	5 97.5 19.5	18

8 240 45	0 0 30			
13 630 75	5 150 60	0 0 30		
18 1170 105	10 450 90	5 150 60	0 0 30	
23 1860 135	15 900 120	10 450 90	5 150 60	0 0 30

TABLE 3

COMMON BRIGHT WIRE NAILS

Penny Designation	Dimensions		Diameter* D (inches)	$D^{3/2}$	Approx. Number per Lb
	Length (inches)	Wire Gage			
2	1	15	.0720	.0193	876
3	1¼	14	.0800	.0227	568
4	1½	12½	.0985	.0309	316
5	1¾	12½	.0985	.0309	271
6	2	11½	.1130	.0380	181
7	2¼	11½	.1130	.0380	161
8	2½	10¼	.1314	.0474	106
9	2¾	10¼	.1314	.0474	96
10	3	9	.1483	.0570	69
12	3¼	9	.1483	.0570	63
16	3½	8	.1620	.0652	49
20	4	6	.1920	.0841	31
30	4½	5	.2070	.0942	24
40	5	4	.2253	.1068	18
50	5½	3	.2437	.1205	14
60	6	2	.2625	.1349	11

* Gage of American Steel and Wire Co. and John A. Roebling Sons.

TABLE 4

LAG SCREWS—SQUARE HEAD AND GIMLET POINT—MANUFACTURERS' STANDARD LIST

Size	Length and Weight per 100										
	1½	2	2½	3	3½	4	5	6	7	8	10
⁵⁄₁₆	3.5	4.4	5.3	6.2	......	......	......	......	......	......	.....
⅜	5.8	7.1	8.5	9.8	11.1	12.5	14.9	17.2	20.0	......	.....
½	.....	15.0	17.3	19.5	21.6	23.8	28.8	33.8	......	44.0	.....
⅝	.....	26.3	......	33.5	37.1	40.7	......	55.7	......	69.3	83.5
¾	.....	......	......	......	......	57.1	......	80.5	......	......	.....

TABLE 5

Teco Split-Ring Data

Nominal Size	$2\frac{1}{2}$	4
Split-ring—dimensions		
Inside diameter at center when closed, inches	$2\frac{1}{2}$	4
Depth, inches	$\frac{3}{4}$	1
Weight, per 100 rings, pounds	28	70
Lumber, minimum dimensions allowed		
Width, inches	$3\frac{5}{8}$	$5\frac{1}{2}$
Thickness, rings in one face, inches	1	1
Thickness, rings opposite in both faces, inches	$1\frac{5}{8}$	$1\frac{5}{8}$
Bolt, diameter, minimum, inches	$\frac{1}{2}$	$\frac{3}{4}$
(With rings of different size, use minimum for larger ring)		
Bolt hole, maximum diameter, inches	$\frac{9}{16}$	$1\frac{3}{16}$
Projected area for portion of one ring within a member, square inches	1.10	2.25
Washers, minimum		
Round, cast or malleable iron, diameter, inches	$2\frac{1}{8}$	3
Square plate		
Length of side, inches	2	3
Thickness, inches	$\frac{1}{8}$	$\frac{3}{16}$
(For trussed rafters and similar light construction standard wrought washers may be used)		

Reprinted from "Teco Design Manual for Teco Timber Connector Construction," by courtesy of the Timber Engineering Co.

TABLE 6

Permissible Increases for Load Duration on Split Rings

	Permanent Loading	Three Months' Loading	Snow Loading	Wind or Earthquake Loading	Impact Loading
Split-rings	0%	15%	15%	50%	100%

Reprinted from "Teco Design Manual for Teco Timber Connector Construction," by courtesy of the Timber Engineering Co.

TABLE 7

DECREASES FOR MOISTURE CONTENT CONDITIONS

Condition when fabricated	Seasoned	Unseasoned	Unseasoned
Condition when used	Seasoned	Seasoned	Unseasoned or wet
Split-rings	0%	20%	33%

Reprinted from "Teco Design Manual for Teco Timber Connector Construction," by courtesy of the Timber Engineering Co.

TABLE 8

MAXIMUM RECOMMENDED VALUES FOR A GROUP OF CONNECTORS ACTING 45 TO 90 DEGREES WITH THE GRAIN

(% of Allowable Loads on One Connector)

Type and Size of Connector	Thickness of Loaded Member, Inches			
	1⅝"	2"	2⅝"	3" and Thicker
2½-in. Split-ring	300%	300%	300%	300%
4-in. Split-ring	233%	248%	269%	300%

For above 3 rings.

For each additional connector exceeding 4, add 33 per cent of the allowable load for one connector.
Reprinted from "Teco Design Manual for Teco Timber Connector Construction," by courtesy of the Timber Engineering Co.

TECO SPLIT RING CONNECTORS

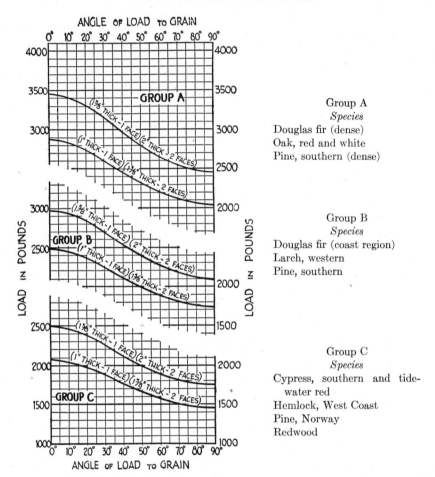

Group A
Species
Douglas fir (dense)
Oak, red and white
Pine, southern (dense)

Group B
Species
Douglas fir (coast region)
Larch, western
Pine, southern

Group C
Species
Cypress, southern and tide-water red
Hemlock, West Coast
Pine, Norway
Redwood

DESIGN CHART I. Safe Load on One $2\frac{1}{2}$-in. Split Ring and Bolt in Single Shear.

(From "Teco Design Manual for Teco Timber Connector Construction," by courtesy of the Timber Engineering Co.)

TECO SPLIT RING CONNECTORS

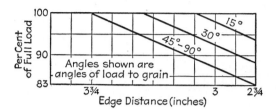

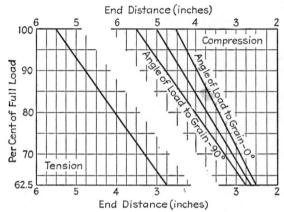

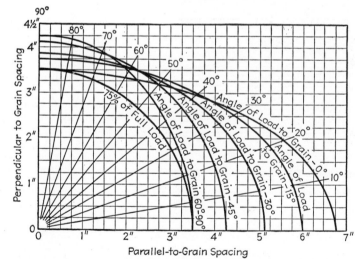

DESIGN CHART II.   Spacing Chart for $2\frac{1}{2}$-in. Split Ring Connectors.

(From "Teco Design Manual for Teco Timber Connector Construction," by courtesy of the Timber Engineering Co.)

TECO SPLIT RING CONNECTORS

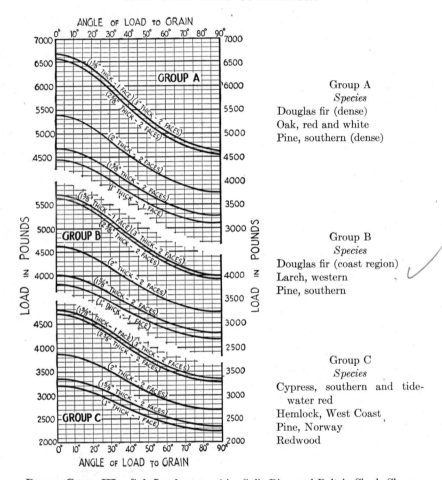

Group A
Species
Douglas fir (dense)
Oak, red and white
Pine, southern (dense)

Group B
Species
Douglas fir (coast region)
Larch, western
Pine, southern

Group C
Species
Cypress, southern and tide-
water red
Hemlock, West Coast
Pine, Norway
Redwood

DESIGN CHART III.   Safe Load on one 4-in. Split Ring and Bolt in Single Shear.

(From "Teco Design Manual for Teco Timber Connector Construction," by courtesy of the Timber Engineering Co.)

TECO SPLIT RING CONNECTORS

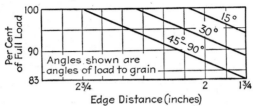

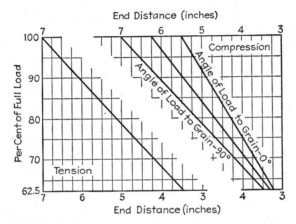

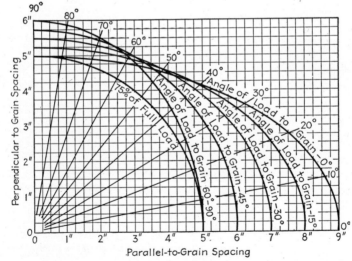

DESIGN CHART IV. Spacing Chart for 4-in. Split Ring Connectors.

(From "Teco Design Manual for Teco Timber Connector Construction," by courtesy of the Timber Engineering Co.)

TABLE 9

BOLT HEADS AND NUTS

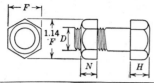 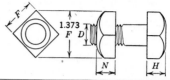

Heads and Nuts		American Standard Regular	American Standard Heavy	American Standard Bolt and Nut Dimensions, rounded to the nearest 1/16 in., are those adopted by American Institute of Bolt, Nut and Rivet Manufacturers, American Standard B 18.2, 1941. "American Standard Regular" formerly called Manufacturers Standard, American Standard, etc. "American Standard Heavy" formerly called United States Standard. Some fabricators have standard heads and nuts differing only slightly from the table. For bolts with countersunk heads the included angle is 78 degrees, the same as for rivets.
Head	Height, H	$\tfrac{2}{3}D$	$\tfrac{3}{4}D + \tfrac{1}{16}$ in.	
	Short Dia., F	$1\tfrac{1}{2}D$	$1\tfrac{1}{2}D + \tfrac{1}{8}$ in.	
Nut	Height, N	$\tfrac{7}{8}D$	D	
	Short Dia., F	$1\tfrac{1}{2}D + \tfrac{1}{16}$ in. ($D = \tfrac{5}{8}$ in. or less) $1\tfrac{1}{2}D$ (D greater than $\tfrac{5}{8}$ in.)	$1\tfrac{1}{2}D + \tfrac{1}{8}$ in.	

Standard Dimensions

Head

Dia. of Bolt, In.	Series	Hexagon Diameter Long	Hexagon Diameter Short	Height, In.	Square Diameter Long	Square Diameter Short
¼	American Standard Regular	7/16	3/8	3/16	½	3/8
3/8		5/8	9/16	¼	¾	9/16
½		7/8	¾	5/16	1	¾
5/8		1 1/16	15/16	7/16	1 5/16	15/16
¾		1 5/16	1 1/8	½	1 9/16	1 1/8
7/8		1½	1 5/16	9/16	1 13/16	1 5/16
1		1 11/16	1½	5/8	2 1/16	1½
1 1/8		1 15/16	1 11/16	¾	2 5/16	1 11/16
1¼		2 1/8	1 7/8	13/16	2 9/16	1 7/8
1 3/8		2 3/8	2 1/16	15/16	2 13/16	2 1/16
1½		2 9/16	2¼	1	3 1/16	2¼
1 5/8		2¾	2 7/16	1 1/16	3 3/8	2 7/16
1¾		3	2 5/8	1 3/16	3 5/8	2 5/8
1 7/8		3 3/16	2 13/16	1¼	3 7/8	2 13/16
2		3 7/16	3	1 5/16	4 1/8	3
2¼		3 7/8	3 3/8	1½	4 5/8	3 3/8
2½		4¼	3¾	1 11/16	5 1/8	3¾
2¾		4 11/16	4 1/8	1 13/16	5 11/16	4 1/8
3		5 1/8	4½	2	6 3/16	4½
3¼	Former Manufacturers Standard	5 9/16	4 7/8	2 3/16	6 11/16	4 7/8
3½		6	5¼	2 5/16	7 3/16	5¼
3¾		6 7/16	5 5/8	2½	7¾	5 5/8
4		6 7/8	6	2 11/16	8¼	6
4¼		7¼	6 3/8	2 13/16	8¾	6 3/8
4½		7 11/16	6¾	3	9¼	6¾
4¾		8 1/8	7 1/8	3 3/16	9 13/16	7 1/8
5		8 9/16	7½	3 5/16	10 5/16	7½
5¼		9	7 7/8	3½	10 13/16	7 7/8
5½		9 3/8	8¼	3 11/16	11 5/16	8¼
5¾		9 13/16	8 5/8	3 13/16	11 13/16	8 5/8
6		10¼	9	4	12 3/8	9

Nut

Dia. of Bolt, In.	Series	Hexagon Diameter Long	Hexagon Diameter Short	Height, In.	Square Diameter Long	Square Diameter Short
¼	American Standard Regular	½	7/16	¼	5/8	7/16
3/8		11/16	5/8	5/16	7/8	5/8
½		15/16	13/16	7/16	1 1/8	13/16
5/8		1 1/8	1	9/16	1 3/8	1
¾		1 5/16	1 1/8	11/16	1 9/16	1 1/8
7/8		1½	1 5/16	¾	1 13/16	1 5/16
1		1 11/16	1½	7/8	2 1/16	1½
1 1/8		1 15/16	1 11/16	1	2 5/16	1 11/16
1¼		2 1/8	1 7/8	1 1/8	2 9/16	1 7/8
1 3/8		2 3/8	2 1/16	1¼	2 13/16	2 1/16
1½		2 9/16	2¼	1 5/16	3 1/8	2¼
1 3/8	American Standard Heavy	2½	2 3/16	1 3/8	3	2 3/16
1½		2 11/16	2 3/8	1½	3¼	2 3/8
1 5/8		2 15/16	2 9/16	1 5/8	3½	2 9/16
1¾		3 1/8	2¾	1¾	3¾	2¾
1 7/8		3 3/8	2 15/16	1 7/8	4 1/16	2 15/16
2		3 9/16	3 1/8	2	4 5/16	3 1/8
2¼		4	3½	2¼	4 13/16	3½
2½		4 7/16	3 7/8	2½	5 5/16	3 7/8
2¾		4 7/8	4¼	2¾	5 13/16	4¼
3		5¼	4 5/8	3	6 3/8	4 5/8
3¼	Former U. S. Standard	5 11/16	5	3¼	6 7/8	5
3½		6 1/8	5 3/8	3½	7 3/8	5 3/8
3¾		6 9/16	5¾	3¾	7 7/8	5¾
4		7	6 1/8	4	8 7/16	6 1/8
4¼		7 7/16	6½	4¼	8 15/16	6½
4½		7 13/16	6 7/8	4½	9 7/16	6 7/8
4¾		8¼	7¼	4¾	9 15/16	7¼
5		8 11/16	7 5/8	5	10½	7 5/8
5¼		9 1/8	8	5¼	11	8
5½		9 9/16	8 3/8	5½	11½	8 3/8
5¾		10	8¾	5¾	12	8¾
6		10 3/8	9 1/8	6	12½	9 1/8

Reprinted from "Steel Construction," by courtesy of the American Institute of Steel Construction.

TABLE 10

SCREW THREADS

American National Form

American Standard, B 1.1, 1935

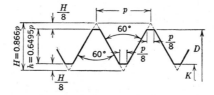

Diameter		Area		Number of Threads per Inch	Diameter		Area		Number of Threads per Inch
Total D, In.	Net K, In.	Total Dia., D, Sq. In.	Net Dia., K, Sq. In.		Total D, In.	Net K, In.	Total Dia., D, Sq. In.	Net Dia., K, Sq. In.	
¼	0.185	0.049	0.027	20	3	2.675	7.069	5.621	4
⅜	0.294	0.110	0.068	16	3¼	2.925	8.296	6.720	4
½	0.400	0.196	0.126	13	3½	3.175	9.621	7.918	4
⅝	0.507	0.307	0.202	11	3¾	3.425	11.045	9.214	4
¾	0.620	0.442	0.302	10	4	3.675	12.566	10.608	4
⅞	0.731	0.601	0.419	9					
1	0.838	0.785	0.551	8	4¼	3.798	14.186	11.330	2⅞
1⅛	0.939	0.994	0.693	7	4½	4.028	15.904	12.741	2¾
1¼	1.064	1.227	0.890	7	4¾	4.255	17.721	14.221	2⅝
1⅜	1.158	1.485	1.054	6					
1½	1.283	1.767	1.294	6	5	4.480	19.635	15.766	2½
1¾	1.490	2.405	1.744	5	5¼	4.730	21.648	17.574	2½
					5½	4.953	23.758	19.268	2⅜
2	1.711	3.142	2.300	4½	5¾	5.203	25.967	21.262	2⅜
2¼	1.961	3.976	3.021	4½					
2½	2.175	4.909	3.716	4	6	5.423	28.274	23.095	3¼
2¾	2.425	5.940	4.619	4					

Sizes over 4 in. are old U. S. Standard; there is no American Standard.

Dimensions are maximum; specify "Free Fit, Class 2." For Bolts from 2½ in. to 6 in. in diameter it is always necessary to bill the number of threads per inch.

Reprinted from "Steel Construction," by courtesy of the American Institute of Steel Construction.

TABLE 11

LENGTH OF BOLT THREADS

American Standard, B 18.2, 1941

Diameter of Bolt, In. — Minimum Thread Length

Length of Bolt, In.	1/4	3/8	1/2	5/8	3/4	7/8	1	1 1/8 1 1/4	1 3/8 1 1/2	1 5/8 1 3/4	1 7/8 2	2 1/4	2 1/2	2 3/4	3
1	3/4	3/4	3/4	3/4											
1 1/4	3/4	3/4	1	1	1										
1 1/2	3/4	7/8	1	1 1/8	1 1/8	1 1/8									
1 3/4	3/4	7/8	1	1 3/16	1 3/8	1 3/8	1 3/8								
2	3/4	1	1 1/4	1 1/4	1 3/8	1 9/16	1 5/8	1 5/8							
2 1/2	3/4	1	1 1/4	1 1/2	1 1/2	1 9/16	1 3/4	2	2						
3	7/8	1	1 1/4	1 1/2	1 3/4	1 3/4	1 3/4	2 1/8	2 1/2	2 1/2					
4	7/8	1	1 1/4	1 1/2	1 3/4	2	2 1/4	2 1/4	2 1/2	2 7/8	3 1/4	3 1/4	3 1/4		
5	7/8	1 3/16	1 1/4	1 1/2	1 3/4	2	2 1/4	2 3/4	2 3/4	2 7/8	3 1/4	3 5/8	4	4 1/8	4 1/4
6	7/8	1 3/16	1 1/2	1 1/2	1 3/4	2	2 1/4	2 3/4	3 1/4	3 1/4	3 1/4	3 5/8	4	4 1/8	4 3/4
8	7/8	1 3/16	1 1/2	1 13/16	2	2	2 1/4	2 3/4	3 1/4	3 3/4	4	4	4	4 1/8	4 3/4
10	7/8	1 3/16	1 1/2	1 13/16	2 1/8	2 7/16	2 1/2	2 3/4	3 1/4	3 3/4	4 1/4	4 3/4	4 3/4	4 3/4	4 3/4
12	7/8	1 3/16	1 1/2	1 13/16	2 1/8	2 7/16	2 3/4	2 3/4	3 1/4	3 3/4	4 1/4	4 3/4	5 1/4	5 3/4	6 1/4
16	1	1 3/16	1 1/2	1 13/16	2 1/8	2 7/16	2 3/4	3 1/4	3 1/4	3 3/4	4 1/4	4 3/4	5 1/4	5 3/4	6 1/4
20	1	1 3/8	1 1/4	1 13/16	2 1/8	2 7/16	2 3/4	3 3/8	4	4 5/8	4 3/4	4 3/4	5 1/4	5 3/4	6 1/4
30			1 3/4	1 13/16	2 1/8	2 7/16	2 3/4	3 3/8	4	4 5/8	5 1/4	5 7/8	6 1/2	6 1/2	6 1/2

For intermediate bolt lengths, same minimum thread length as for next shorter tabulated length.
Reprinted from "Steel Construction" by courtesy of the American Institute of Steel Construction.

TABLE 12

BASIC STRESSES FOR CALCULATING SAFE LOADS FOR BOLTED JOINTS [1]

Group	Species of Wood	Basic Stress	
		Parallel to the grain	Perpendicular to the grain
		Pounds per square inch	*Pounds per square inch*
	Softwoods:		
1	Cedar, northern and southern white......... Fir, balsam and commercial white.......... Hemlock, eastern......................... Pine, ponderosa, sugar, northern white, and western white....................... Spruce, Engelmann, red, Sitka, and white....	800	150
2	Cedar, Alaska, Port Orford, and western red.. Douglas fir (Rocky Mountain type)........ Hemlock, western........................ Pine, Norway...........................	1,000	200
3	Cypress, southern........................ Douglas fir (coast type)................... Larch, western.......................... Pine, southern yellow.................... Redwood................................ Tamarack...............................	1,300	275
	Hardwoods:		
1	Ash, black............................. Aspen and largetooth aspen............... Basswood.............................. Birch, paper............................ Chestnut............................... Cottonwood, black and eastern............ Yellow poplar...........................	925	175
2	Maple (soft), red and silver............... Elm, American and slippery............... Gum, black, red, and tupelo.............. Sycamore...............................	1,200	250
3	Ash, commercial white.................... Beech................................. Birch, sweet and yellow................... Elm, rock.............................. Hickory, true and pecan.................. Maple (hard), black and sugar............. Oak, commercial red and white............	1,500	400

[1] These stresses, when used in conjunction with Tables 13 and 14, give safe bolt-bearing stresses. They apply to seasoned timbers used in a dry, inside location. For other conditions, reduce each stress as follows: When the timbers are occasionally wet but quickly dried, use three-fourths of the stress listed; if damp or wet most of the time, use two-thirds.

From U. S. Dept. of Agriculture Technical Bulletin 332.

TABLE 13

PERCENTAGE OF BASIC STRESS PARALLEL TO THE GRAIN [1] FOR CALCULATING
SAFE BEARING STRESSES UNDER BOLTS

Length of Bolt in Main Member Divided by Its Diameter (L/D)	Percentage of Basic Stress for					
	Common bolts [2]			High-strength bolts [3]		
	Group 1 woods	Group 2 woods	Group 3 woods	Group 1 woods	Group 2 woods	Group 3 woods
1.0	100.0	100.0	100.0	100.0	100.0	100.0
1.5	100.0	100.0	100.0	100.0	100.0	100.0
2.0	100.0	100.0	100.0	100.0	100.0	100.0
2.5	100.0	100.0	99.7	100.0	100.0	100.0
3.0	100.0	100.0	99.0	100.0	100.0	100.0
3.5	100.0	99.3	96.7	100.0	100.0	99.7
4.0	99.5	97.4	92.5	100.0	100.0	99.0
4.5	97.9	93.8	86.8	100.0	100.0	97.8
5.0	95.4	88.3	80.0	100.0	99.8	96.0
5.5	91.4	82.2	73.0	100.0	98.2	93.0
6.0	85.6	75.8	67.2	100.0	95.4	89.5
6.5	79.0	70.0	62.0	98.5	92.2	85.2
7.0	73.4	65.0	57.6	95.8	88.8	81.0
7.5	68.5	60.6	53.7	92.7	85.0	76.8
8.0	64.2	56.9	50.4	89.3	81.2	73.0
8.5	60.4	53.5	47.4	85.9	77.7	69.6
9.0	57.1	50.6	44.8	82.5	74.2	66.4
9.5	54.1	47.9	42.4	79.0	71.0	63.2
10.0	51.4	45.5	40.3	75.8	68.0	60.2
10.5	48.9	43.3	38.4	72.5	64.8	57.4
11.0	46.7	41.4	36.6	69.7	61.9	54.8
11.5	44.7	39.6	35.0	66.8	59.2	52.4
12.0	42.8	37.9	33.6	64.0	56.7	50.2
12.5	41.1	36.4	32.2	61.4	54.4	48.2
13.0	39.5	35.0	31.0	59.1	52.4	46.3

[1] The product of the basic stress parallel to the grain selected from Table 12 and the percentage for the particular L/D ratio and species group, taken from this table, is the safe working stress at that ratio for joints with metal splice plates. When wood splice plates are used, each one-half the thickness of the main timber, 80 per cent of this product is the safe working stress.

[2] Bolts having a yield point of approximately 45,000 pounds per square inch.

[3] Bolts having a yield point of approximately 125,000 pounds per square inch.

From U. S. Dept. of Agriculture Technical Bulletin 332.

TABLE 14

Percentages of Basic Stress Perpendicular to the Grain Used in Calculating Safe Bearing Stresses under Bolts [1]

Length of Bolt in Main Member Divided by Its Diameter (L/D)	Percentage for Common Bolts [2]				Percentage for High-Strength Bolts [3]
	Group 1 conifers and group 1 hardwoods	Group 2 conifers	Group 2 hardwoods and group 3 conifers	Group 3 hardwoods	All groups
1.0 to 5.0, inclusive....	100.0	100.0	100.0	100.0	100.0
5.5.................	100.0	100.0	100.0	99.0	100.0
6.0.................	100.0	100.0	100.0	96.3	100.0
6.5.................	100.0	100.0	99.5	92.3	100.0
7.0.................	100.0	100.0	97.3	86.9	100.0
7.5.................	100.0	99.1	93.3	81.2	100.0
8.0.................	100.0	96.1	88.1	75.0	100.0
8.5.................	98.1	91.7	82.1	69.9	99.8
9.0.................	94.6	86.3	76.7	64.6	97.7
9.5.................	90.0	80.9	71.9	60.0	94.2
10.0.................	85.0	76.2	67.2	55.4	90.0
10.5.................	80.1	71.6	62.9	51.6	85.7
11.0.................	76.1	67.6	59.3	48.4	81.5
11.5.................	72.1	64.1	55.6	45.4	77.4
12.0.................	68.6	61.0	62.0	42.5	73.6
12.5.................	65.3	58.0	49.0	40.0	70.2
13.0.................	62.2	55.3	45.9	37.5	66.9

Diameter of bolt, inches........	¼	⅜	½	⅝	¾	⅞	1	1¼	1½	1¾	2	2½	3 and over
Diameter factor.	2.50	1.95	1.68	1.52	1.41	1.33	1.27	1.19	1.14	1.10	1.07	1.03	1.00

[1] The safe working stress for a given value of L/D is the product of three factors: (1) the basic stress perpendicular to the grain taken from Table 12, (2) the percentage from this table, and (3) the factor for bolt diameter, also from this table. No reduction need be made when wood splice plates are used except that the safe load perpendicular to the grain should never exceed the safe load parallel to the grain for any given size and quality of bolt and timber.

[2] Bolts having a yield point of approximately 45,000 pounds per square inch.

[3] Bolts having a yield point of approximately 125,000 pounds per square inch.

From U. S. Dept. of Agriculture Technical Bulletin 332.

TABLE 15

DIMENSIONS OF STRUCTURAL RIVETS

Driven Heads　　Manufactured Heads　　Die　　Driving Clearance

"Basic Dimensions," High Button (Acorn) Heads, American Institute of Bolt, Nut and Rivet Manufacturers, 1937

			Dia. of Rivet, In.	1/2	5/8	3/4	7/8	1	1 1/8	1 1/4	1 3/8	1 1/2
Driven Head, In.	Full	A	1.5D + 1/8	7/8	1 1/16	1 1/4	1 7/16	1 5/8	1 13/16	2	2 3/16	2 3/8
		H	0.425A	3/8	7/16	17/32	5/8	11/16	3/4	27/32	15/16	1
		F	1.5H	9/16	11/16	13/16	15/16	1 1/32	1 5/32	1 9/32	1 13/32	1 1/2
	Counter-sunk	C	1.81D	29/32	1 1/8	1 11/32	1 19/32	1 13/16	2 1/32	2 1/4	2 1/2	2 23/32
		K	0.5D	1/4	5/16	3/8	7/16	1/2	9/16	5/8	11/16	3/4
Manufactured Head, In.	Full	A	1.5D + 1/32	25/32	31/32	1 5/32	1 11/32	1 17/32	1 23/32	1 29/32	2 3/32	2 9/32
		H	0.75D + 1/8	1/2	19/32	11/16	25/32	7/8	31/32	1 1/16	1 5/32	1 1/4
		F	0.75D + 9/32	21/32	3/4	27/32	15/16	1 1/32	1 1/8	1 7/32	1 5/16	1 13/32
		M	0.50	1/2	1/2	1/2	1/2	1/2	1/2	1/2	1/2	1/2
		N	0.094	3/32	3/32	3/32	3/32	3/32	3/32	3/32	3/32	3/32
		G	0.75D − 9/32	3/32	3/16	9/32	3/8	15/32	9/16	21/32	3/4	27/32
	Counter-sunk	C	1.81D	29/32	1 1/8	1 11/32	1 19/32	1 13/16	2 1/32	2 1/4	2 1/2	2 23/32
		K	0.5D	1/4	5/16	3/8	7/16	1/2	9/16	5/8	11/16	3/4
Die, In.		B		1 3/4	2	2 1/4	2 1/2	2 3/4	3	3 1/4	3 1/2	3 3/4
Driving Clearance Inches			E (min)	3/4	7/8	1	1 1/8	1 1/4	1 3/8	1 1/2	1 5/8	1 3/4
			E (pref.)	1	1 1/8	1 1/4	1 3/8	1 1/2	1 5/8	1 3/4	1 7/8	2

Reprinted from "Steel Construction," by courtesy of the American Institute of Steel Construction.

TABLE 16

Allowable Working Values for Power-Driven Rivets

Unit Shearing Stress $= 15{,}000\#/\text{in}^2$

Unit Bearing Stress $\begin{cases} \text{Single Bearing} = 32{,}000\#/\text{in}^2 \\ \text{Double Bearing} = 40{,}000\#/\text{in}^2 \end{cases}$

Diameter of Rivet	$\frac{5}{8}''$		$\frac{3}{4}''$		$\frac{7}{8}''$		$1''$		$1\frac{1}{8}''$	
Area of Rivet	0.3068		0.4418		0.6013		0.7854		0.9940	
Single Shear, Pounds	4,600		6,630		9,020		11,780		14,910	
Double Shear, Pounds	9,200		13,250		18,040		23,560		29,820	
Bearing	Single, Lb	Double, Lb	Single, Lb	Double, Lb	Single, Lb	Double, Lb	Single, Lb	Double, Lb	Single, Lb	Double, Lb
$\frac{1}{4}$	....	6,250	6,000	7,500	7,000	8,750	8,000	10,000	9,000	11,250
$\frac{5}{16}$	....	7,810	....	9,380	8,750	10,900	10,000	12,500	11,300	14,100
$\frac{3}{8}$	....	9,380	....	11,300	....	13,100	12,000	15,000	13,500	16,900
$\frac{7}{16}$	....	.....	....	13,100	....	15,300	.....	17,500	.....	19,700
$\frac{1}{2}$	....	.....	....	.....	....	17,500	.....	20,000	.....	22,500
$\frac{9}{16}$	....	.....	....	.....	....	.....	.....	22,500	.....	25,300
$\frac{5}{8}$	....	.....	....	.....	....	.....	.....	.....	.....	28,100

(Left vertical label: Thickness of plate in inches)

Compiled from data in "Manual of Steel Construction," by permission of the American Institute of Steel Construction.

TABLE 17

Unfinished Bolts

Allowable Loads in Kips

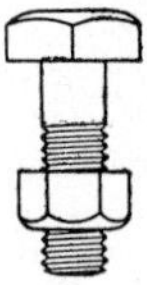

Shear	10,000 psi
Bearing: S. S.	20,000 psi
D. S.	25,000 psi

For bolts with washers under nuts and with unthreaded shanks extending completely through joined parts, values may be increased by 12.5 percent

Bolt. Dia.	½		⅝		¾		⅞		1		1⅛		1¼	
Area	0.1963		0.3068		0.4418		0.6013		0.7854		0.9940		1.2272	
Single Shear	1.96		3.07		4.42		6.01		7.85		9.94		12.27	
Double Shear	3.93		6.14		8.84		12.03		15.71		19.88		24.54	
Thickness of Plate	Bearing		Bearing		Bearing		Bearing		Bearing		Bearing		Bearing	
	20.0	25.0	20.0	25.0	20.0	25.0	20.0	25.0	20.0	25.0	20.0	25.0	20.0	25.0
0.125 ⅛	1.25	1.56	1.56	1.95	1.88	2.35								
0.140	1.40	1.75	1.75	2.19	2.10	2.63	2.45	3.06						
0.160	1.60	2.00	2.00	2.50	2.40	3.00	2.80	3.50						
0.180	1.80	2.25	2.25	2.81	2.70	3.38	3.15	3.94						
0.1875 3/16	1.88	2.38	2.34	2.93	2.81	3.52	3.28	4.10						
0.200	2.00	2.50	2.50	3.13	3.00	3.75	3.50	4.38	4.00	5.00				
0.220	...	2.75	2.75	3.44	3.30	4.13	3.85	4.81	4.40	5.50				
0.240	...	3.00	3.00	3.75	3.60	4.50	4.20	5.25	4.80	6.00				
0.250 ¼	...	3.13	3.13	3.91	3.75	4.69	4.38	5.47	5.00	6.25				
0.260	...	3.25	...	4.06	3.90	4.88	4.55	5.69	5.20	6.50	5.85	7.31		
0.280	...	3.50	...	4.38	4.20	5.25	4.90	6.13	5.60	7.00	6.30	7.88		
0.300	...	3.75	...	4.69	4.50	5.63	5.25	6.56	6.00	7.50	6.75	8.44		
0.3125 5/16	...	3.91	...	4.88	...	5.86	5.47	6.84	6.25	7.81	7.03	8.79		
0.320	...	4.00	...	5.00	...	6.00	5.60	7.00	6.40	8.00	7.20	9.00	8.00	10.0
0.340	...	...	...	5.31	...	6.38	5.95	7.44	6.80	8.50	7.65	9.56	8.50	10.6
0.360	...	...	...	5.63	...	6.75	...	7.88	7.20	9.00	8.10	10.1	9.00	11.3
0.375 ⅜	...	...	...	5.86	...	7.03	...	8.20	7.50	9.38	8.44	10.6	9.38	11.7
0.380	...	...	...	5.94	...	7.13	...	8.31	7.60	9.50	8.55	10.7	9.50	11.9
0.400	...	...	...	6.25	...	7.50	...	8.75	8.00	10.0	9.00	11.3	10.0	12.5
0.420	...	...	...	...	...	7.88	...	9.19	...	10.5	9.45	11.8	10.5	13.1
0.4375 7/16	...	...	...	...	...	8.20	...	9.57	...	10.9	9.84	12.3	10.9	13.7
0.440	...	...	...	...	...	8.25	...	9.63	...	11.0	9.90	12.4	11.0	13.8
0.460	...	...	...	...	...	8.63	...	10.1	...	11.5	...	12.9	11.5	14.4
0.480	...	...	...	...	...	9.00	...	10.5	...	12.0	...	13.5	12.0	15.0
0.500 ½	...	...	...	...	...	...	...	10.9	...	12.5	...	14.1	12.5	15.6
0.520	...	...	...	...	...	...	...	11.4	...	13.0	...	14.6	....	16.3
0.540	...	...	...	...	...	...	...	11.8	...	13.5	...	15.2	....	16.9
0.560	...	...	...	...	...	...	...	12.3	...	14.0	...	15.7	....	17.5
0.5625 9/16	...	...	...	...	...	...	...	....	...	14.1	...	15.8	....	17.6
0.580	...	...	...	...	...	...	...	....	...	14.5	...	16.3	....	18.1
0.600	...	...	...	...	...	...	...	....	...	15.0	...	16.9	....	18.8
0.620	...	...	...	...	...	...	...	....	...	15.5	...	17.4	....	19.4
0.625 ⅝	...	...	...	...	...	...	...	....	...	15.6	...	17.6	....	19.5
0.6875 11/16	...	...	...	...	...	...	...	....	...	17.2	...	19.3	....	21.5
0.750 ¾	...	...	...	...	...	...	...	....	...	....	...	21.1	....	23.4
0.8125 13/16	...	...	...	...	...	...	...	....	...	....	...	....	....	25.4

Reprinted from "Steel Construction" by courtesy of the American Institute of Steel Construction.

TABLE 18

Erection Clearances for Inserting and Driving Rivets

No.	Max. Rivet	Diam. D Ins.	Str. Ins.	Wt., Lb	A: Length L In.	A: Clear. C In.	B: Length L_1 In.	B: Clear. C In.	All hammers except No. 130 and No. 11 can be fitted with inverted handles. These are for crowded work and are only provided by special arrangement. No. 130 is a jam riveter for close-quarter work.
130	7/8	3 1/16	4	15	....	..	9	12	} Used only to drive in close quarters
50	3/4	2 5/16	5	20	....	..	14	17	
60	3/4	2 7/16	6	23	19 1/2	24	15 1/2	19	Rarely used
80	1	2 7/16	8	25	21 1/2	26	17 1/2	21	Used for all except heaviest riveting
90	1 1/4	2 7/16	9	26	23 3/4	28	19 3/4	23	} Used for heaviest riveting
11	1 1/2	2 7/16	11	32	26 1/2	31	....	..	

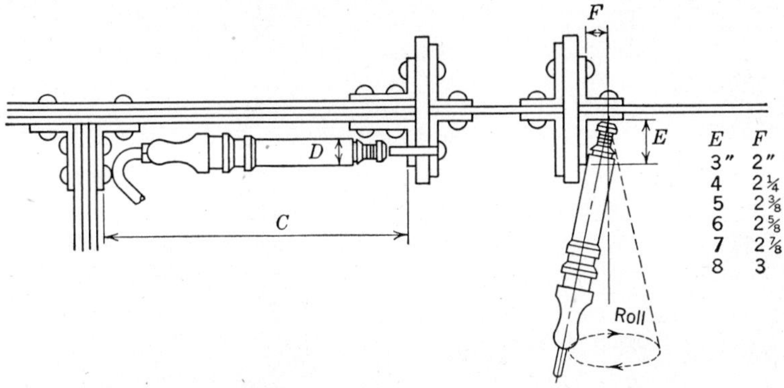
F
D
E
C
Roll
E F
3" 2"
4 2 1/4
5 2 3/8
6 2 5/8
7 2 7/8
8 3

If hammer can be "rolled," easier driving and more symmetrical heads are obtained. To permit this, distance "F" must be as given here and field rivets must have a perfect stagger with shop rivets.

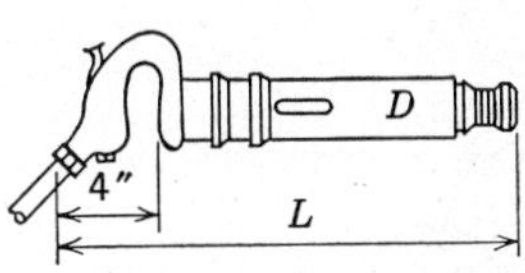
D
4"
L

(a) Standard Open Handle

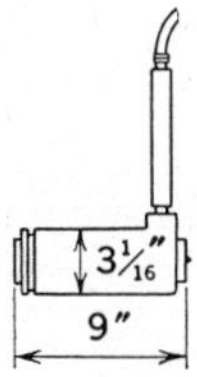
3 1/16"
9"

Jam Riveter No. 130

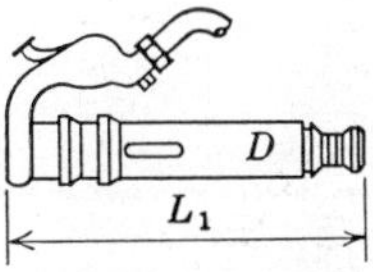
D
L_1

(b) Inverted Handle

Reprinted from "Steel Construction," by courtesy of the American Institute of Steel Construction.

TABLE 19

PHYSICAL PROPERTIES OF METAL DEPOSITED BY BARE AND COATED
ELECTRODES

Property	Bare Electrode		Coated Electrode	
	Min	Max	Min	Max
Yield point, lb per sq in...........	35,000	40,000	42,000	55,000
Ultimate strength, lb per sq in.....	45,000	55,000	60,000	70,000
Elongation in 2 in., per cent.......	8	15	25	35
Reduction of area, per cent........	15	20	45	65
Endurance limit, lb per sq in.......	16,000	20,000	26,000	30,000
Impact strength, Izod, ft-lb........	5	15	40	50
Density, g per cc.................	7.5	7.6	7.81	7.85

From paper on welding design, by Chas. H. Jennings, *A.S.M.E. Transactions* for October, 1936.

TABLE 20

PERMISSIBLE UNIT STRESSES

(Values in Kips per sq in.)

Kind of Stress	For Welds Made with Filler Metal of	
	Grade 2, 4, 10, or 15	Grade 20, 30, or 40
Shear on section through weld throat............	13.6	11.3
Tension on section through weld throat..........	15.6	13.0
Compression (crushing) on section through throat of butt weld..............................	18.0	18.0

Note that this code specifies that the stress in a fillet weld shall be considered as shear, for any direction of the applied stress.

TABLE 21

WORKING STRESSES AND STRESS-CONCENTRATION FACTORS FOR WELDS
ON LOW-CARBON STEELS

Type of Weld	—Working Stresses— Bare Electrodes		—Coated Electrodes—	
	Static Loads, lb per sq in.	Dynamic Loads, lb per sq in.	Static Loads, lb per sq in.	Dynamic Loads, lb per sq in.
Butt welds:				
Tension..................	13,000	5,000	16,000	8,000
Compression..............	15,000	5,000	18,000	8,000
Shear....................	8,000	3,000	10,000	5,000
Fillet welds:				
Transverse and parallel welds	11,300	3,000	14,000	5,000

Stress-Concentration Factors

Location	Stress-Concentration Factor, K
Reinforced butt welds...	1.2
Toe of transverse fillet weld.................................	1.5
End of parallel fillet weld...................................	2.7
T butt joint with sharp corners..............................	2.0

From paper on welding design by Chas. H. Jennings, *A.S.M.E. Transactions* for October, 1936.

TABLE 22

Yard Lumber—Standard Sizes

Finish, Common Boards and Strips, Dimension and Heavy Joist

Product	Rough Size		Dressed Dimensions		
	Thickness, inches	Width, inches	Yard Thickness, inches	Industrial Thickness, inches	Width, inches
Finish	. . . .	3	$\frac{5}{16}$	. . . .	$2\frac{5}{8}$
	. . . .	4	$\frac{7}{16}$	. . . .	$3\frac{1}{2}$
	. . . .	5	$\frac{9}{16}$	. . . .	$4\frac{1}{2}$
	. . . .	6	$1\frac{1}{16}$	. . . .	$5\frac{1}{2}$
	1	7	$2\frac{5}{32}$	$2\frac{6}{32}$	$6\frac{1}{2}$
	$1\frac{1}{4}$	8	$1\frac{1}{16}$	. . . .	$7\frac{1}{4}$
	$1\frac{1}{2}$	9	$1\frac{5}{16}$	. . . .	$8\frac{1}{4}$
	$1\frac{3}{4}$	10	$1\frac{7}{16}$	. . . .	$9\frac{1}{4}$
	2	11	$1\frac{5}{8}$	$1\frac{6}{8}$	$10\frac{1}{4}$
	$2\frac{1}{2}$	12	$2\frac{1}{8}$	. . . .	$11\frac{1}{4}$
	3	. . . .	$2\frac{5}{8}$	. . . .	. . . .
Common boards and strips	1	3	$2\frac{5}{32}$	$2\frac{6}{32}$	$2\frac{5}{8}$
	$1\frac{1}{4}$	4	$1\frac{1}{16}$	. . . .	$3\frac{5}{8}$
	$1\frac{1}{2}$	5	$1\frac{5}{16}$	. . . .	$4\frac{5}{8}$
	. . . .	6	. . . .	. . . .	$5\frac{5}{8}$
	. . . .	7	. . . .	. . . .	$6\frac{5}{8}$
	. . . .	8	. . . .	. . . .	$7\frac{1}{2}$
	. . . .	9	. . . .	. . . .	$8\frac{1}{2}$
	. . . .	10	. . . .	. . . .	$9\frac{1}{2}$
	. . . .	11	. . . .	. . . .	$10\frac{1}{2}$
	. . . .	12	. . . .	. . . .	$11\frac{1}{2}$
Dimension and heavy joist	2	2	$1\frac{5}{8}$	$1\frac{6}{8}$	$1\frac{5}{8}$
	$2\frac{1}{2}$	4	$2\frac{1}{8}$	. . . .	$3\frac{5}{8}$
	3	6	$2\frac{5}{8}$	. . . .	$5\frac{5}{8}$
	4	8	$3\frac{5}{8}$	. . . .	$7\frac{1}{2}$
	. . . .	10	. . . .	. . . .	$9\frac{1}{2}$
	. . . .	12	. . . .	. . . .	$11\frac{1}{2}$

Note: Thicknesses apply to all widths and widths to all thicknesses.

TABLE 23

Standard Sizes of Structural Timbers

Item	Nominal Thickness	Nominal Width	Nominal Length
Joists and planks...	2, 3 and 4 in.	4 in. and up in multiples of 2 in.	6, 8, 9, and 10 ft to 40 ft in multiples of 2 ft
Beams and stringers	5, 6 in. and up in multiples of 2 in.	8 in. and up in multiples of 2 in.	6, 8, 9, and 10 ft and up in multiples of 2 ft
Posts and timbers..	5, 6 in. and up in multiples of 2 in.	5, 6 in. and up in multiples of 2 in.	6, 8, 9, and 10 ft and up in multiples of 2 ft

TABLE 24

Structural Timbers—Standard Sizes Joist and Plank, Beams and Stringers, Posts and Timbers

Tolerances and Surfacing Allowances

Product	Thickness			Width		
		Minimum			Minimum	
	Nominal, inches	Rough, inches	S1S or S2S, inches	Nominal, inches	Rough, inches	S1E or S2E, inches
Joist and plank	2	$\frac{1}{8}$ off	$\frac{3}{8}$ off	4	$\frac{3}{16}$ off	$\frac{3}{8}$ off
	3	$\frac{3}{16}$ off	$\frac{3}{8}$ off	6	$\frac{3}{16}$ off	$\frac{3}{8}$ off
	4	$\frac{3}{16}$ off	$\frac{3}{8}$ off	8 and up	$\frac{1}{4}$ off	$\frac{1}{2}$ off
Beams and stringers	5	$\frac{3}{16}$ off	$\frac{1}{2}$ off	8 and up	$\frac{1}{4}$ off	$\frac{1}{2}$ off
	6	$\frac{3}{16}$ off	$\frac{1}{2}$ off	....	....	....
	8 and up	$\frac{1}{4}$ off	$\frac{1}{2}$ off	....	....	....
Posts and timbers	5	$\frac{3}{16}$ off	$\frac{1}{2}$ off	5	$\frac{3}{16}$ off	$\frac{1}{2}$ off
	6	$\frac{3}{16}$ off	$\frac{1}{2}$ off	6	$\frac{3}{16}$ off	$\frac{1}{2}$ off
	8 and up	$\frac{1}{4}$ off	$\frac{1}{2}$ off	8 and up	$\frac{1}{4}$ off	$\frac{1}{2}$ off

Note: Thicknesses apply to all widths and widths to all thicknesses.

APPENDIX

TABLE 25

ALLOWABLE UNIT STRESSES—STRESS-GRADE LUMBER

The allowable unit stresses below are for permanent loading.

Species and Commercial Grade [1]	Rules Under Which Graded	Allowable Unit Stresses in Pounds per Square Inch					Modulus of Elasticity E
		Extreme Fiber in Bending f and Tension Parallel to Grain [2] t	Horizontal Shear H	Compression Perpendicular to Grain $c\perp$	Compression Parallel to Grain [3] c		
1	2	3	4	5	6		7
Cypress, southern:	National Hardwood Lumber Association			360			1,200,000
1700 f Grade	J.&P.–B.&S.	1,700	145		1,425		
1300 f Grade	J.&P.–B.&S.	1,300	120		1,125		
1450 c Grade	P.&T.	.....	...		1,450		
1200 c Grade	P.&T.	.....	...		1,200		
Cypress, tidewater red:	Southern Cypress Manufacturers Association			360			1,200,000
1700 f Grade	J.&P.–B.&S.	1,700	145		1,425		
1300 f Grade	J.&P.–B.&S.	1,300	120		1,125		
1450 c Grade	P.&T.	.....	...		1,450		
1200 c Grade	P.&T.	.....	...		1,200		
Douglas fir coast region: [4]	West Coast Bureau of Lumber Grades and Inspection						1,600,000
Par. 214a Grade [5]	J.&P.	2,150	145	455	1,550		
Par. 218a Grade [5]	B.&S.	2,150	145	455	1,550		
Par. 214 Grade	J.&P.	1,900	120	415	1,450		
Par. 218 Grade	B.&S.	1,900	120	415	1,450		
Par. 215a Grade [5]	J.&P.	1,700	145	455	1,325		
Par. 219a Grade [5]	B.&S.	1,700	145	455	1,325		
Par. 215 Grade	J.&P.	1,450	120	390	1,200		
Par. 219 Grade	B.&S.	1,450	120	390	1,200		
Par. 216 Grade	J.&P.	1,100	110	390	1,075		
Par. 210a Grade [5]	P.&T.	.....	...	455	1,550		
Par. 210 Grade	P.&T.	.....	...	415	1,450		
Par. 200 Grade	P.&T.	.....	...	390	1,325 [6]		
Douglas fir, inland empire:	Western Pine Association						
Select structural [5]	J.&P.	2,150	145	455	1,750		1,600,000
Structural	J.&P.	1,900	100	400	1,400		1,500,000
Common structural	J.&P.	1,450	95	380	1,250		1,500,000
Select structural [5]	P.&T.	.....	...	455	1,750		1,600,000
Structural	P.&T.	.....	...	400	1,400		1,500,000
Common structural	P.&T.	.....	...	380	1,250		1,500,000
Hemlock, eastern:	Northern Hemlock and Hardwood Manufacturers Association			360			1,100,000
Select structural	J.&P.–B.&S.	1,300	85		850		
Prime structural	J.&P.[7]	1,200	60		775		
Common structural	J.&P.[7]	1,100	60		650		
Utility structural	J.&P.[7]	950	60		600		
Select structural	P.&T.	.....	...		850		
Hemlock, West Coast: [4]	West Coast Bureau of Lumber Grades and Inspection			360			1,400,000
Par. 498 Grade	J.&P.	1,450	100		1,075		
Par. 500 Grade	B.&S.	1,450	100		1,075		
Par. 499 Grade	J.&P.	1,100	90		850		
Par. 503 Grade	P.&T.	.....	...		1,075 [6]		

See footnotes at end of table.

TABLE 25—*Continued*

ALLOWABLE UNIT STRESSES—STRESS-GRADE LUMBER

The allowable unit stresses below are for permanent loading.

Species and Commercial Grade [1]	Rules Under Which Graded	Extreme Fiber in Bending f and Tension Parallel to Grain [2] t	Horizontal Shear H	Compression Perpendicular to Grain $c\perp$	Compression Parallel to Grain [3] c	Modulus of Elasticity E
1	2	3	4	5	6	7
Maple, hard:		National Hardwood Lumber Association		600		1,600,000
2150 f Grade	J.&P.	2,150	145		1,750	
1900 f Grade	J.&P.–B.&S.	1,900	145		1,525	
1700 f Grade	J.&P.–B.&S.	1,700	145		1,350	
1450 f Grade	J.&P.–B.&S.	1,450	120		1,150	
1550 c Grade	P.&T.	.....	...		1,550	
1450 c Grade	P.&T.	.....	...		1,450	
1200 c Grade	P.&T.	.....	...		1,200	
Oak, red and white:		National Hardwood Lumber Association		600		1,500,000
2150 f Grade	J.&P.	2,150	145		1,550	
1900 f Grade	J.&P.–B.&S.	1,900	145		1,375	
1700 f Grade	J.&P.–B.&S.	1,700	145		1,200	
1450 f Grade	J.&P.–B.&S.	1,450	120		1,050	
1300 f Grade	B.&S.	1,300	120		950	
1325 c Grade	P.&T.	.....	...		1,325	
1200 c Grade	P.&T.	.....	...		1,200	
1075 c Grade	P.&T.	.....	...		1,075	
Pine, Norway:		Northern Hemlock and Hardwood Manufacturers Association		360		1,200,000
Prime structural	J.&P.[7]	1,200	75		900	
Common structural	J.&P.[7]	1,100	75		775	
Utility structural	J.&P.[7]	950	75		650	
Pine, southern longleaf:		Southern Pine Inspection Bureau of the Southern Pine Association		455		1,600,000
Select structural[5]	J.&P.–B.&S.	2,400	120[8]		1,750	
Prime structural[5]	J.&P.–B.&S.	2,150	120[8]		1,550	
Merchantable structural[5]	J.&P.–B.&S.	1,900	120[8]		1,450	
Structural S.E.&S.[5]	J.&P.–B.&S.	1,900	120[8]		1,450	
No. 1 structural[5]	J.&P.–B.&S.	1,700	120[8]		1,200	
No. 1 dimension[5]	J.&P.[7]	1,700	...		1,200	
No. 2 stress dimension[5]	J.&P.[7]	1,250	...		1,025	
Select structural[5]	P.&T.	.....	...		1,750	
Prime structural[5]	P.&T.	.....	...		1,550	
Merchantable structural[5]	P.&T.	.....	...		1,450	
Structural S.E.&S.[5]	P.&T.	.....	...		1,450	
No. 1 structural[5]	P.&T.	.....	...		1,200	
Pine, southern shortleaf:		Southern Pine Inspection Bureau of the Southern Pine Association				1,600,000
Dense select structural[5]	J.&P.–B.&S.	2,400	120[8]	455	1,750	
Dense Structural[5]	J.&P.–B.&S.	2,150	120[8]	455	1,550	
Dense structural S.E.&S.[5]	J.&P.–B.&S.	1,900	120[8]	455	1,450	

See footnotes at end of table.

TABLE 25—*Continued*

ALLOWABLE UNIT STRESSES—STRESS-GRADE LUMBER

The allowable unit stresses below are for permanent loading.

Species and Commercial Grade [1]	Rules Under Which Graded	Allowable Unit Stresses in Pounds per Square Inch				Modulus of Elasticity E
		Extreme Fiber in Bending f and Tension Parallel to Grain [2] t	Horizontal Shear H	Compression Perpendicular to Grain $c\perp$	Compression Parallel to Grain [3] c	
1	2	3	4	5	6	7
Pine, southern shortleaf: *Continued*						
Dense No. 1 structural [5]	J.&P.–B.&S.	1,700	120 [8]	455	1,200	
No. 1 dense dimension [5]	J.&P. [7]	1,700	. . .	455	1,200	
No. 1 dimension	J.&P. [7]	1,450	. . .	390	1,075	
No. 2 dense stress dimension [5]	J.&P. [7]	1,250	. . .	455	1,025	
No. 2 medium grain stress dimension	J.&P. [7]	1,100	. . .	390	875	
Dense select structural [5]	P.&T.	. . . . .	. . .	455	1,750	
Dense structural [5]	P.&T.	. . . . .	. . .	455	1,550	
Dense structural S.E. & S. [5]	P.&T.	. . . . .	. . .	455	1,450	
Dense No. 1 structural [5]	P.&T.	. . . . .	. . .	455	1,200	
Redwood:	California Redwood Association			320		1,200,000
Dense select all-heart structural [5]	J.&P.–B.&S.	1,700	110		1,450	
Select all-heart structural [5]	J.&P.–B.&S.	1,450	95		1,325	
Bulkhead structural [5]	J.&P.	1,300	95		1,325	
Heart structural	J.&P.	1,300	95		1,325	
Dense select all-heart structural [5]	P.&T.	. . . . .	. . .		1,450	
Select all-heart structural [5]	P.&T.	. . . . .	. . .		1,325	
Spruce, eastern:	Northeastern Lumber Manufacturers Association, Inc.			300		1,200,000
1450 f structural grade	J.&P.	1,450	110		1,050	
1300 f structural grade	J.&P.	1,300	95		975	
1200 f structural grade	J.&P.	1,200	95		900	

[1] Abbreviations: J.&P., Joists and Planks; B.&S., Beams and Stringers; P.&T., Posts and Timbers; S.E.&S., Square Edge and Sound.

[2] When graded in accordance with specification.

[3] When graded according to specification and when the l/d ratio is 11 or less.

[4] These paragraph numbers refer to paragraphs in the Standard Grading and Dressing Rules of the West Coast Bureau of Lumber Grades and Inspection.

[5] These grades include requirements for density.

[6] When slope of grain is not more than 1 in 10.

[7] Available in thickness of 2 in. only.

[8] Allowable unit shearing stresses of 145, 170, and 190 psi may be used when these grades are specified to conform to the standard 120, 140, and 160 lb shear grades respectively in the grading rules.

Consider actual size

TABLE 26

TIMBER

AMERICAN STANDARD SIZES

Properties for Designing

National Lumber Manufacturers' Association

Nominal Size	American Standard Dressed Size	Area of Section	Wt per Foot	Moment of Inertia	Section Modulus
In.	In.	In.²	Lb	In.⁴	In.³
2 × 4	1⅝×3⅝	5.89	1.64	6.45	3.56
6	5⅝	9.14	2.54	24.1	8.57
8	7½	12.2	3.39	57.1	15.3
10	9½	15.4	4.29	116	24.4
12	11½	18.7	5.19	206	35.8
14	13½	21.9	6.09	333	49.4
16	15½	25.2	6.99	504	65.1
18	17½	28.4	7.90	726	82.9
3 × 4	2⅝×3⅝	9.52	2.64	10.4	5.75
6	5⅝	14.8	4.10	38.9	13.8
8	7½	19.7	5.47	92.3	24.6
10	9½	24.9	6.93	188	39.5
12	11½	30.2	8.39	333	57.9
14	13½	35.4	9.84	538	79.7
16	15½	40.7	11.3	815	105
18	17½	45.9	12.8	1172	134
4 × 4	3⅝×3⅝	13.1	3.65	14.4	7.94
6	5⅝	20.4	5.66	53.8	19.1
8	7½	27.2	7.55	127	34.0
10	9½	34.4	9.57	259	54.5
12	11½	41.7	11.6	459	79.9
14	13½	48.9	13.6	743	110
16	15½	56.2	15.6	1125	145
18	17½	63.4	17.6	1619	185
6 × 6	5½×5½	30.3	8.40	76.3	27.7
8	7½	41.3	11.4	193	51.6
10	9½	52.3	14.5	393	82.7
12	11½	63.3	17.5	697	121
14	13½	74.3	20.6	1128	167
16	15½	85.3	23.6	1707	220
18	17½	96.3	26.7	2456	281
20	19½	107.3	29.8	3398	349
8 × 8	7½×7½	56.3	15.6	264	70.3
10	9½	71.3	19.8	536	113
12	11½	86.3	23.9	951	165
14	13½	101.3	28.0	1538	228
16	15½	116.3	32.0	2327	300
18	17½	131.3	36.4	3350	383
20	19½	146.3	40.6	4634	475
22	21½	161.3	44.8	6211	578

Nominal Size	American Standard Dressed Size	Area of Section	Wt per Foot	Moment of Inertia	Section Modulus
In.	In.	In.²	Lb	In.⁴	In.³
10×10	9½ × 9½	90.3	25.0	679	143
12	11½	109	30.3	1,204	209
14	13½	128	35.6	1,948	289
16	15½	147	40.9	2,948	380
18	17½	166	46.1	4,243	485
20	19½	185	51.4	5,870	602
22	21½	204	56.7	7,868	732
24	23½	223	62.0	10,274	874
12×12	11½×11½	132	36.7	1,458	253
14	13½	155	43.1	2,358	349
16	15½	178	49.5	3,569	460
18	17½	201	55.9	5,136	587
20	19½	224	62.3	7,106	729
22	21½	247	68.7	9,524	886
24	23½	270	75.0	12,437	1058
14×14	13½×13½	182	50.6	2,768	410
16	15½	209	58.1	4,189	541
18	17½	236	65.6	6,029	689
20	19½	263	73.1	8,342	856
22	21½	290	80.6	11,181	1040
24	23½	317	88.1	14,600	1243
16×16	15½×15½	240	66.7	4,810	621
18	17½	271	75.3	6,923	791
20	19½	302	83.9	9,578	982
22	21½	333	92.5	12,837	1194
24	23½	364	101	16,763	1427
18×18	17½×17½	306	85.0	7,816	893
20	19½	341	94.8	10,813	1109
22	21½	376	105	14,493	1348
24	23½	411	114	18,926	1611
26	25½	446	124	24,181	1897
20×20	19½×19½	380	106	12,049	1236
22	21½	419	116	16,150	1502
24	23½	458	127	21,089	1795
26	25½	497	138	26,945	2113
28	27½	536	149	33,795	2458
24×24	23½×23½	552	153	25,415	2163
26	25½	599	166	32,472	2547
28	27½	646	180	40,727	2962
30	29½	693	193	50,275	3408

All properties and weights given are for dressed size only.

The weights given above are based on assumed average weight of 40 pounds per cubic foot.

Reproduced from "Manual of Steel Construction," by courtesy of the American Institute of Steel Construction.

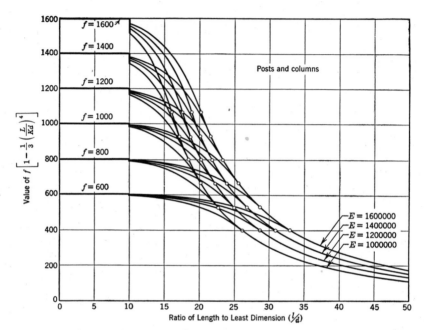

DESIGN CHART V. Allowable Unit Stress in Timber Columns.

(From *Douglas Fir Use Book*, by permission of West Coast Lumberman's Assoc.)

TABLE 27

Steel for Bridges and Buildings   ASTM A 7-39
Structural Rivet Steel   ASTM A 141-39
Structural Silicon Steel   ASTM A 94-39

Property	Steel for Bridges and Buildings		Structural Rivet Steel	Structural Silicon Steel
	Plates, Sections, and Bars	Eye-Bar Flats, Unannealed		
Tensile strength, psi	60,000 to 72,000	67,000 to 82,000	52,000 to 62,000	80,000 to 95,000
Yield point, psi, but never less than	0.5 tens. str. 33,000	0.5 tens. str. 36,000	0.5 tens. str. 28,000	45,000
Elongation in 8-in. minimum percentage	$\dfrac{1,500,000\ [1]}{\text{tens. str.}}$	$\dfrac{1,500,000\ [1]}{\text{tens. str.}}$	$\dfrac{1,500,000}{\text{tens. str.}}$	$\dfrac{1,500,000[1]}{\text{tens. str.}}$
Elongation in 2-in. minimum percentage	22	20	. . .	$\dfrac{1,600,000}{\text{tens. str.}}$

[1] The specifications permit a modification of this requirement for material over ¾ in. in thickness or under 5⁄16 in.

TABLE 28

W Shapes

Properties for Designing

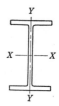

Nominal Size	Weight per Foot	Area	Depth	Flange		Web Thickness	Axis X–X			Axis Y–Y		
				Width	Thickness		I	S	r	I	S	r
In.	Lb	In.²	In.	In.	In.	In.	In.⁴	In.³	In.	In.⁴	In.³	In.
36 × 16½	300	88.17	36.72	16.655	1.680	0.945	20290.2	1105.1	15.17	1225.2	147.1	3.73
	280	82.32	36.50	16.595	1.570	0.885	18819.3	1031.2	15.12	1127.5	135.9	3.70
	260	76.56	36.24	16.555	1.440	0.845	17233.8	951.1	15.00	1020.6	123.3	3.65
	245	72.03	36.06	16.512	1.350	0.802	16092.2	892.5	14.95	944.7	114.4	3.67
	230	67.73	35.88	16.475	1.260	0.765	14988.4	835.5	14.88	870.9	105.7	3.59
36 × 12	194	57.11	36.48	12.117	1.260	0.770	12103.4	663.6	14.56	355.4	58.7	2.49
	182	53.54	36.32	12.072	1.180	0.725	11281.5	621.2	14.52	327.7	54.3	2.47
	170	49.98	36.16	12.027	1.100	0.680	10470.0	579.1	14.47	300.6	50.0	2.45
	160	47.09	36.00	12.000	1.020	0.653	9738.8	541.0	14.38	275.4	45.9	2.42
	150	44.16	35.84	11.972	0.940	0.625	9012.1	502.9	14.29	250.4	41.8	2.38
33 × 15¾	240	70.52	33.50	15.865	1.400	0.830	13585.1	811.1	13.88	874.3	110.2	3.52
	220	64.73	33.25	15.810	1.275	0.775	12312.1	740.6	13.79	782.4	99.0	3.48
	200	58.79	33.00	15.750	1.150	0.715	11048.2	669.6	13.71	691.7	87.8	3.43
33 × 11½	152	44.71	33.50	11.565	1.055	0.635	8147.6	486.4	13.50	256.1	44.3	2.39
	141	41.51	33.31	11.535	0.960	0.605	7442.2	446.8	13.39	229.7	39.8	2.35
	130	38.26	33.10	11.510	0.855	0.580	6699.0	404.8	13.23	201.4	35.0	2.29
30 × 15	210	61.78	30.38	15.105	1.315	0.775	9872.4	649.9	12.64	707.9	93.7	3.38
	190	55.90	30.12	15.040	1.185	0.710	8825.9	586.1	12.57	624.6	83.1	3.34
	172	50.65	29.88	14.985	1.065	0.655	7891.5	528.2	12.48	550.1	73.4	3.30
30 × 10½	132	38.83	30.30	10.551	1.000	0.615	5753.1	379.7	12.17	185.0	35.1	2.18
	124	36.45	30.16	10.521	0.930	0.585	5347.1	354.6	12.11	169.7	32.3	2.16
	116	34.13	30.00	10.500	0.850	0.564	4919.1	327.9	12.00	153.2	29.2	2.12
	108	31.77	29.82	10.484	0.760	0.548	4461.0	299.2	11.85	135.1	25.8	2.06
27 × 14	177	52.10	27.31	14.090	1.190	0.725	6728.6	492.8	11.36	518.9	73.7	3.16
	160	47.04	27.08	14.023	1.075	0.658	6018.6	444.5	11.31	458.0	65.3	3.12
	145	42.68	26.88	13.965	0.975	0.600	5414.3	402.9	11.26	406.9	58.3	3.09
27 × 10	114	33.53	27.28	10.070	0.932	0.570	4080.5	299.2	11.03	149.6	29.7	2.11
	102	30.01	27.07	10.018	0.827	0.518	3604.1	266.3	10.96	129.5	25.9	2.08
	94	27.65	26.91	9.990	0.747	0.490	3266.7	242.8	10.87	115.1	23.0	2.04
24 × 14	160	47.04	24.72	14.091	1.135	0.656	5110.3	413.5	10.42	492.6	69.9	3.23
	145	42.62	24.49	14.043	1.020	0.608	4561.0	372.5	10.34	434.3	61.8	3.19
	130	38.21	24.25	14.000	0.900	0.565	4009.5	330.7	10.24	375.2	53.6	3.13

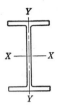

TABLE 28 (*Continued*)

W̄ SHAPES

Properties for Designing

Nominal Size	Weight per Foot	Area	Depth	Flange		Web Thick-ness	Axis X–X			Axis Y–Y		
				Width	Thick-ness		I	S	r	I	S	r
In.	Lb	In.²	In.	In.	In.	In.	In.⁴	In.³	In.	In.⁴	In.³	In.
24 × 12	120	35.29	24.31	12.088	0.930	0.556	3635.3	299.1	10.15	254.0	42.0	2.68
	110	32.36	24.16	12.042	0.855	0.510	3315.0	274.4	10.12	229.1	38.0	2.66
	100	29.43	24.00	12.000	0.775	0.468	2987.3	248.9	10.08	203.5	33.9	2.63
24 × 9	94	27.63	24.29	9.061	0.872	0.516	2683.0	220.9	9.85	102.2	22.6	1.92
	84	24.71	24.09	9.015	0.772	0.470	2364.3	196.3	9.78	88.3	19.6	1.89
	76	22.37	23.91	8.985	0.682	0.440	2096.4	175.4	9.68	76.5	17.0	1.85
21 × 13	142	41.76	21.46	13.132	1.095	0.659	3403.1	317.2	9.03	385.9	58.8	3.04
	127	37.34	21.24	13.061	0.985	0.588	3017.2	284.1	8.99	338.6	51.8	3.01
	112	32.93	21.00	13.000	0.865	0.527	2620.6	249.6	8.92	289.7	44.6	2.96
21 × 9	96	28.21	21.14	9.038	0.935	0.575	2088.9	197.6	8.60	109.3	24.2	1.97
	82	24.10	20.86	8.962	0.795	0.499	1752.4	168.0	8.53	89.6	20.0	1.93
21 × 8¼	73	21.46	21.24	8.295	0.740	0.455	1600.3	150.7	8.64	66.2	16.0	1.76
	68	20.02	21.13	8.270	0.685	0.430	1478.3	139.9	8.59	60.4	14.6	1.74
	62	18.23	20.99	8.240	0.615	0.400	1326.8	126.4	8.53	53.1	12.9	1.71
18 × 11¾	114	33.51	18.48	11.833	0.991	0.595	2033.8	220.1	7.79	255.6	43.2	2.76
	105	30.86	18.32	11.792	0.911	0.554	1852.5	202.2	7.75	231.0	39.2	2.73
	96	28.22	18.16	11.750	0.831	0.512	1674.7	184.4	7.70	206.8	35.2	2.71
18 × 8¾	85	24.97	18.32	8.838	0.911	0.526	1429.9	156.1	7.57	99.4	22.5	2.00
	77	22.63	18.16	8.787	0.831	0.475	1286.8	141.7	7.54	88.6	20.2	1.98
	70	20.56	18.00	8.750	0.751	0.438	1153.9	128.2	7.49	78.5	17.9	1.95
	64	18.80	17.87	8.715	0.686	0.403	1045.8	117.0	7.46	70.3	16.1	1.93
18 × 7½	60	17.64	18.25	7.558	0.695	0.416	984.0	107.8	7.47	47.1	12.5	1.63
	55	16.19	18.12	7.532	0.630	0.390	889.9	98.2	7.41	42.0	11.1	1.61
	50	14.71	18.00	7.500	0.570	0.358	800.6	89.0	7.38	37.2	9.9	1.59
16 × 11½	96	28.22	16.32	11.533	0.875	0.535	1355.1	166.1	6.93	207.2	35.9	2.71
	88	25.87	16.16	11.502	0.795	0.504	1222.6	151.3	6.87	185.2	32.2	2.67
16 × 8½	78	22.92	16.32	8.586	0.875	0.529	1042.6	127.8	6.74	87.5	20.4	1.95
	71	20.86	16.16	8.543	0.795	0.486	936.9	115.9	6.70	77.9	18.2	1.93
	64	18.80	16.00	8.500	0.715	0.443	833.8	104.2	6.66	68.4	16.1	1.91
	58	17.04	15.86	8.464	0.645	0.407	746.4	94.1	6.62	60.5	14.3	1.88

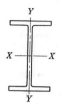

TABLE 28 (*Continued*)

W⊏ Shapes

Properties for Designing

| Nominal Size | Weight per Foot | Area | Depth | Flange | | Web Thick-ness | Axis X–X | | | Axis Y–Y | | |
				Width	Thick-ness		I	S	r	I	S	r
In.	Lb	In.²	In.	In.	In.	In.	In.⁴	In.³	In.	In.⁴	In.³	In.
16 × 7	50	14.70	16.25	7.073	0.628	0.380	655.4	80.7	6.68	34.8	9.8	1.54
	45	13.24	16.12	7.039	0.563	0.346	583.3	72.4	6.64	30.5	8.7	1.52
	40	11.77	16.00	7.000	0.503	0.307	515.5	64.4	6.62	26.5	7.6	1.50
	36	10.59	15.85	6.992	0.428	0.299	446.3	56.3	6.49	22.1	6.3	1.45
14 × 16	426	125.25	18.69	16.695	3.033	1.875	6610.3	707.4	7.26	2359.5	282.7	4.34
	398	116.98	18.31	16.590	2.843	1.770	6013.7	656.9	7.17	2169.7	261.6	4.31
	370	108.78	17.94	16.475	2.658	1.655	5454.2	608.1	7.08	1986.0	241.1	4.27
	342	100.59	17.56	16.365	2.468	1.545	4911.5	559.4	6.99	1806.9	220.8	4.24
	314	92.30	17.19	16.235	2.283	1.415	4399.4	511.9	6.90	1631.4	201.0	4.20
	287	84.37	16.81	16.130	2.093	1.310	3912.1	465.5	6.81	1466.5	181.8	4.17
	264	77.63	16.50	16.025	1.938	1.205	3526.0	427.4	6.74	1331.2	166.1	4.14
	246	72.33	16.25	15.945	1.813	1.125	3228.9	397.4	6.68	1226.6	153.9	4.12
	237	69.69	16.12	15.910	1.748	1.090	3080.9	382.2	6.65	1174.8	147.7	4.11
	228	67.06	16.00	15.865	1.688	1.045	2942.4	367.8	6.62	1124.8	141.8	4.10
	219	64.36	15.87	15.825	1.623	1.005	2798.2	352.6	6.59	1073.2	135.6	4.08
	211	62.07	15.75	15.800	1.563	0.980	2671.4	339.2	6.56	1028.6	130.2	4.07
	202	59.39	15.63	15.750	1.503	0.930	2538.8	324.9	6.54	979.7	124.4	4.06
	193	56.73	15.50	15.710	1.438	0.890	2402.4	310.0	6.51	930.1	118.4	4.05
	184	54.07	15.38	15.660	1.378	0.840	2274.8	295.8	6.49	882.7	112.7	4.04
	176	51.73	15.25	15.640	1.313	0.820	2149.6	281.9	6.45	837.9	107.1	4.02
	167	49.09	15.12	15.600	1.248	0.780	2020.8	267.3	6.42	790.2	101.3	4.01
	158	46.47	15.00	15.550	1.188	0.730	1900.6	253.4	6.40	745.0	95.8	4.00
	150	44.08	14.88	15.515	1.128	0.695	1786.9	240.2	6.37	702.5	90.6	3.99
	142	41.85	14.75	15.500	1.063	0.680	1672.2	226.7	6.32	660.1	85.2	3.97
	320 [1]	94.12	16.81	16.710	2.093	1.890	4141.7	492.8	6.63	1635.1	195.7	4.17
14 × 14½	136	39.98	14.75	14.740	1.063	0.660	1593.0	216.0	6.31	567.7	77.0	3.77
	127	37.33	14.62	14.690	0.998	0.610	1476.7	202.0	6.29	527.6	71.8	3.76
	119	34.99	14.50	14.650	0.938	0.570	1373.1	189.4	6.26	491.8	67.1	3.75
	111	32.65	14.37	14.620	0.873	0.540	1266.5	176.3	6.23	454.9	62.2	3.73
	103	30.26	14.25	14.575	0.813	0.495	1165.8	163.6	6.21	419.7	57.6	3.72
	95	27.94	14.12	14.545	0.748	0.465	1063.5	150.6	6.17	383.7	52.8	3.71
	87	25.56	14.00	14.500	0.688	0.420	966.9	138.1	6.15	349.7	48.2	3.70
14 × 12	84	24.71	14.18	12.023	0.778	0.451	928.4	130.9	6.13	225.5	37.5	3.02
	78	22.94	14.06	12.000	0.718	0.428	851.2	121.1	6.09	206.9	34.5	3.00
14 × 10	74	21.76	14.19	10.072	0.783	0.450	796.8	112.3	6.05	133.5	26.5	2.48
	68	20.00	14.06	10.040	0.718	0.418	724.1	103.0	6.02	121.2	24.1	2.46
	61	17.94	13.91	10.000	0.643	0.378	641.5	92.2	5.98	107.3	21.5	2.45

TABLE 28 (*Continued*)

WF SHAPES

Properties for Designing

Nominal Size	Weight per Foot	Area	Depth	Flange		Web Thickness	Axis X–X			Axis Y–Y		
				Width	Thickness		I	S	r	I	S	r
In.	Lb	In.²	In.	In.	In.	In.	In.⁴	In.³	In.	In.⁴	In.³	In.
14 × 8	53	15.59	13.94	8.062	0.658	0.370	542.1	77.8	5.90	57.5	14.3	1.92
	48	14.11	13.81	8.031	0.593	0.339	484.9	70.2	5.86	51.3	12.8	1.91
	43	12.65	13.68	8.000	0.528	0.308	429.0	62.7	5.82	45.1	11.3	1.89
14 × 6¾	38	11.17	14.12	6.776	0.513	0.313	385.3	54.6	5.87	24.6	7.3	1.49
	34	10.00	14.00	6.750	0.453	0.287	339.2	48.5	5.83	21.3	6.3	1.46
	30	8.81	13.86	6.733	0.383	0.270	289.6	41.8	5.73	17.5	5.2	1.41
12 × 12	190	55.86	14.38	12.670	1.736	1.060	1892.5	263.2	5.82	589.7	93.1	3.25
	161	47.38	13.88	12.515	1.486	0.905	1541.8	222.2	5.70	486.2	77.7	3.20
	133	39.11	13.38	12.365	1.236	0.755	1221.2	182.5	5.59	389.9	63.1	3.16
	120	35.31	13.12	12.320	1.106	0.710	1071.7	163.4	5.51	345.1	56.0	3.13
	106	31.19	12.88	12.230	0.986	0.620	930.7	144.5	5.46	300.9	49.2	3.11
	99	29.09	12.75	12.190	0.921	0.580	858.5	134.7	5.43	278.2	45.7	3.09
	92	27.06	12.62	12.155	0.856	0.545	788.9	125.0	5.40	256.4	42.2	3.08
	85	24.98	12.50	12.105	0.796	0.495	723.3	115.7	5.38	235.5	38.9	3.07
	79	23.22	12.38	12.080	0.736	0.470	663.0	107.1	5.34	216.4	35.8	3.05
	72	21.16	12.25	12.040	0.671	0.430	597.4	97.5	5.31	195.3	32.4	3.04
	65	19.11	12.12	12.000	0.606	0.390	533.4	88.0	5.28	174.6	29.1	3.02
12 × 10	58	17.06	12.19	10.014	0.641	0.359	476.1	78.1	5.28	107.4	21.4	2.51
	53	15.59	12.06	10.000	0.576	0.345	426.2	70.7	5.23	96.1	19.2	2.48
12 × 8	50	14.71	12.19	8.077	0.641	0.371	394.5	64.7	5.18	56.4	14.0	1.96
	45	13.24	12.06	8.042	0.576	0.336	350.8	58.2	5.15	50.0	12.4	1.94
	40	11.77	11.94	8.000	0.516	0.294	310.1	51.9	5.13	44.1	11.0	1.94
12 × 6½	36	10.59	12.24	6.565	0.540	0.305	280.8	45.9	5.15	23.7	7.2	1.50
	31	9.12	12.09	6.525	0.465	0.265	238.4	39.4	5.11	19.8	6.1	1.47
	27	7.97	11.95	5.500	0.400	0.240	204.1	34.1	5.06	16.6	5.1	1.44
10 × 10	112	32.92	11.38	10.415	1.248	0.755	718.7	126.3	4.67	235.4	45.2	2.67
	100	29.43	11.12	10.345	1.118	0.685	625.0	112.4	4.61	206.6	39.9	2.65
	89	26.19	10.88	10.275	0.998	0.615	542.4	99.7	4.55	180.6	35.2	2.63
	77	22.67	10.62	10.195	0.868	0.535	457.2	86.1	4.49	153.4	30.1	2.60
	72	21.18	10.50	10.170	0.808	0.510	420.7	80.1	4.46	141.8	27.9	2.59
	66	19.41	10.38	10.117	0.748	0.457	382.5	73.7	4.44	129.2	25.5	2.58
	60	17.66	10.25	10.075	0.683	0.415	343.7	67.1	4.41	116.5	23.1	2.57
	54	15.88	10.12	10.028	0.618	0.368	305.7	60.4	4.39	103.9	20.7	2.56
	49	14.40	10.00	10.000	0.558	0.340	272.9	54.6	4.35	93.0	18.6	2.54

I

TABLE 28 (*Continued*)

WF Shapes

Properties for Designing

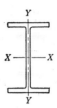

Nominal Size	Weight per Foot	Area	Depth	Flange		Web Thickness	Axis X–X			Axis Y–Y		
				Width	Thickness		I	S	r	I	S	r
In.	Lb	In.²	In.	In.	In.	In.	In.⁴	In.³	In.	In.⁴	In.³	In.
10 × 8	45	13.24	10.12	8.022	0.618	0.350	248.6	49.1	4.33	53.2	13.3	2.00
	39	11.48	9.94	7.990	0.528	0.318	209.7	42.2	4.27	44.9	11.2	1.98
	33	9.71	9.75	7.964	0.433	0.292	170.9	35.0	4.20	36.5	9.2	1.94
10 × 5¾	29	8.53	10.22	5.799	0.500	0.289	157.3	30.8	4.29	15.2	5.2	1.34
	25	7.35	10.08	5.762	0.430	0.252	133.2	26.4	4.26	12.7	4.4	1.31
	21	6.19	9.90	5.750	0.340	0.240	106.3	21.5	4.14	9.7	3.4	1.25
8 × 8	67	19.70	9.00	8.287	0.933	0.575	271.8	60.4	3.71	88.6	21.4	2.12
	58	17.06	8.75	8.222	0.808	0.510	227.3	52.0	3.65	74.9	18.2	2.10
	48	14.11	8.50	8.117	0.683	0.405	183.7	43.2	3.61	60.9	15.0	2.08
	40	11.76	8.25	8.077	0.558	0.365	146.3	35.5	3.53	49.0	12.1	2.04
	35	10.30	8.12	8.027	0.493	0.315	126.5	31.1	3.50	42.5	10.6	2.03
	31	9.12	8.00	8.000	0.433	0.288	109.7	27.4	3.47	37.0	9.2	2.01
8 × 6½	28	8.23	8.06	6.540	0.463	0.285	97.8	24.3	3.45	21.6	6.6	1.62
	24	7.06	7.93	6.500	0.398	0.245	82.5	20.8	3.42	18.2	5.6	1.61
8 × 5¼	20	5.88	8.14	5.268	0.378	0.248	69.2	17.0	3.43	8.5	3.2	1.20
	17	5.00	8.00	5.250	0.308	0.230	56.4	14.1	3.36	6.7	2.6	1.16

Reprinted from "Steel Construction," by courtesy of the American Institute of Steel Construction.

TABLE 29

W⁻ Shapes

Miscellaneous (B) Columns and Beams

Properties for Designing

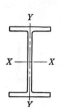

Nominal Size	Weight per Foot	Area	Depth	Flange		Web Thickness	Axis X–X			Axis Y–Y		
				Width	Thickness		I	S	r	I	S	r
In.	Lb	In.²	In.	In.	In.	In.	In.⁴	In.³	In.	In.⁴	In.³	In.

W⁻ Shapes and Light Columns

Nominal Size	Weight per Foot	Area	Depth	Width	Thickness	Web Thickness	I	S	r	I	S	r
6 W⁻	25	7.37	6.37	6.080	0.456	0.320	53.5	16.8	2.69	17.1	5.6	1.52
6 × 6	20	5.90	6.20	6.018	0.367	0.258	41.7	13.4	2.66	13.3	4.4	1.50
	15.5	4.62	6.00	6.000	0.269	0.240	30.3	10.1	2.56	9.69	3.2	1.45
5 W⁻	18.5	5.45	5.12	5.025	0.420	0.265	25.4	9.94	2.16	8.89	3.54	1.28
5 × 5	16	4.70	5.00	5.000	0.360	0.240	21.3	8.53	2.13	7.51	3.00	1.26
4 W⁻	13	3.82	4.16	4.060	0.345	0.280	11.3	5.45	1.72	3.76	1.85	0.99
4 × 4	10	2.93	4.00	4.000	0.265	0.220	8.31	4.16	1.68	2.74	1.37	0.97

Light Beams

Nominal Size	Weight per Foot	Area	Depth	Width	Thickness	Web Thickness	I	S	r	I	S	r
12 × 4	22	6.47	12.31	4.030	0.424	0.260	155.7	25.3	4.91	4.55	2.26	0.84
	19	5.62	12.16	4.010	0.349	0.240	130.1	21.4	4.81	3.67	1.83	0.81
	16½	4.86	12.00	4.000	0.269	0.230	105.3	17.5	4.65	2.79	1.39	0.76
10 × 4	19	5.61	10.25	4.020	0.394	0.250	96.2	18.8	4.14	4.19	2.08	0.86
	17	4.98	10.12	4.010	0.329	0.240	81.8	16.2	4.05	3.45	1.72	0.83
	15	4.40	10.00	4.000	0.269	0.230	68.8	13.8	3.95	2.79	1.39	0.80
8 × 4	15	4.43	8.12	4.015	0.314	0.245	48.0	11.8	3.29	3.30	1.65	0.86
	13	3.83	8.00	4.000	0.254	0.230	39.5	9.88	3.21	2.62	1.31	0.83
6 × 4	16	4.72	6.25	4.030	0.404	0.260	31.7	10.1	2.59	4.32	2.14	0.96
	12	3.53	6.00	4.000	0.279	0.230	21.7	7.24	2.48	2.89	1.44	0.90

Joists

Nominal Size	Weight per Foot	Area	Depth	Width	Thickness	Web Thickness	I	S	r	I	S	r
12 × 4	14	4.14	11.91	3.970	0.224	0.200	88.2	14.8	4.61	2.25	1.13	0.74
10 × 4	11½	3.39	9.87	3.950	0.204	0.180	51.9	10.5	3.92	2.01	1.02	0.77
8 × 4	10	2.95	7.90	3.940	0.204	0.170	30.8	7.79	3.23	1.99	1.01	0.82
6 × 4	8½	2.50	5.83	3.940	0.194	0.170	14.8	5.07	2.43	1.89	0.96	0.87

Above shapes are all rolled by Bethlehem Steel Co. and Carnegie-Illinois Steel Corp., except 4 W⁻ 13 which is rolled by Bethlehem Steel Co. only.

Reprinted from "Steel Construction," by courtesy of the American Institute of Steel Construction.

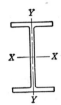

TABLE 30

Miscellaneous Shapes

Properties for Designing

Nominal Size	Weight per Foot	Area	Depth	Width of Flange	Web Thickness	Axis X–X			Axis Y–Y		
						I	S	r	I	S	r
In.	Lb	In.²	In.	In.	In.	In.⁴	In.³	In.	In.⁴	In.³	In.
Light Columns											
8 × 8 [1]	34.3	10.09	8.00	8.000	0.375	115.5	28.9	3.40	35.1	8.8	1.87
6 × 6 [1]	25.0	7.35	6.00	5.938	0.313	47.0	15.7	2.53	14.9	5.0	1.43
	20.0	5.88	6.00	5.938	0.250	38.8	12.9	2.57	11.4	3.8	1.39
5 × 5 [2]	18.9	5.56	5.00	5.000	0.313	23.8	9.5	2.08	7.8	3.1	1.20
4 × 4 [3]	13.0	3.82	4.00	3.937	0.250	10.4	5.2	1.65	3.4	1.7	0.94
Standard Mill Beams											
10 × 5¾ [4]	25	7.35	9.90	5.86	0.35	117.0	23.6	3.99	9.84	3.36	1.16
	21	6.18	9.90	5.74	0.24	107.5	21.7	4.17	9.30	3.24	1.22
8 × 6½ [4]	28	8.23	8.00	6.65	0.39	90.1	22.5	3.31	17.73	5.33	1.47
	24	7.06	8.00	6.50	0.24	83.8	21.0	3.45	16.52	5.08	1.53
8 × 5¼ [4]	20	5.88	8.00	5.36	0.35	60.7	15.2	3.22	6.60	2.46	1.06
	17	5.00	8.00	5.25	0.24	56.0	14.0	3.35	6.16	2.35	1.11
Junior Beams											
12 × 3 [5]	11.8	3.45	12.00	3.063	0.175	72.2	12.0	4.57	0.98	0.64	0.53
11 × 2⅞ [5]	10.3	3.01	11.00	2.844	0.165	53.1	9.6	4.20	0.75	0.52	0.50
10 × 2¾ [5]	9.0	2.64	10.00	2.688	0.155	39.0	7.8	3.85	0.61	0.45	0.48
9 × 2⅜ [5]	7.5	2.20	9.00	2.375	0.145	26.2	5.8	3.45	0.39	0.33	0.42
8 × 2¼ [5]	6.5	1.92	8.00	2.281	0.135	18.7	4.7	3.12	0.34	0.30	0.42
7 × 2⅛ [5]	5.5	1.61	7.00	2.078	0.126	12.1	3.5	2.74	0.25	0.24	0.39
6 × 1⅞ [5]	4.4	1.30	6.00	1.844	0.114	7.3	2.4	2.37	0.17	0.18	0.36

Junior Channels

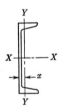

Nominal Size	Weight per Foot	Area	Depth	Width of Flange	Web Thickness	Axis X–X			Axis Y–Y			
						I	S	r	I	S	r	x
In.	Lb	In.²	In.	In.	In.	In.⁴	In.³	In.	In.⁴	In.³	In.	In.
12 × 1½ [5]	10.6	3.12	12.00	1.500	0.190	55.8	9.3	4.23	0.39	0.32	0.35	0.27
10 × 1½ [5]	8.4	2.47	10.00	1.500	0.170	32.3	6.5	3.61	0.33	0.28	0.37	0.29
10 × 1⅛ [5]	6.5	1.91	10.00	1.125	0.150	22.1	4.4	3.47	0.12	0.13	0.25	0.19

[1] Rolled by Carnegie-Illinois Steel Corp., Inland Steel Co., and The Phoenix Iron Co.-M.
[2] Rolled by Carnegie-Illinois Steel Corp. and Bethlehem Steel Co.-B.
[3] Rolled by Carnegie-Illinois Steel Corp.-B.
[4] Rolled by The Phoenix Iron Co.-M.
[5] Rolled by Jones & Laughlin Steel Corp.-Jr.
Reprinted from "Steel Construction," by courtesy of the American Institute of Steel Construction.

TABLE 31

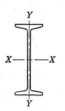

American Standard

Beams

Properties for Designing

Nominal Size	Weight per Foot	Area	Depth	Flange		Web Thick-ness	Axis X–X			Axis Y–Y		
				Width	Thick-ness		I	S	r	I	S	r
In.	Lb	In.²	In.	In.	In.	In.	In.⁴	In.³	In.	In.⁴	In.³	In.
24 × 7⅞	120.0	35.13	24.00	8.048	1.102	0.798	3010.8	250.9	9.26	84.9	21.1	1.56
	105.9	30.98	24.00	7.875	1.102	0.625	2811.5	234.3	9.53	78.9	20.0	1.60
24 × 7	100.0	29.25	24.00	7.247	0.871	0.747	2371.8	197.6	9.05	48.4	13.4	1.29
	90.0	26.30	24.00	7.124	0.871	0.624	2230.1	185.8	9.21	45.5	12.8	1.32
	79.9	23.33	24.00	7.000	0.871	0.500	2087.2	173.9	9.46	42.9	12.2	1.36
20 × 7	95.0	27.74	20.00	7.200	0.916	0.800	1599.7	160.0	7.59	50.5	14.0	1.35
	85.0	24.80	20.00	7.053	0.916	0.653	1501.7	150.2	7.78	47.0	13.3	1.38
20 × 6¼	75.0	21.90	20.00	6.391	0.789	0.641	1263.5	126.3	7.60	30.1	9.4	1.17
	65.4	19.08	20.00	6.250	0.789	0.500	1169.5	116.9	7.83	27.9	8.9	1.21
18 × 6	70.0	20.46	18.00	6.251	0.691	0.711	917.5	101.9	6.70	24.5	7.8	1.09
	54.7	15.94	18.00	6.000	0.691	0.460	795.5	88.4	7.07	21.2	7.1	1.15
15 × 5½	50.0	14.59	15.00	5.640	0.622	0.550	481.1	64.2	5.74	16.0	5.7	1.05
	42.9	12.49	15.00	5.500	0.622	0.410	441.8	58.9	5.95	14.6	5.3	1.08
12 × 5¼	50.0	14.57	12.00	5.477	0.659	0.687	301.6	50.3	4.55	16.0	5.8	1.05
	40.8	11.84	12.00	5.250	0.659	0.460	268.9	44.8	4.77	13.8	5.3	1.08
12 × 5	35.0	10.20	12.00	5.078	0.544	0.428	227.0	37.8	4.72	10.0	3.9	0.99
	31.8	9.26	12.00	5.000	0.544	0.350	215.8	36.0	4.83	9.5	3.8	1.01
10 × 4⅝	35.0	10.22	10.00	4.944	0.491	0.594	145.8	29.2	3.78	8.5	3.4	0.91
	25.4	7.38	10.00	4.660	0.491	0.310	122.1	24.4	4.07	6.9	3.0	0.97
8 × 4	23.0	6.71	8.00	4.171	0.425	0.441	64.2	16.0	3.09	4.4	2.1	0.81
	18.4	5.34	8.00	4.000	0.425	0.270	56.9	14.2	3.26	3.8	1.9	0.84
7 × 3⅝	20.0	5.83	7.00	3.860	0.392	0.450	41.9	12.0	2.68	3.1	1.6	0.74
	15.3	4.43	7.00	3.660	0.392	0.250	36.2	10.4	2.86	2.7	1.5	0.78
6 × 3⅜	17.25	5.02	6.00	3.565	0.359	0.465	26.0	8.7	2.28	2.3	1.3	0.68
	12.5	3.61	6.00	3.330	0.359	0.230	21.8	7.3	2.46	1.8	1.1	0.72
5 × 3	14.75	4.29	5.00	3.284	0.326	0.494	15.0	6.0	1.87	1.7	1.0	0.63
	10.0	2.87	5.00	3.000	0.326	0.210	12.1	4.8	2.05	1.2	0.82	0.65
4 × 2⅝	9.5	2.76	4.00	2.796	0.293	0.326	6.7	3.3	1.56	0.91	0.65	0.58
	7.7	2.21	4.00	2.660	0.293	0.190	6.0	3.0	1.64	0.77	0.58	0.59
3 × 2⅜	7.5	2.17	3.00	2.509	0.260	0.349	2.9	1.9	1.15	0.59	0.47	0.52
	5.7	1.64	3.00	2.330	0.260	0.170	2.5	1.7	1.23	0.46	0.40	0.53

TABLE 32

AMERICAN STANDARD

CHANNELS

Properties for Designing

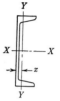

Nominal Size	Weight per Foot	Area	Depth	Flange		Web Thick-ness	Axis X–X			Axis Y–Y			
				Width	Average Thick-ness		I	S	r	I	S	r	x
In.	Lb	In.²	In.	In.	In.	In.	In.⁴	In.³	In.	In.⁴	In.³	In.	In.
18 × 4 [1]	58.0	16.98	18.00	4.200	0.625	0.700	670.7	74.5	6.29	18.5	5.6	1.04	0.88
	51.9	15.18	18.00	4.100	0.625	0.600	622.1	69.1	6.40	17.1	5.3	1.06	0.87
	45.8	13.38	18.00	4.000	0.625	0.500	573.5	63.7	6.55	15.8	5.1	1.09	0.89
	42.7	12.48	18.00	3.950	0.625	0.450	549.2	61.0	6.64	15.0	4.9	1.10	0.90
15 × 3⅜	50.0	14.64	15.00	3.716	0.650	0.716	401.4	53.6	5.24	11.2	3.8	0.87	0.80
	40.0	11.70	15.00	3.520	0.650	0.520	346.3	46.2	5.44	9.3	3.4	0.89	0.78
	33.9	9.90	15.00	3.400	0.650	0.400	312.6	41.7	5.62	8.2	3.2	0.91	0.79
12 × 3	30.0	8.79	12.00	3.170	0.501	0.510	161.2	26.9	4.28	5.2	2.1	0.77	0.68
	25.0	7.32	12.00	3.047	0.501	0.387	143.5	23.9	4.43	4.5	1.9	0.79	0.68
	20.7	6.03	12.00	2.940	0.501	0.280	128.1	21.4	4.61	3.9	1.7	0.81	0.70
10 × 2⅝	30.0	8.80	10.00	3.033	0.436	0.673	103.0	20.6	3.42	4.0	1.7	0.67	0.65
	25.0	7.33	10.00	2.886	0.436	0.526	90.7	18.1	3.52	3.4	1.5	0.68	0.62
	20.0	5.86	10.00	2.739	0.436	0.379	78.5	15.7	3.66	2.8	1.3	0.70	0.61
	15.3	4.47	10.00	2.600	0.436	0.240	66.9	13.4	3.87	2.3	1.2	0.72	0.64
9 × 2½	20.0	5.86	9.00	2.648	0.413	0.448	60.6	13.5	3.22	2.4	1.2	0.65	0.59
	15.0	4.39	9.00	2.485	0.413	0.285	50.7	11.3	3.40	1.9	1.0	0.67	0.59
	13.4	3.89	9.00	2.430	0.413	0.230	47.3	10.5	3.49	1.8	0.97	0.67	0.61
8 × 2¼	18.75	5.49	8.00	2.527	0.390	0.487	43.7	10.9	2.82	2.0	1.0	0.60	0.57
	13.75	4.02	8.00	2.343	0.390	0.303	35.8	9.0	2.99	1.5	0.86	0.62	0.56
	11.5	3.36	8.00	2.260	0.390	0.220	32.3	8.1	3.10	1.3	0.79	0.63	0.58
7 × 2⅛	14.75	4.32	7.00	2.299	0.366	0.419	27.1	7.7	2.51	1.4	0.79	0.57	0.53
	12.25	3.58	7.00	2.194	0.366	0.314	24.1	6.9	2.59	1.2	0.71	0.58	0.53
	9.8	2.85	7.00	2.090	0.366	0.210	21.1	6.0	2.72	0.98	0.63	0.59	0.55
6 × 2	13.0	3.81	6.00	2.157	0.343	0.437	17.3	5.8	2.13	1.1	0.65	0.53	0.52
	10.5	3.07	6.00	2.034	0.343	0.314	15.1	5.0	2.22	0.87	0.57	0.53	0.50
	8.2	2.39	6.00	1.920	0.343	0.200	13.0	4.3	2.34	0.70	0.50	0.54	0.52
5 × 1¾	9.0	2.63	5.00	1.885	0.320	0.325	8.8	3.5	1.83	0.64	0.45	0.49	0.48
	6.7	1.95	5.00	1.750	0.320	0.190	7.4	3.0	1.95	0.48	0.38	0.50	0.49
4 × 1⅝	7.25	2.12	4.00	1.720	0.296	0.320	4.5	2.3	1.47	0.44	0.35	0.46	0.46
	5.4	1.56	4.00	1.580	0.296	0.180	3.8	1.9	1.56	0.32	0.29	0.45	0.46
3 × 1½	6.0	1.75	3.00	1.596	0.273	0.356	2.1	1.4	1.08	0.31	0.27	0.42	0.46
	5.0	1.46	3.00	1.498	0.273	0.258	1.8	1.2	1.12	0.25	0.24	0.41	0.44
	4.1	1.19	3.00	1.410	0.273	0.170	1.6	1.1	1.17	0.20	0.21	0.41	0.44

[1] Car and Shipbuilding Channel; not an American Standard.
Reprinted from "Steel Construction," by courtesy of the American Institute of Steel Construction.

TABLE 33

ANGLES

EQUAL LEGS

Properties for Designing

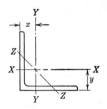

Size	Thickness	Weight per Foot	Area	Axis X–X and Axis Y–Y				Axis Z–Z
				I	S	r	x or y	r
In.	In.	Lb	In.²	In.⁴	In.³	In.	In.	In.
8 × 8	1⅛	56.9	16.73	98.0	17.5	2.42	2.41	1.56
	1	51.0	15.00	89.0	15.8	2.44	2.37	1.56
	⅞	45.0	13.23	79.6	14.0	2.45	2.32	1.57
	¾	38.9	11.44	69.7	12.2	2.47	2.28	1.57
	⅝	32.7	9.61	59.5	10.3	2.49	2.23	1.58
	⁹⁄₁₆	29.6	8.68	54.1	9.3	2.50	2.21	1.58
	½	26.4	7.75	48.6	8.4	2.50	2.19	1.59
6 × 6	1	37.4	11.00	35.5	8.6	1.80	1.86	1.17
	⅞	33.1	9.73	31.9	7.6	1.81	1.82	1.17
	¾	28.7	8.44	28.2	6.7	1.83	1.78	1.17
	⅝	24.2	7.11	24.2	5.7	1.84	1.73	1.18
	⁹⁄₁₆	21.9	6.43	22.1	5.1	1.85	1.71	1.18
	½	19.6	5.75	19.9	4.6	1.86	1.68	1.18
	⁷⁄₁₆	17.2	5.06	17.7	4.1	1.87	1.66	1.19
	⅜	14.9	4.36	15.4	3.5	1.88	1.64	1.19
	⁵⁄₁₆	12.5	3.66	13.0	3.0	1.89	1.61	1.19
5 × 5	⅞	27.2	7.98	17.8	5.2	1.49	1.57	0.97
	¾	23.6	6.94	15.7	4.5	1.51	1.52	0.97
	⅝	20.0	5.86	13.6	3.9	1.52	1.48	0.98
	½	16.2	4.75	11.3	3.2	1.54	1.43	0.98
	⁷⁄₁₆	14.3	4.18	10.0	2.8	1.55	1.41	0.98
	⅜	12.3	3.61	8.7	2.4	1.56	1.39	0.99
	⁵⁄₁₆	10.3	3.03	7.4	2.0	1.57	1.37	0.99
4 × 4	¾	18.5	5.44	7.7	2.8	1.19	1.27	0.78
	⅝	15.7	4.61	6.7	2.4	1.20	1.23	0.78
	½	12.8	3.75	5.6	2.0	1.22	1.18	0.78
	⁷⁄₁₆	11.3	3.31	5.0	1.8	1.23	1.16	0.78
	⅜	9.8	2.86	4.4	1.5	1.23	1.14	0.79
	⁵⁄₁₆	8.2	2.40	3.7	1.3	1.24	1.12	0.79
	¼	6.6	1.94	3.0	1.1	1.25	1.09	0.80

TABLE 33 (*Continued*)

ANGLES

EQUAL LEGS

Properties for Designing

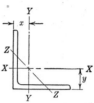

Size	Thick-ness	Weight per Foot	Area	Axis X–X and Axis Y–Y				Axis Z–Z
				I	S	r	x or y	r
In.	In.	Lb	In.²	In.⁴	In.³	In.	In.	In.
3½ × 3½	½	11.1	3.25	3.6	1.5	1.06	1.06	0.68
	⁷⁄₁₆	9.8	2.87	3.3	1.3	1.07	1.04	0.68
	⅜	8.5	2.48	2.9	1.2	1.07	1.01	0.69
	⁵⁄₁₆	7.2	2.09	2.5	0.98	1.08	0.99	0.69
	¼	5.8	1.69	2.0	0.79	1.09	0.97	0.69
3 × 3	½	9.4	2.75	2.2	1.1	0.90	0.93	0.58
	⁷⁄₁₆	8.3	2.43	2.0	0.95	0.91	0.91	0.58
	⅜	7.2	2.11	1.8	0.83	0.91	0.89	0.58
	⁵⁄₁₆	6.1	1.78	1.5	0.71	0.92	0.87	0.59
	¼	4.9	1.44	1.2	0.58	0.93	0.84	0.59
	³⁄₁₆	3.71	1.09	0.96	0.44	0.94	0.82	0.59
2½ × 2½	½	7.7	2.25	1.2	0.72	0.74	0.81	0.49
	⅜	5.9	1.73	0.98	0.57	0.75	0.76	0.49
	⁵⁄₁₆	5.0	1.47	0.85	0.48	0.76	0.74	0.49
	¼	4.1	1.19	0.70	0.39	0.77	0.72	0.49
	³⁄₁₆	3.07	0.90	0.55	0.30	0.78	0.69	0.49
2 × 2	⅜	4.7	1.36	0.48	0.35	0.59	0.64	0.39
	⁵⁄₁₆	3.92	1.15	0.42	0.30	0.60	0.61	0.39
	¼	3.19	0.94	0.35	0.25	0.61	0.59	0.39
	³⁄₁₆	2.44	0.71	0.27	0.19	0.62	0.57	0.39
	⅛	1.65	0.48	0.19	0.13	0.63	0.55	0.40
1¾ × 1¾	¼	2.77	0.81	0.23	0.19	0.53	0.53	0.34
	³⁄₁₆	2.12	0.62	0.18	0.14	0.54	0.51	0.34
	⅛	1.44	0.42	0.13	0.10	0.55	0.48	0.35
1½ × 1½	¼	2.34	0.69	0.14	0.13	0.45	0.47	0.29
	³⁄₁₆	1.80	0.53	0.11	0.10	0.46	0.44	0.29
	⅛	1.23	0.36	0.08	0.07	0.47	0.42	0.30
1¼ × 1¼	¼	1.92	0.56	0.08	0.09	0.37	0.40	0.24
	³⁄₁₆	1.48	0.43	0.06	0.07	0.38	0.38	0.24
	⅛	1.01	0.30	0.04	0.05	0.38	0.36	0.25
1 × 1	¼	1.49	0.44	0.04	0.06	0.29	0.34	0.20
	³⁄₁₆	1.16	0.34	0.03	0.04	0.30	0.32	0.19
	⅛	0.80	0.23	0.02	0.03	0.30	0.30	0.20

Reprinted from "Steel Construction," by courtesy of the American Institute of Steel Construction.

TABLE 34

ANGLES

UNEQUAL LEGS

Properties for Designing

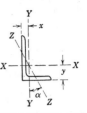

Size	Thick-ness	Weight per Foot	Area	Axis X–X				Axis Y–Y				Axis Z–Z	
				I	S	r	y	I	S	r	x	r	Tan α
In.	In.	Lb	In.²	In.⁴	In.³	In.	In.	In.⁴	In.³	In.	In.	In.	In.
9 × 4	1	40.8	12.00	97.0	17.6	2.84	3.50	12.0	4.0	1.00	1.00	0.83	0.203
	⅞	36.1	10.61	86.8	15.7	2.86	3.45	10.8	3.6	1.01	0.95	0.84	0.208
	¾	31.3	9.19	76.1	13.6	2.88	3.41	9.6	3.1	1.02	0.91	0.84	0.212
	⅝	26.3	7.73	64.9	11.5	2.90	3.36	8.3	2.6	1.04	0.86	0.85	0.216
	9⁄16	23.8	7.00	59.1	10.4	2.91	3.33	7.6	2.4	1.04	0.83	0.85	0.218
	½	21.3	6.25	53.2	9.3	2.92	3.31	6.9	2.2	1.05	0.81	0.85	0.220
8 × 6	1	44.2	13.00	80.8	15.1	2.49	2.65	38.8	8.9	1.73	1.65	1.28	0.543
	⅞	39.1	11.48	72.3	13.4	2.51	2.61	34.9	7.9	1.74	1.61	1.28	0.547
	¾	33.8	9.94	63.4	11.7	2.53	2.56	30.7	6.9	1.76	1.56	1.29	0.551
	⅝	28.5	8.36	54.1	9.9	2.54	2.52	26.3	5.9	1.77	1.52	1.29	0.554
	9⁄16	25.7	7.56	49.3	9.0	2.55	2.50	24.0	5.3	1.78	1.50	1.30	0.556
	½	23.0	6.75	44.3	8.0	2.56	2.47	21.7	4.8	1.79	1.47	1.30	0.558
	7⁄16	20.2	5.93	39.2	7.1	2.57	2.45	19.3	4.2	1.80	1.45	1.31	0.560
8 × 4	1	37.4	11.00	69.6	14.1	2.52	3.05	11.6	3.9	1.03	1.05	0.85	0.247
	⅞	33.1	9.73	62.5	12.5	2.53	3.00	10.5	3.5	1.04	1.00	0.85	0.253
	¾	28.7	8.44	54.9	10.9	2.55	2.95	9.4	3.1	1.05	0.95	0.85	0.258
	⅝	24.2	7.11	46.9	9.2	2.57	2.91	8.1	2.6	1.07	0.91	0.86	0.262
	9⁄16	21.9	6.43	42.8	8.4	2.58	2.88	7.4	2.4	1.07	0.88	0.86	0.265
	½	19.6	5.75	38.5	7.5	2.59	2.86	6.7	2.2	1.08	0.86	0.86	0.267
	7⁄16	17.2	5.06	34.1	6.6	2.60	2.83	6.0	1.9	1.09	0.83	0.87	0.269
7 × 4	⅞	30.2	8.86	42.9	9.7	2.20	2.55	10.2	3.5	1.07	1.05	0.86	0.318
	¾	26.2	7.69	37.8	8.4	2.22	2.51	9.1	3.0	1.09	1.01	0.86	0.324
	⅝	22.1	6.48	32.4	7.1	2.24	2.46	7.8	2.6	1.10	0.96	0.86	0.329
	9⁄16	20.0	5.87	29.6	6.5	2.24	2.44	7.2	2.4	1.11	0.94	0.87	0.332
	½	17.9	5.25	26.7	5.8	2.25	2.42	6.5	2.1	1.11	0.92	0.87	0.335
	7⁄16	15.8	4.62	23.7	5.1	2.26	2.39	5.8	1.9	1.12	0.89	0.88	0.337
	⅜	13.6	3.98	20.6	4.4	2.27	2.37	5.1	1.6	1.13	0.87	0.88	0.339
6 × 4	⅞	27.2	7.98	27.7	7.2	1.86	2.12	9.8	3.4	1.11	1.12	0.86	0.421
	¾	23.6	6.94	24.5	6.3	1.88	2.08	8.7	3.0	1.12	1.08	0.86	0.428
	⅝	20.0	5.86	21.1	5.3	1.90	2.03	7.5	2.5	1.13	1.03	0.86	0.435
	9⁄16	18.1	5.31	19.3	4.8	1.90	2.01	6.9	2.3	1.14	1.01	0.87	0.438
	½	16.2	4.75	17.4	4.3	1.91	1.99	6.3	2.1	1.15	0.99	0.87	0.440
	7⁄16	14.3	4.18	15.5	3.8	1.92	1.96	5.6	1.9	1.16	0.96	0.87	0.443
	⅜	12.3	3.61	13.5	3.3	1.93	1.94	4.9	1.6	1.17	0.94	0.88	0.446
	5⁄16	10.3	3.03	11.4	2.8	1.94	1.92	4.2	1.4	1.17	0.92	0.88	0.449

TABLE 34 (*Continued*)

ANGLES

UNEQUAL LEGS

Properties for Designing

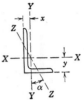

Size	Thick-ness	Weight per Foot	Area	Axis X–X				Axis Y–Y				Axis Z–Z	
				I	S	r	y	I	S	r	x	r	Tan α
In.	In.	Lb	In.²	In.⁴	In.³	In.	In.	In.⁴	In.³	In.	In.	In.	In.
6 × 3½	½	15.3	4.50	16.6	4.2	1.92	2.08	4.3	1.6	0.97	0.83	0.76	0.344
	⅜	11.7	3.42	12.9	3.2	1.94	2.04	3.3	1.2	0.99	0.79	0.77	0.350
	⁵⁄₁₆	9.8	2.87	10.9	2.7	1.95	2.01	2.9	1.0	1.00	0.76	0.77	0.352
	¼	7.9	2.31	8.9	2.2	1.96	1.99	2.3	0.85	1.01	0.74	0.78	0.355
5 × 3½	¾	19.8	5.81	13.9	4.3	1.55	1.75	5.6	2.2	0.98	1.00	0.75	0.464
	⅝	16.8	4.92	12.0	3.7	1.56	1.70	4.8	1.9	0.99	0.95	0.75	0.472
	½	13.6	4.00	10.0	3.0	1.58	1.66	4.1	1.6	1.01	0.91	0.75	0.479
	⁷⁄₁₆	12.0	3.53	8.9	2.6	1.59	1.63	3.6	1.4	1.01	0.88	0.76	0.482
	⅜	10.4	3.05	7.8	2.3	1.60	1.61	3.2	1.2	1.02	0.86	0.76	0.486
	⁵⁄₁₆	8.7	2.56	6.6	1.9	1.61	1.59	2.7	1.0	1.03	0.84	0.76	0.489
	¼	7.0	2.06	5.4	1.6	1.61	1.56	2.2	0.83	1.04	0.81	0.76	0.492
5 × 3	½	12.8	3.75	9.5	2.9	1.59	1.75	2.6	1.1	0.83	0.75	0.65	0.357
	⁷⁄₁₆	11.3	3.31	8.4	2.6	1.60	1.73	2.3	1.0	0.84	0.73	0.65	0.361
	⅜	9.8	2.86	7.4	2.2	1.61	1.70	2.0	0.89	0.84	0.70	0.65	0.364
	⁵⁄₁₆	8.2	2.40	6.3	1.9	1.61	1.68	1.8	0.75	0.85	0.68	0.66	0.368
	¼	6.6	1.94	5.1	1.5	1.62	1.66	1.4	0.61	0.86	0.66	0.66	0.371
4 × 3½	⅝	14.7	4.30	6.4	2.4	1.22	1.29	4.5	1.8	1.03	1.04	0.72	0.745
	½	11.9	3.50	5.3	1.9	1.23	1.25	3.8	1.5	1.04	1.00	0.72	0.750
	⁷⁄₁₆	10.6	3.09	4.8	1.7	1.24	1.23	3.4	1.4	1.05	0.98	0.72	0.753
	⅜	9.1	2.67	4.2	1.5	1.25	1.21	3.0	1.2	1.06	0.96	0.73	0.755
	⁵⁄₁₆	7.7	2.25	3.6	1.3	1.26	1.18	2.6	1.0	1.07	0.93	0.73	0.757
	¼	6.2	1.81	2.9	1.0	1.27	1.16	2.1	0.81	1.07	0.91	0.73	0.759
4 × 3	⅝	13.6	3.98	6.0	2.3	1.23	1.37	2.9	1.4	0.85	0.87	0.64	0.534
	½	11.1	3.25	5.1	1.9	1.25	1.33	2.4	1.1	0.86	0.83	0.64	0.543
	⁷⁄₁₆	9.8	2.87	4.5	1.7	1.25	1.30	2.2	1.0	0.87	0.80	0.64	0.547
	⅜	8.5	2.48	4.0	1.5	1.26	1.28	1.9	0.87	0.88	0.78	0.64	0.551
	⁵⁄₁₆	7.2	2.09	3.4	1.2	1.27	1.26	1.7	0.73	0.89	0.76	0.65	0.554
	¼	5.8	1.69	2.8	1.0	1.28	1.24	1.4	0.60	0.90	0.74	0.65	0.558
3½ × 3	½	10.2	3.00	3.5	1.5	1.07	1.13	2.3	1.1	0.88	0.88	0.62	0.714
	⁷⁄₁₆	9.1	2.65	3.1	1.3	1.08	1.10	2.1	0.98	0.89	0.85	0.62	0.718
	⅜	7.9	2.30	2.7	1.1	1.09	1.08	1.9	0.85	0.90	0.83	0.62	0.721
	⁵⁄₁₆	6.6	1.93	2.3	0.95	1.10	1.06	1.6	0.72	0.90	0.81	0.63	0.724
	¼	5.4	1.56	1.9	0.78	1.11	1.04	1.3	0.59	0.91	0.79	0.63	0.727

TABLE 34 (*Continued*)

ANGLES

UNEQUAL LEGS

Properties for Designing

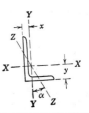

Size	Thickness	Weight per Foot	Area	Axis X–X				Axis Y–Y				Axis Z–Z	
				I	S	r	y	I	S	r	x	r	Tan α
In.	In.	Lb	In.²	In.⁴	In.³	In.	In.	In.⁴	In.³	In.	In.	In.	In.
3½ × 2½	½	9.4	2.75	3.2	1.4	1.09	1.20	1.4	0.76	0.70	0.70	0.53	0.486
	⁷⁄₁₆	8.3	2.43	2.9	1.3	1.09	1.18	1.2	0.68	0.71	0.68	0.54	0.491
	⅜	7.2	2.11	2.6	1.1	1.10	1.16	1.1	0.59	0.72	0.66	0.54	0.496
	⁵⁄₁₆	6.1	1.78	2.2	0.93	1.11	1.14	0.94	0.50	0.73	0.64	0.54	0.501
	¼	4.9	1.44	1.8	0.75	1.12	1.11	0.78	0.41	0.74	0.61	0.54	0.506
3 × 2½	½	8.5	2.50	2.1	1.0	0.91	1.00	1.3	0.74	0.72	0.75	0.52	0.667
	⁷⁄₁₆	7.6	2.21	1.9	0.93	0.92	0.98	1.2	0.66	0.73	0.73	0.52	0.672
	⅜	6.6	1.92	1.7	0.81	0.93	0.96	1.0	0.58	0.74	0.71	0.52	0.676
	⁵⁄₁₆	5.6	1.62	1.4	0.69	0.94	0.93	0.90	9.49	0.74	0.68	0.53	0.680
	¼	4.5	1.31	1.2	0.56	0.95	0.91	0.74	0.40	0.75	0.66	0.53	0.684
3 × 2	½	7.7	2.25	1.9	1.0	0.92	1.08	0.67	0.47	0.55	0.58	0.43	0.414
	⁷⁄₁₆	6.8	2.00	1.7	0.89	0.93	1.06	0.61	0.42	0.55	0.56	0.43	0.421
	⅜	5.9	1.73	1.5	0.78	0.94	1.04	0.54	0.37	0.56	0.54	0.43	0.428
	⁵⁄₁₆	5.0	1.47	1.3	0.66	0.95	1.02	0.47	0.32	0.57	0.52	0.43	0.435
	¼	4.1	1.19	1.1	0.54	0.95	0.99	0.39	0.26	0.57	0.49	0.43	0.440
	³⁄₁₆	3.07	0.90	0.84	0.41	0.97	0.97	0.31	0.20	0.58	0.47	0.44	0.446
2½ × 2	⅜	5.3	1.55	0.91	0.55	0.77	0.83	0.51	0.36	0.58	0.58	0.42	0.614
	⁵⁄₁₆	4.5	1.31	0.79	0.47	0.78	0.81	0.45	0.31	0.58	0.56	0.42	0.620
	¼	3.62	1.06	0.65	0.38	0.78	0.79	0.37	0.25	0.59	0.54	0.42	0.626
	³⁄₁₆	2.75	0.81	0.51	0.29	0.79	0.76	0.29	0.20	0.60	0.51	0.43	0.631
2½ × 1½	⅜	4.7	1.36	0.82	0.52	0.78	0.92	0.22	0.20	0.40	0.42	0.32	0.340
	⁵⁄₁₆	3.92	1.15	0.71	0.44	0.79	0.90	0.19	0.17	0.41	0.40	0.32	0.349
	¼	3.19	0.94	0.59	0.36	0.79	0.88	0.16	0.14	0.41	0.38	0.32	0.357
	³⁄₁₆	2.44	0.72	0.46	0.28	0.80	0.85	0.13	0.11	0.42	0.35	0.33	0.364
2 × 1½	¼	2.77	0.81	0.32	0.24	0.62	0.66	0.15	0.14	0.43	0.41	0.32	0.543
	³⁄₁₆	2.12	0.62	0.25	0.18	0.63	0.64	0.12	0.11	0.44	0.39	0.32	0.551
	⅛	1.44	0.42	0.17	0.13	0.64	0.62	0.09	0.08	0.45	0.37	0.33	0.558
1¾ × 1¼	¼	2.34	0.69	0.20	0.18	0.54	0.60	0.09	0.10	0.35	0.35	0.27	0.486
	³⁄₁₆	1.80	0.53	0.16	0.14	0.55	0.58	0.07	0.08	0.36	0.33	0.27	0.496
	⅛	1.23	0.36	0.11	0.09	0.56	0.56	0.05	0.05	0.37	0.31	0.27	0.506

Reprinted from "Steel Construction," by courtesy of the American Institute of Steel Construction.

TABLE 35

PROPERTIES OF STRAN-STEEL MEMBERS

Properties of Member	Overall Dimension	Nominal Gage Number	Metal Thickness	Area of Section	Weight per Foot	About Major Axis				About Minor Axis			
						I	S	r	x	I	S	r	x
6-in. joist	2 × 6	14	0.0781	0.982	3.339	4.855	1.618	2.225		0.1147	0.1122	0.338	
	2 × 6	16	0.0625	0.7930	2.696	3.928	1.309	2.228		0.0916	0.0895	0.336	
8-in. joist	2 × 8	12	0.1094	1.573	5.327	14.0	3.50	2.970		0.163	0.160	0.320	
	2 × 8	14	0.0781	1.140	3.870	10.178	2.545	2.984		0.113	0.112	0.315	
	2 × 8	16	0.0625	0.918	3.121	8.219	2.055	2.992		0.090	0.089	0.313	
9-in. joist	2 × 9	12	0.1094	1.729	5.878	18.845	4.188	3.301		0.162	0.152	0.306	
	2 × 9	14	0.0781	1.218	4.135	13.620	3.027	3.341		0.118	0.117	0.308	
	2 × 9	16	0.0625	0.981	3.333	10.992	2.443	3.348		0.093	0.093	0.306	
3⅝-in. stud	2 × 3⅝	16	0.0625	0.660	2.244	1.163	0.641	1.327		0.090	0.086	0.368	
2⁵⁄₁₆-in. stud	2 × 2⁵⁄₁₆	16	0.0625	0.500	1.700	0.393	0.340	0.886		0.090	0.085	0.423	
Half stud	2 × 1¹¹⁄₁₆	16	0.0625	0.313	1.062	0.098	0.089	0.561	0.589	0.045	0.043	0.378	
Standard channel plate	3¹³⁄₁₆ × 1⅝	16	0.0625	0.368	1.461	0.842	0.442	1.504		0.080	0.063	0.465	0.343
Narrow channel plate	2½ × 1⅝	16	0.0625	0.286	1.182	0.309	0.247	1.030		0.070	0.059	0.491	0.431

TABLE 36

TENSILE REQUIREMENTS

Properties Considered	Plain Bars			Deformed Bars			Cold-Twisted Bars
	Structural-Steel Grade	Intermediate Grade	Hard Grade	Structural-Steel Grade	Intermediate Grade	Hard Grade	
Tensile strength, psi	55,000 to 75,000	70,000 to 90,000	80,000 min	55,000 to 75,000	70,000 to 90,000	80,000 min	Recorded only
Yield point, min, psi	33,000	40,000	50,000	33,000	40,000	50,000	55,000
Elongation in 8 in., min percentage	1,400,000 Tens. str. but not less than 20%	1,300,000 Tens. str. but not less than 16%	1,200,000 Tens. str.	1,250,000 Tens. str. but not less than 20%	1,125,000 Tens. str. but not less than 14%	1,000,000 Tens. str.	5

From "Standard Specifications for Billet-Steel Concrete Reinforcement Bars," ASTM Designation A 15–39.

TABLE 37

BEND-TEST REQUIREMENTS

Thickness or Diameter of Bar	Plain Bars			Deformed Bars			Cold-Twisted Bars
	Structural-Steel Grade	Intermediate Grade	Hard Grade	Structural-Steel Grade	Intermediate Grade	Hard Grade	
Under ¾ in.	180 deg. $d = t$	180 deg. $d = 2t$	180 deg. $d = 3t$	180 deg. $d = t$	180 deg. $d = 3t$	180 deg. $d = 4t$	180 deg. $d = 2t$
¾ in. or over	180 deg. $d = t$	90 deg. $d = 2t$	90 deg. $d = 3t$	180 deg. $d = 2t$	90 deg. $d = 3t$	90 deg. $d = 4t$	180 deg. $d = 3t$

Explanatory note. d = the diameter of pin about which the specimen is bent.
t = the thickness or diameter of the specimen.

From "Standard Specifications for Billet-Steel Concrete Reinforcement Bars," ASTM Designation A 15–39.

TABLE 38

REINFORCING STEEL BARS

Size*	Shape of Section	Area (sq in.)	Perimeter (in.)	Weight per foot (lb)
⅜	Round	0.11	1.178	0.376
½	Round	0.20	1.571	0.668
½	Square	0.25	2.000	0.850
⅝	Round	0.31	1.963	1.043
¾	Round	0.44	2.356	1.502
⅞	Round	0.60	2.749	2.044
1	Round	0.79	3.142	2.670
1	Square	1.00	4.000	3.400
1⅛	Square	1.27	4.500	4.303
1¼	Square	1.56	5.000	5.313

* Diameter or side in inches.

TABLE 39

Allowable Unit Stresses in Concrete *

Description		For any strength of concrete as fixed by test $n = \dfrac{30{,}000}{f'_c}$	When strength of concrete is fixed by the water-content			
			$f'_c =$ 2,000#/in² $n = 15$	$f'_c =$ 2,500#/in² $n = 12$	$f'_c =$ 3,000#/in² $n = 10$	$f'_c =$ 3,750#/in² $n = 8$
Flexure: f_c						
Extreme fiber stress in compression..................	f_c	$0.45f'_c$	900	1,125	1,350	1,688
Shear: v						
Beams with no web reinforcement and without special anchorage of longitudinal steel	v_c	$0.02f'_c$	40	50	60	75
Beams with no web reinforcement but with special anchorage of longitudinal steel	v_c	$0.03f'_c$	60	75	90	113
Beams with properly designed web reinforcement but without special anchorage of longitudinal steel..........	v	$0.06f'_c$	120	150	180	225
Beams with properly designed web reinforcement and with special anchorage of longitudinal steel..........	v	$0.12f'_c$	240	300	360	450
Flat slabs at distance d from edge of column capital or drop panel..............	v_c	$0.03f'_c$	60	75	90	113
Footings..................	v_c	$0.03f'_c$ but not to exceed 75#/in²	60	75	75	75
Bond †: u						
In beams and slabs and one-way footings:						
Plain bars.	u	$0.04f'_c$ but not to exceed 160#/in²	80	100	120	150
Deformed bars...........	u	$0.05f'_c$ but not to exceed 200#/in²	100	125	150	188
In two-way footings:						
Plain bars (hooked).......	u	$0.045f'_c$ but not to exceed 160#/in²	90	113	135	160
Deformed bars (hooked)...	u	$0.056f'_c$ but not to exceed 200#/in²	112	140	168	200
Bearing: f_c						
On full area..............	f_c	$0.25f'_c$	500	625	750	938
On one-third area or less ‡....	f_c	$0.375f'_c$	750	938	1,125	1,405

* Taken by permission from "Building Regulations for Reinforced Concrete," published by the American Concrete Institute.

† Where special anchorage is provided, one and one-half times these values in bond may be used in beams, slabs and one-way footings, but in no case to exceed 200#/in² for plain bars and 250#/in² for deformed bars. The values given for two-way footings include an allowance for special anchorage.

‡ The allowable bearing stress on an area greater than one-third but less than the full area shall be interpolated between the values given.

TABLE 40

REINFORCED CONCRETE BEAMS

Design Constants for Rectangular Beams

$$p = \frac{\frac{1}{2}}{\frac{f_s}{f_c}\left(\frac{f_s}{nf_c}+1\right)} \;;\; k = \frac{nf_c}{f_s+nf_c} \;;\; j = 1 - \tfrac{1}{3}k; \; K = \frac{M}{bd^2} = f_s pj \text{ or } \tfrac{1}{2}f_c kj$$

n	f_c	$f_s = 18,000$				$f_s = 20,000$			
		p	k	j	K	p	k	j	K
8	1315	0.0134	0.368	0.877	212	0.0103	0.345	0.885	182
	1500	0.0167	0.400	0.867	261	0.0140	0.375	0.875	246
	1688	0.0201	0.428	0.857	311	0.0170	0.403	0.866	294
10	1050	0.0108	0.368	0.877	170	0.0090	0.345	0.885	160
	1200	0.0133	0.400	0.867	208	0.0113	0.375	0.875	197
	1350	0.0161	0.428	0.857	248	0.0136	0.403	0.866	236
12	875	0.0089	0.368	0.877	140	0.0076	0.345	0.885	134
	1000	0.0111	0.400	0.867	173	0.0094	0.375	0.875	164
	1125	0.0133	0.428	0.857	206	0.0113	0.403	0.866	194
15	700	0.0072	0.368	0.877	113	0.0060	0.345	0.885	107
	800	0.0089	0.400	0.867	139	0.0075	0.375	0.875	131
	900	0.0107	0.428	0.857	165	0.0091	0.403	0.866	157

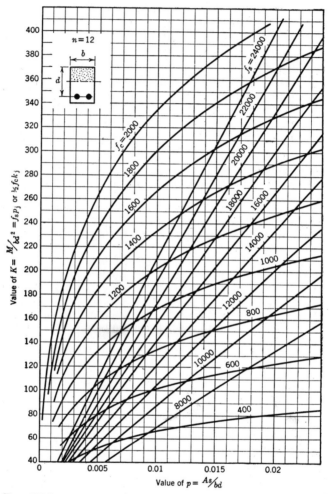

Design Chart VI for Analysis of Rectangular Reinforced Concrete Beams; $n = 12$.

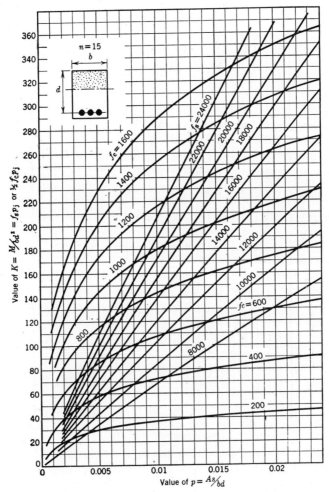

Design Chart VII for Analysis of Rectangular Reinforced Concrete Beams; $n = 15$.

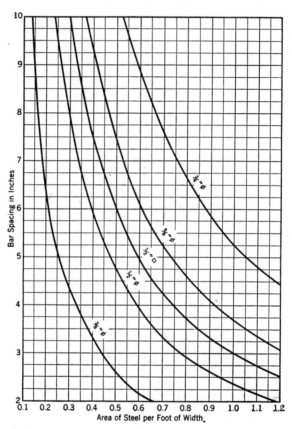

DESIGN CHART VIII. Spacing of Bars in Slabs.

INDEX

415

Inclined chord truss, dimension determinations, 144
  influence lines, 155
  uniform live load, 154
Influence line, 59
  for bending-moment, 68
  for reactions, 59
  for shear, 65
Internal forces, 60

Joint loads, 110
Joist, 2
Joist and plank, standard sizes, 387

Kip, 55

Lacing for steel columns, 253
Lag screw, 189
  dimension and weights, 367
Lane loading for highway bridges, 15
Lateral pressure, in high bins, 29
  on walls, 26
Light-gage steel beams, 310
Light-gage steel columns, 311
Light-gage steel construction, 294
Live loads, 8
  for floors of buildings, 10, 11
  for highway bridges, 15
  for railway bridges, 17
  for roofs, 12
  for sidewalks, 11
Lumber, 218
  standard sizes, 386

Masonry dams, 182
Mill bent, 129
  fixed column bases, 133
  hinged column bases, 129
Moment distribution at a joint, 92
Moment of inertia, graphical determina-
  tion, 42
Moment table Cooper's E60, 366

Nails, 188
  dimensions of, 367
National Board of Fire Underwriters,
  specifications for roof loads, 15
Net section of steel tension members, 244
Normal thrust, 61

Panel load, 116
Parallel chord truss, chord stresses, 137

Parallel chord truss, concentrated load
  systems, 153
  dead-load stress coefficients, 142
  dead-load stresses, 136
  influence lines for, 149
  live-load stresses, 147
  stress, in diagonals, 138
    in verticals, 141
  uniform live loading, 148
Pile foundations, 175
Piling, 175
Pins, 202
Plate girder, 270
  design procedure, 277
  riveting, 275
  web stiffeners, 272
Posts and timbers, standard sizes, 387
Pratt truss, 109
Primary stress, 109
Purlin, 110

Rafter, 2
Railway bridge loading, 17
Rankine theory for lateral pressure, 27
Reaction, 9
  character of, 49
  determined analytically, 53
  determined graphically, 51
  due to live loads, 59
  for continuous beams, 99
  for fixed loads, 54
  for three-hinged arch, 56
  influence line for, 59
Reduction of live loads, 13
Reinforced concrete, allowable unit
  stresses, 410
Reinforced concrete beams, bond stress,
  335
  design charts, 412, 413
  design constants, 411
  design of rectangular sections, 339
  shear and diagonal tension, 337
  theory of flexure, 330
  transformed section, 332
Reinforced concrete columns, 350
Reinforced concrete retaining walls, 181
Reinforced concrete slabs, 343
Reinforced concrete T-beams, 346
Reinforcing steel, allowable unit stress,
  327